TEACHING SCIENCE THROUGH DISCOVERY

TEACHING
SCIENCE

Arthur Carin
Robert B. Sund

THROUGH
DISCOVERY

CHARLES E. MERRILL BOOKS, INC. Columbus, Ohio

LINE DRAWINGS PREPARED BY DENNIS WILLIAMS
TONE DRAWINGS PREPARED BY RAE D. CHAMBERS

Library of Congress Catalog Card Number: 64-8366

PRINTED IN THE UNITED STATES OF AMERICA

PREFACE

Although science education has been long accepted and established in the elementary school curriculum, many improvements are being made in teaching science to children. Much of the progress in science teaching is due to a more successful alignment of the general elementary school curriculum with the goals and activities of science for children. This book combines the rationale and framework of science education with good, solid classroom activities that elementary teachers have found most rewarding and efficient. These areas are expanded to clarify problems related to objectives for teaching science, development of curriculum, and teaching methods and materials for science education.

Part 1 presents a framework for modern, forward looking science education. Documented by research and the best-known practices, full attention is given to such fundamental questions as: "What Is Science?" "Why Should Science Be Taught to Children?" "How Do Children Best Learn Science?" Stressing the ways in which science education contributes to the needs and interests of children, Part 1 explores further how science education contributes to the needs and goals of our society in a scientific age. The concepts of teaching science as inquiry and as methods for investigation are developed and coupled with the vast accumulation of tested ideas and principles. Evidence points clearly toward an active program of science education utilizing problem solving techniques. Procedures for the active involvement of professional scientists, blended into cooperative planning and teaching of science with children, are given as guidelines for teachers and supervisors, who recognize the need for greater structure and continuity in the science program. Teachers will find needed background materials upon which to keep pace with the shifts of science which require proper perspectives in the total elementary school program.

Specific and detailed step-by-step activities are given in Part 2 for organizing, planning, and teaching science. For instance, the teacher is shown how to develop science units, to plan individual science lessons, to arrange time in the daily and weekly curriculum for science, and to locate and use science materials effectively.

Part 3 offers enrichment activities to the teachers who wish to be prepared to meet every student with perceptiveness and depth of understanding. Methods of teaching to meet the individual differences of children in the science program are emphasized. Specific suggestions are made for the demands placed on the teacher by the slow learner and the exceptional student. The material of Part 3 provides classroom-tested science experiences for the elementary teacher's use in the encouragement of creativity and self-evaluation. Special emphasis is placed on evaluation as an important teacher-learning experience.

Additional aid is given in Part 4 through the lesson plans which are grouped into the basic areas of science. They offer teaching suggestions, experiments, demonstrations, and pictorial riddles for science learning through discovery. Although these lesson plans are merely suggestive material, the elementary teacher will find that they present unlimited possibilities for adaption to specific classroom situations. Due to the wide variations in the curriculum of school districts and the differences between individual classes, the lessons have purposely been designed as resources and not as a specific curriculum for any school. Thus, it is important for the teacher to have the freedom to design the science unit for the particular situation. With this book, the teacher can incorporate the principles and methods of science education presented in the first parts with specific discovery lesson plans of Part 4 for the greatest benefit to the student in science education. The lists of supplies, the sources for obtaining materials and information, and the numerous references for both children and teachers in the Appendix provide additional help to the individual planning and teaching science in the elementary school.

The authors gratefully acknowledge the support and encouragement of their colleagues at Queens College and Colorado State College. Acknowledgments are also due to Drs. Bert Thomas, Al Hendricks, and Mr. Hayes for insuring the scientific accuracy of the manuscript through their critical review of the activity sections; to Dr. Wesley Staton for comments and helpful criticism; to Mr. J. Reilly Sinnett, Assistant Superintendent, and the thirty-six teachers of Colorado School District RE 7 who tested the activities of Part 4 and gave us their reactions to them. Thanks to Drs. Harley Glidden, Paul Merrick, Leslie Trowbridge, Kenneth Olson, Edith Selberg, Louise Neal, Mrs. Tillie Mathews, Mrs. Esther Banek, Mrs. Olive McNeil, Mrs. Barbara Weber, Mrs. Grace Burly, Mr. Schuyler Van Gordon, and our students for various kinds of help and enlightenment relative to elementary science teaching.

Thanks are due to the following organizations and governmental agencies for providing information and other data: The American Association for the Advancement of Science; National Science Foundation; The Department of Health, Education, and Welfare; the Elementary Science Study; Educational Services, Inc.; The University of California, Science Curriculum Improvement Study; The Elementary School Science Project; the University of Illinois Elementary School Science Project; the Princeton Study; The National Foundation of the Princeton Study; the Coordinated Science and Mathematics Curriculum; University of Minnesota; the School Mathematics Study Group.

Sincere gratitude is extended to Terry, Jill, and Amy Carin without whose inspiration, patience, and sacrifices this book would never have been written.

August 1, 1964

ARTHUR CARIN

ROBERT SUND

PHOTO CREDITS

Grateful acknowledgment is made to the following school systems, individuals, and organizations that cooperated in supplying illustrative materials. (Figures refer to the pages on which the illustrations appear.)

Board of Education, Worthington, Ohio, 50.

Cedar Hill School, Oak Ridge Schools, Oak Ridge, Tennessee, James M. Yonts, Jr., Assistant Superintendent, 38, 62(b), 71(b), 138(b).

Cincinnati, Ohio, Public Schools, Wendell H. Pierce, Superintendent, 26, 52, 59(2), 61, 62(a), 63, 65(b), 72, 74, 101, 125(2), 128(2), 138(a), 139, 150.

Charles Phelps Cushing (McKeown), New York, 1, 65(a).

A. Devaney, Inc., New York, 4, 22, 60, 92, 104, 122(a), 123, 130, 135.

Elementary Science Study of Educational Services, Incorporated, Watertown, Massachusetts, 15, 34, 64(b), 113, 136, 148, 149, 161.

S. A. Hirsh Manufacturing Co., Chicago, Illinois, 110.

International Business Machines, Inc., White Plains, New York, 127.

Jewel Aquarium Company, Chicago, Illinois, 106(b), 112(2).

Learning Center, Princeton, New Jersey, xii, 11, 106(a), 107(b), 116.

George Lichty, Publishers Newspaper Syndicate, "Grin & Bear It," 29.

Monkmeyer Press Photo Service (Hays), New York, New York, 6, 31.

H. Armstrong Roberts, Philadelphia, Pennsylvania, 2, 27, 28, 55(b), 56, 64(a), 94, 118, 121, 134, 142.

Science Kit Lab., Corp., Tonawanda, New York, 107(a).

Bob Waters, Colorado State College, 24, 45(2), 55(a), 68, 71(a), 88, 122(b), 137, 152.

TABLE OF CONTENTS

Part 4 Discovery Lesson Plans and Other Activities for Teaching Science, 163

Appendix, 489

Index, 505

TEACHING SCIENCE THROUGH DISCOVERY

What Is Modern Science?
Why Teach Science in the Elementary School?
Nature of Science Teaching-Learning

Shaping Science Education in the Elementary School

Part 1

What Is
Modern Science?

1

INTRODUCTION

Why should we include science in the educational program? Let us first define science and then develop its implications for a program for elementary school children.

WHAT IS SCIENCE?

The Columbia Encyclopedia defines science as:

> . . . an *accumulated and systematized* learning, in general usage restricted to natural phenomena. The progress of science is marked not only by an accumulation of fact, but by the emergence of *scientific method* and of the *scientific attitude*.[1]

This definition includes three of the basic principles of modern science; namely, (1) an accumulated and systematized body of knowledge, (2) scientific attitudes, and (3) scientific methods of inquiry. While the first point is the PRODUCT OF

---

[1]"Science," *The Columbia Encyclopedia,* (3rd ed., 1963), p. 1990. (authors' italics)

SCIENCE, the second and third points constitute the PROCESS OF SCIENCE. The following discussion provides a more detailed account of the product and process of modern science.

THE PRODUCT OF SCIENCE:
An Accumulated and Systematized Body of Knowledge

Ivan Pavlov pointed out in a speech to the youth of his country: "Perfect as the wing of a bird may be, it will never enable the bird to fly if unsupported by the air. Facts are the air of science. Without them the men of science can never rise. Without them your theories are vain surmises."

The accumulated facts gathered by scientists as an outgrowth of their studies of nature have resulted in a large body of verified knowledge. This knowledge has been organized into subject matter fields; such as, biology, geology, physics, and chemistry. This organized and systematized subject matter is the *product* of scientific investigation. Schools have, however, traditionally overemphasized this product of science, the subject matter, and underemphasized or forgotten the *process* of science. A look at the process by which the subject matter is obtained reveals the dynamic nature of the scientific process, for facts become valid and cumulative only after they survive unrelenting scrutiny. Thus, scientific facts — although extremely necessary for any scientific investigation — are only a product of the greater contribution of modern science, *the process of inquiry*.

THE PROCESS OF SCIENCE:
Scientific Attitudes and Methods

> True science teaches, above all, to doubt and to be ignorant.
> Miguel de Unamuno, *The Tragic Sense of Life*

Science is fundamentally a means of understanding why things happen as they do.

Man has found in science a process by which his search for answers to his unlimited questions can be approached systematically. Science as a process of inquiry stems from human urges and needs and is guided by scientific attitudes and methods. Either by intent or by accident, many people describe scientific attitudes and methods in such ways as to indicate that there is one, and only one, approach to solving problems scientifically. Case histories of famous scientists reveal that there are as many scientific methods as there are scientists. Nevertheless, an attempt to abstract basic scientific attitudes and methods is not hopeless, for there are some common denominators in the work of scientists that give us insights into their patterns of thinking and working. We can then observe the scientific ways of thinking as a natural outgrowth of modern scientific attitudes.

Just as the young child enjoys discovering the texture, color, size, weight, and taste of sand at the seashore or sandbox because it intrigues him, the scientists studies the wonders of nature because he delights in them.

This dynamic and almost compulsive involvement of the child or adult investigator searching for answers provides the fuel for the vehicle of investigation. Without this hunger for answers there could not be scientific inquiry. It is not always important that practical uses be found from the answers. The scientist many times is not concerned with nor aware of the uses for his discoveries. The sheer joy of discovery is justification enough for scientific inquiry as revealed in this statement:

> Anyone who has ever worked in any science knows how much esthetic joy he has obtained. That is, in the actual activity of science, in the process of making a discovery, however humble it is, one can't help feeling an awareness of beauty.[2]

The Sense of Humility

The scientist is quick to realize that there is not one method of scientific thinking and this realization gives him a sense of humility in relation to his work and the ways in which he approaches problem solving. Humility can be defined as freedom from pride and arrogance. Most scientists cautiously guard against the human tendency to be opinionated, dogmatic, or pedantic. Through this humility and reluctance to be categorical or dogmatic, a second element of scientific attitudes is derived. All findings are tentative.

Scientific Facts Are Tentative

The fund of scientific information has been described as the product of a process similar to building a brick wall. Facts represent the bricks. The bricks, however, are removable in such a manner that the weaker ones, when discovered, may be replaced by stronger ones without unduly endangering the strength and structure of the brick wall. Most of our scientific bricks are quite strong and withstand the scientific elements that test their strength. Some of the corroding scientific elements represent new and more reliable information used in evolving new theories.

These scientific elements can be compared to the weather elements heat and rain which are at work attempting to break down real brick walls.

Occasionally a large part or even the whole scientific wall may come tumbling down as a result of new and more reliable information. Such a breakdown occurred when Nicolaus Copernicus upset the then prevalent view of the relationship between the earth, the sun, and the planets. He showed that the sun rather than the earth was the center of the solar system, thus laying a foundation for a new wall.

Later works by Galileo, Kepler, and Newton resulted in the correction and enlargement of the Copernican ideas. The history of the development of these ideas indicates that a series of revised judgments advances the progress of science. We should heed Oliver Cromwell's warning:

> My Brethren, by the bowels of Christ, I beseech you, bethink you may be mistaken.

Positive Approach to Failure

In accepting constant testing, the scientist develops a very realistic and healthy approach to research in which failure is but a point on the continuum of study. Failure, as a step along the path in research, makes it necessary to try other routes for answers to problems.

In a way, failure is a type of success. It says: "At least it's not this particular answer." In effect, the failure can actually be interpreted as an addition to the great storehouse of cumulative scientific information. An example of success from failures can be seen in the work of Dr. Paul Ehrlich, 1908 Nobel Prize winner in medicine and physiology. Dr. Ehrlich developed Salvarsan for the treatment of syphilis after 605 unsuccessful experiments. As a matter of fact, Salvarsan was called "606" by Dr. Ehrlich because of the numerical order in his experimental series. The 605 failures experienced by Paul Ehrlich contributed positively to medical

---

[2]Charles P. Snow, "Appreciations in Science," *Science,* 133 (January 27, 1961), pp. 256-59.

research by contributing the information that lead to the development of the 606th formula.

Another example of this positive approach to failure can be found in the modern day quest for sixty-second, color pictures developed by the Polaroid Camera Company. Howard Rogers, a chemist, spent 15 years searching for just the right chemical compound needed for instant color pictures. It took 5000 different chemical compounds before Rogers actually invented an entirely new chemical molecule. His 5000 failures added to the knowledge in the field of chemistry.[3]

Failures enable scientists to know what has been tried, to avoid repeating errors, and to advance in new directions. The Ehrlichs have enabled us to reap the inheritance of a vast, cumulative body of tested information from which our investigations advance.

SCIENTIFIC WAYS OF THINKING AND WORKING

Scientists Are Human

Once a person in a scientific field has developed an intense desire to search for answers to problems, it is mistakenly thought that all he has to do is to apply the scientific method of investigation and his troubles are over. The scientific method as widely perceived by too many people has taken on almost an aura of magic as the complete antithesis of science. The popular stereotype of the scientist is the magician who stands before elaborate, clinical glassware and meticulously mixes liquids that bubble, steam, and periodically change color. The "science" of Professor Frankenstein and his monster and of Dr. Jekyll and Mr. Hyde typify the popular misconception of the scientist. However, anyone who has done any reading about the work of famous scientists immediately begins to recognize that there is

not a stereotype of the scientist as there is no one scientific method of investigation. The reason that no one series of steps will work for all people is that the emotional stability, the awareness of chance discovery, and the prepared mind of the individual varies. These factors influence the methods in which the scientific approach is used in solving problems.

Control of Emotions

The scientist does not have the single-minded, robot approach to problem solving often observed in electronic computing machines; instead, the ways in which he thinks and works are influenced by human traits and weaknesses. Alfred North Whitehead recognized one of the human difficulties of organizing the initial stages of scientific studies by describing this stage as a "state of imaginative muddled suspense which precedes successful inductive generalization."[4] Setting up the organization of a study taxes man's creative powers, for man approaches problems with a tendency toward the much

---

[3]For an absorbing and colorful story of the search for a new chemical *see:* "Instant Color Pictures," *Life* (January 25, 1963), pp. 74-88.

[4]Alfred North Whitehead, *Science and the Modern World* (New York: The Macmillan Company, 1925).

used methods of the past. The scientist must force himself each time he approaches a new problem to search for all possible ways of organizing his study.

Another frailty of man is his tendency to allow his emotions to influence and at times to control his thought processes. In fact, psychologists have advanced the idea that much, if not all, of our learning is affected by our feelings. James Bryant Conant acknowledges the scientist's efforts to control the emotions by referring to . . .

> the stumbling ways in which even the ablest of the early scientists had to fight through thickets of erroneous observations, misleading generalizations, inadequate formulations, and unconscious prejudice.[5]

Recognition by the scientist of his tendency to be influenced by his emotions has led him to set up a protection to guard against himself.

The Place of Chance in Scientific Discovery

Another factor that enters into scientific ways of working is the element of chance, the brilliant flash of imagination, the accidental discovery, the educated guess, or intuition. Many occurrences of great scientific import have had such an element in their scientific investigation. Case histories of such scientific investigation in which chance played an important role are presented in Dr. Conant's *On Understanding Science, An Historical Approach.* Among these cases those of Luigi Galvani and Allesandro Volta merit elaboration. Galvani reports his accidental discovery in his own words:

> I had dissected and prepared a frog . . . and while I was attending to something else . . . I laid it on a table on which stood an electrical machine at some distance . . . Now when one of the persons who were present touched accidentally and lightly the inner

crural nerves of the frog with the point of a scalpel all the muscles of the legs seemed to contract again and again.

> . . . Another one who was there, who was helping us in electrical researches, thought that he had noticed that the action was excited when a spark was discharged from the conductor of the machine. Being astonished by this new phenomenon, he called my attention to it, who at the time had something else in mind and was deep in thought. Whereupon I was inflamed with an incredible zeal and eagerness to test the same and to bring to light what was concealed in it.[6]

While working with frogs on an entirely different experiment, Galvani stumbled onto his now famous "animal electricity" discovery.

Years later while working on Galvani's original problem, "animal electricity," Volta found by accident that he no longer needed frogs in his experiments and that any moist material would give the same results. His discovery of the electrical battery followed Galvani's work and these steps were observed:

CHANCE HAPPENING: 1. An accidental discovery (by Galvani and the associates that interrupted his original work)

CONTROLLED EXPERIMENTS: 2. A series of controlled experiments (by Galvani once he was "inflamed with an incredible zeal and eagerness to test the same and to bring to light what was concealed in it")

TENTATIVE HYPOTHESIS: 3. The formulation of a working hypothesis to explain the fact (animal electricity)

MORE EXPERIMENTS: 4. More controlled experiments by another experimenter (Volta)

NEW HYPOTHESIS: 5. The formulation of an entirely different hypothesis and the development of an entirely new conceptual scheme into which the facts about electric batteries neatly fit.

---

[5]James B. Conant, *On Understanding Science: An Historical Approach* (New Haven: Yale University Press, 1947).

[6]*Ibid.*

Although both Galvani and Volta were fascinated by their experimentation with "animal electricity," this chance happening has now become lost in the greater and more famous result of Volta's discovery, the electric battery. Frequently in scientific history, we end up solving a problem very different from the original one.

Granting that chance does play a great part in our lives both personally and professionally, one is reminded of Louis Pasteur who aptly placed chance in its proper perspective by stating that: "Chance favors only the prepared mind." What are some of the elements of the "prepared mind" as they pertain to solving problems?

The Prepared Mind

The scientific method is nothing more than approaching problems from as many directions as possible. Although we have observed that there is not any one scientific method common to all the sciences, there are definite methods of reasoning from available evidence, and they are essentially the same in all the sciences. Certain mental activities developed and usually used by individuals in scientific investigations constitute the prepared mind, controlled and ready to use chance happenings. They are:

observation (including experimentation)
analysis and synthesis
imagination
supposition and idealization
inference (inductive and deductive)
comparison (including analogy) at first
glance

We should remember, however, that the prepared mind is not the sole property of the scientist. Every alert, intelligent human being is not only capable of but also engages in the mental activities of the prepared mind. Verification of these characteristics can be seen in man's everyday problem solving.

Everyday Problem Solving

All of us use similar mental processes in our everyday problem solving like those described as the prepared mind. Many times these mental activities are labeled common sense, a term most frequently used to describe alert, intelligent, mental activities. Oliver Wendell Holmes has presented the analogy of scientific thinking as a first-rate piece of furniture for a man's upper floor only if he has common sense on the ground floor.

Common sense has also been referred to as the residue of science which has been well digested. An example of common sense in a very familiar everyday situation shows the ways in which we exercise many of the processes of thinking so often attributed only to scientists:

You go into a fruit store to buy some apples. You take an apple, bite it, and find it sour. You look at the apple and observe that it is hard and green. You take another apple and that is also hard, green, and . . . sour.

The fruitman offers you a third apple; but before biting it, you examine it and find that it too is hard and green. You immediately say that you do not want it as it must be sour like the ones you have already tried.

Although you may not even be conscious of the process, you can now discern some of these mental activities: observation, analysis and synthesis, imagination, supposition and idealization, inference and comparison.

The intent of showing the prepared mind as an everyday occurrence is not to minimize this magnificent advance in human progress but rather to place it in the proper perspective. Scientific thinking is a product of man belonging to men and not to a small group of persons regardless of training or importance.

In summary, the prepared mind or scientific mode of thought was examined in items of:

No single, scientific method exists due to the uniqueness of each investigator, situation, and problem to be solved.

The element of chance or accidental occurrences plays a great part in scientific investigation.

All findings from studies are tentative and cumulative.

Hypotheses and findings are exposed to every possible verification.

Due to the tentativeness, cumulativeness, and constant testing of ideas, failures are only steps toward more answers and not toward finality.

The prepared mind uses these mental activities:

observation (including experimentation)
analysis and synthesis
imagination
supposition and idealization
inference (inductive and deductive)
comparison (including analogy)

Everyone practices ways of looking at problems scientifically (common sense) and can improve their abilities in this area.

IMPLICATIONS FOR SCIENCE EDUCATION

Planned and Structured Science Education

It is no longer adequate to relegate science in the elementary school exclusively to the incidental or chance-happening style of teaching although both have a place in the elementary science program and will be discussed later in the book. The hit-and-miss approach is inadequate today. For example, a brief discussion of the bird's nest brought in by Sally should not comprise all the science to which the class is exposed. This is not to say that some very fine teaching has not been done without a structural program; however, the following aspects of a structural science program seem necessary in light of today's scientific advancement:

a. A structured program provides a framework of science principles which can help teachers unify their own experiences and give them confidence in meeting difficult classroom situations that arise. The answer suggested a decade ago to children's questions — "I don't know, but let's find out together" — is not sufficient for all of today's needs.

b. A structured program does not have to be a rigid one. Within the broad content areas, there are many choices which permit the teacher to adapt the program to the needs of the class. Both the unit approach and the provision of a variety of materials and situations which foster children's creativity and originality are possible within a structured program.

c. The freshness engendered by the use of unanticipated incidents is not lost in a structured program. Indeed, the incident becomes more significant because the teacher sees it as a part of the whole and thus may be able to convey its importance to the pupil. A structured program helps the teacher anticipate, identify, and incorporate into the program the many incidents which arise during the school year.

d. While it is true that children come to school with many interests, it is also true that interest can be aroused and cultivated by what takes place in school.

e. A structured program makes it easier for children to acquire the science concepts essential for their understanding of the complex world they live in.

f. A structured program is a democratic one: many can share in building it and changing it. It provides a common framework for testing and evaluation by the children as well as by the teachers.[7]

A planned and structured but flexible program of science concepts is as much a necessity to the elementary school as the structured programs we have in mathematics, social studies, and language arts. A planned program presents an overall scope and sequence of possible science concepts from which the teacher can select learning experiences for his specific class. The scope gives an overview of the concepts suggested in each content area to which we hope to expose our children from kindergarten to eighth grade while the sequence presents a general idea of the expected difficulty of the concepts. One of the big questions in the selection of science concepts for an elementary school science program has been the criteria upon which to make the selection.

One of the first questions to answer in content organization is what science areas should be included? Science education in the elementary school should not be limited to one of the separate sciences, but should draw upon all of the sciences. From all of these sciences, broad concept areas should be developed allowing for development of skills, attitudes, and scientific techniques that apply to many science areas. The next question that arises concerns the selection of those broad concept areas.

Agreement on Broad Concept Areas

In an effort to give directions, organization, and continuity to elementary and junior high school science education, the American Association for the Advancement of Science, with the aid of a grant from the National Science Foundation conducted a study.[8] A series of conferences were held in St. Louis, Missouri; Berkeley, California; and Washington, D. C.; they consisted of participants drawn from the ranks of elementary and junior high school science instruction, science educators, scientists from various disciplines, representatives from psychological disciplines interested in learning theory. The broad science concept areas agreed upon for organization of the elementary school science education program were: cosmology, character of the universe as an orderly system; evolution; ecology, mutual relations between organisms and their environment; structure and function; reproduction and development; structure of matter; and energy interrelations and change of matter.[9] Although many broad areas such as these appear in many present science programs under such headings as the universe, conditions necessary for life, and physical and chemical phenomena, it is apparent that much revision and reorganization is needed for a refinement of science content areas.

The refinement and limiting of science areas has to be a continual activity due to the increase in the amount of new scientific knowledge and theory. Paul de Hurd, one of our leading science educators, describes the need for an ordering of science in this way:

> The pupil needs at each grade level to acquire a background of ordered knowledge, to develop an adequate vocabulary in science for effective communication and to learn some facts because they are important in every day living, such as knowledge useful in maintaining health, promoting safety, and interpreting the immediate environment. Recent theories and new knowledge should have priority in science teaching when they are significant and can be made understandable at a specified grade level. The generalized concepts selected for teaching should be those

[7]*Rethinking Science Education*, Part I, National Society for Study of Education (Chicago: University of Chicago Press, 1960), p. 128.

[8]John R. Mayor and Dael Wolfle, *Feasibility Study on Major Efforts to Improve Science Courses in Elementary and Junior High School* (Washington, D. C.: American Association for the Advancement of Science, 1960-61).

(References to excerpts can be found in the following footnote.)

[9]John R. Mayor, "Science Teaching in the Elementary and Junior High Schools," *Science*, 1331, No. 3469 (June 23, 1961), p. 2021.

which tend to explain or involve many science facts.[10]

As we revise and strengthen our science education, we should keep in mind another criteria, the need for continuity in science education from kindergarten to twelfth grade.

Need for Continuity

Our planned and structured science education program should be coordinated as a twelve year program. Haphazard samplings of science concepts, as well as uncoordinated repetition and omissions, should yield to a more systematic and developmental program based upon science, its process and product, as well as the individual child and the way he learns. Too often programs of science education are a boring and wasteful repetition of a purely descriptive treatment of such subjects as the solar system, weather, and classification of trees, leaves, and birds. How familiar we all are with hearing from children, "Oh, we did that in science last year." Although complete overlap is unavoidable and is even desirable for reinforcement and review, we should strive to minimize unnecessary repetition. One purpose of a planned program is minimizing boredom and repetition; this, in turn, provides for the

[10]*Rethinking Science Education,* Part I, National Society for Study of Education (Chicago: University of Chicago Press, 1960), p. 35.

early introduction of the methods and systematic characteristics of scientific inquiry.

Science Discovery Versus Memory

Science education should stress the spirit of discovery characteristic of science. Both teachers and students find that science teaching and learning becomes a chore when approached as a series of facts to be memorized and regurgitated back on exams; nothing is more contrary to the spirit of science than this lecture-memorize-test method. This does not mean that concepts, theories, principles, and content areas are abandoned in our science curriculum; to the contrary, they can be learned better when approached from a discovery method. The student, while learning concepts, develops his skills in observing, checking, measuring, criticizing, and interpreting discoveries as well as other skills inherent in the prepared or scientific mind. Students cannot learn the skills nor grasp the true spirit of science unless they engage in discovery. Fortunately, discovery is possible at all levels, with the simplest being a child discovering and observing phenomena that are new to him. On a higher level, the child can learn to observe relationships by actual experimentation. Still later, discoveries can be made by utilizing the child's increasing ability to engage in abstract reasoning. Help in devising situations and pro-

cedures that encourage scientific discovery can be obtained by jointly using scientists with a knowledge of the discovery spirit of their discipline as well as educators with a knowledge of children and the ways in which they learn and mature.

Professional Scientists and Educators Combine Skills

Elementary school science programs and textbooks have been criticized by scientists for not teaching how scientists discover knowledge of our universe. Instead they have traditionally emphasized the products of science. Because of this concern, groups of professional scientists working in conjunction with educators are beginning to produce science materials and programs of instruction for the elementary schools. These materials and programs stress the ways in which scientists find answers to their questions. Professional scientists are naturally in the most favorable position to identify the scientific processes and concepts of greatest value in their respective scientific fields. Professional educators contribute their skills, knowledge, and experiences with children to assist in selecting appropriate learning experiences for children to grasp these scientific processes and concepts on their own levels. Three of these scientist-educator projects that have attracted much publicity are: J. Myron Atkin and Associates in the University of Illinois Elementary School Science Project,[11] Robert Karplus and Associates in the University of California Elementary School Science Project,[12] the Educational Services Incorporated, Elementary Science

Study, Watertown, Massachusetts.[13] A brief description follows of each of these projects including a sample of the materials developed for use with elementary school teachers and children.

University of Illinois Science Project

A staff of professional astronomers and educators collaborated on a series of children's books with teaching guides. Their purpose was to present a new organization of elementary school science content based upon an identification of fundamental concepts and principles that incorporate a given scientific field and that help students make their own entity of what otherwise is solely a collection of disparate facts. Each of their booklets were tested with elementary school children and revised where necessary.

The following is a sample of the type of activities included in their first booklet, *Astronomy, Charting the Universe*. In the message to the student at the front of the booklet, the authors reveal the *process of science* approach that they wish to instill:

To the Student:

> You have studied astronomy in school. You have read about astronomy in newspapers and seen programs about astronomy on TV. Probably you know some of the facts of astronomy; the size of the moon; the distance to the sun; the temperature of a star. In this book you are going to take a new look at astronomy. You will discover how we know about objects in the sky. The astronomers and teachers who wrote this book feel it is as important to know the "hows" of astronomy as it is to know the answers. . . .[14]

[11]J. Myron Atkin, "Teaching Concepts of Modern Astronomy to Elementary School Children," *Science Education,* 45 (February, 1961), p. 54. (and) J. Myron Atkin, "The University of Illinois School Science Project," *Elementary School Science Bulletin,* 66 (December, 1961), p. 3.

[12]Lloyd Scott, "Research Scientists Build an Elementary School Science Program," *Elementary School Science Bulletin,* 66 (December, 1961), p. 3.

[13]"Elementary Science Study," *Quarterly Report* (Watertown, Massachusetts: Educational Services, Inc., Winter 1962-63), pp. 9-16.

[14]J. Myron Atkin and Stanley P. Wyatt, *Astronomy: Charting the Universe* (Urbana, Illinois: Elementary-School Science Project, University of Illinois, 1961). Prepared under a grant from the National Science Foundation.

INDIRECT MEASUREMENTS

Shape of the Earth—How big is the earth? What is its shape? You may know the answers to these questions already, but perhaps you do not know *how* the answers were obtained. Let's study the shape of the earth first.

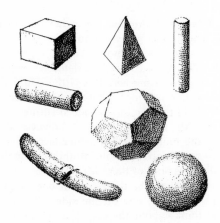

People often say that the earth is a sphere because you can travel all the way around it. But this is not a complete proof. You could travel around the surface of the earth if it were shaped like a square box or a telephone pole, a frankfurter or a pyramid. Of course, if you were to travel around some of these objects you would come to some sharp edges. Since you don't, you know that the earth is fairly smooth. But an ant walks around a frankfurter without coming to any edges. Is the earth shaped like a frankfurter?

The shadow of the earth shows this idea to be false. When the earth comes between the sun and the moon, its shadow sometimes falls on the moon. Then we can observe that the edge of its shadow is always circular, no matter how the earth is turned. The only object which *always* has a circular shadow is a sphere. The earth must be a sphere.

But why don't we see the roundness of the earth? For thousands of years men thought the earth was flat. It certainly *looks* flat. The reason it doesn't look round is that you don't see enough of it at one

time. A small part of the surface of a very large sphere looks flat.

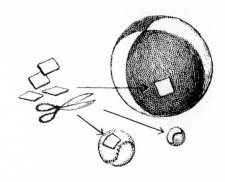

ACTIVITY

To demonstrate this idea, get some balls of various sizes (a beach ball and a ping-pong ball, for example). Cut out paper squares about one inch on a side. Press a square firmly against each ball. Notice how much flatter a square appears on the largest ball.[15]

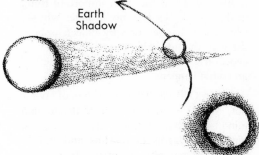

Earth Shadow

University of California Science Project

Robert Karplus, a physicist, is exploring a concept of science education based upon communicating scientific literacy. His own definition of scientific literacy requires students to develop "sufficient knowledge and experience so that they will be able to have some understanding of scientific work being carried out by others even though they themselves do not become scientists."[16] Stress in

---

[15]*Ibid.,* pp. 4-5.

[16]Robert Karplus, "One Physicist Looks at Science Education," (College Park, Maryland: University of Maryland), p. 12. Paper presented at the Eighth ASCD Curriculum Research Institute, April 27, 1963, Washington, D. C.

this study is upon teaching pupils to look at natural phenomena from the scientific point of view, encompassing a scientific conceptual framework and language. Karplus, like many other scientists, feels that only by carrying out investigations himself can the student become acquainted with the experience of wrestling with a scientific problem. He has worked directly with children in an effort to help them make personal investigations. Below is an excerpt of such experiences from *Meet Mr. O*,[17] a booklet describing experiments carried out by the author with elementary school children in Berkeley, California:

MEET MR. O

Allow me to introduce Mr. O. Mr. O. is an artificial observer. He knows where every object is at all times, but he describes the location of everything always relative to himself. He is the most important thing in the world. He does not wonder why — why events happen or why objects appear the way they do. He "reports" in his very egocentric way only what can be observed and what happens.

Is Mr. O like a real person? No, of course not. Mr. O is an invention of the human mind. His characteristics are assigned to him for pedagogical reasons and not to make him resemble a person. In his "reports" he summarizes the knowledge of the person who uses the Mr. O concept, and he is not confined by perceptual limitations of his own.

If a Mr. O on a table is asked, "Where are you?" he can only answer, "I am right here," perhaps while pointing to himself. If he were asked, "Where is the table?" he would say, "Underneath my feet." For the pupils in a class, of course, Mr. O is on the table. Such a point of view, however, subordinates Mr. O to the table. For Mr. O, he himself is the central reference point, and the way he faces defines the reference directions. Since he accepts no external reference object, he has no way

to describe where he is other than by pointing at himself. For himself he is always in the same place, namely, "Right here."

As was pointed out above, Mr. O is an artificial observer. His characteristics are unlike common sense. Yet three examples will show everyone's common sense outlook involves the use of the Mr. O concept in an unconscious way.

Example 1. Mother drives her daughter to school. The girl starts to climb into the back seat. "Don't move around so much. Sit still," mother says. The daughter obeys. That satisfies mother. But is the daughter really not moving? That depends. For a Mr. O in the car, she is indeed sitting still. For a Mr. O on the sidewalk, however, the car, the mother, and daughter are moving past at perhaps 30 mph. Mother automatically uses both of these Mr. O's: one inside the car when she thinks about her daughter's behavior; one on the sidewalk when she thinks about the car as a whole.

Example 2. In a bus, the situation is still more interesting. As the bus starts suddenly, the passengers seem to fall backwards. Do they really fall backwards? Not for a Mr. O on the road; for him, they are moving forward, but more slowly than the bus. For a Mr. O on the bus, of course, they do move backwards. Who is right?

Example 3. In astronomy, everyone learns that the earth rotates on its axis and moves around the sun. Is this true? For an observer on the sun, it is. But for an observer on the earth, the earth doesn't move at all; it is fixed beneath his feet. Instead, the sun and the moon move around the earth and show certain seasonal variations. Which idea is right?

Once the observer fixed on the earth was the only one considered consciously. Nowadays, man's thinking is nimble, and he can conceive of the different observers that have been mentioned and many more. Each Mr. O is right for himself, from his point of view. The question, "What is really happening?" has no scientific meaning anymore. Instead, the scientific mind thinks about a phenomenon from several points of view and then chooses the one that permits the simplest description and

---

[17]Robert Karplus, *Meet Mr. O* (College Park, Maryland: Department of Physics and Astronomy, University of Maryland, March, 1963), pp. 1–3.

that leads to the best understanding. For this reason, everyone thinks about the solar system like an observer on the sun. Which observer to choose for studying the passengers on the bus is less clear.

Elementary Science Study

The evidence of change in the natural world and in certain scientific values can be understood and appreciated by even the youngest children. The work of the Elementary Science Study indicates that a new coherence in the elementary science curriculum is possible and that some of the aims and methods of science, assimilated in the earliest years, can be effectively related to many other disciplines during the earliest school years.

Seven programs or units of elementary science study were developed during the 1962 Summer Conference at the Newton South High School, Newton, Massachusetts. A group of twenty-five research scientists in a variety of fields, an equal number of experienced elementary school teachers and supervisors, a few researchers in the area of the learning process, together with artists, photographers, and laboratory and shop technicians were brought together to prepare materials for introducing the spirit and concepts of science to elementary school children. Units were developed in these areas: microecology, plant growth, laboratory science, elementary physics, charges and currents, gases and airs, animal coloration, cell unit, astronomy, animal behavior and locomotion, carbon and energy, chemical reactions, geology, physics and light, and psychology of learning. In addition to the units, texts, graphic materials, apparatus, and teacher aids were devised. The following is a sample from the unit, *Growing Seeds*.[18]

GROWING SEEDS

Introduction — Growing seeds provides an opportunity to touch upon one of two cen-

tral themes of science as early as first grade. Classifying or distinguishing among things on the basis of similarities and differences is the key activity. What makes a seed a seed? Because it grows into a plant? Here children classify not as a brittle mechanical exercise, but as a lively, functional part of their "finding out." While they find out what seeds do, they are also deciding what seeds are.

Measurement can also be introduced in a meaningful way as children themselves come to feel the need for it. They see that measuring is a good way of keeping track, that it can help answer questions which could not be answered otherwise. They can develop their own methods for recording their measurements and discover that some are more helpful than others.

Designing their techniques themselves, the children really understand what they are for, what they do, and how they might be modified in another situation to do something differently.

Are They Seeds? Our procedure is to give each child a little package of ten to twelve different things that we think look like

[18]*Growing Seeds* (Watertown, Massachusetts: Educational Services, Inc., March, 1963), pp. 1-2.

seeds — some of them actually are, and some are not. Some of the things we have used are listed.

Indian corn	yellow-eye beans
popping corn	red kidney beans
miniature corn	morning-glory seeds
beet seeds	acorns
radish seeds	gravel
orange seeds	lead shot
mung beans	vermiculite
dried peas	charcoal

Acorns take three to four weeks to germinate, orange seeds seven to eight. (It is sometimes fun to use one of these because they take so much longer than any other kinds of seeds.)

It is important that most of the ones which are seeds should be kinds that will start to grow within a week or two. As for the non-seeds, the main thing is that they should look as if they might be seeds. These "seeds" can be distributed in small envelopes, plastic pill boxes, or just twists of paper.

Considerable interest and excitement are usually aroused simply by asking the student what the objects are. If you feel you need more structuring, you could start casually planting some in a paper cupful of soil, so the children will start to wonder what you are doing. Before long they will suggest that they are seeds. Now you can simply ask them, "Are you sure?" and encourage them to look closely.

Many of them are likely to object that some of the things they have are not seeds. Let them get into discussions with each other about which are seeds and which are not. All sorts of ideas about seeds will come out in their remarks; try to keep track of these as best as you can. Here is a sample of the remarks we overheard:

"This can't be a seed. It's too hard."
"Yes, that's a seed, because it has that little mark."
  (This was a very astute observation of the small scar on the outside coat of most seeds.)
"This is too flaky to be a seed."
"Seeds aren't black."

The children themselves will be highly critical of each other's criteria; try to encourage this interplay whenever possible. You can also take part in their discussions from time to time, by pointing out when they are inconsistent. For example, if they say seeds cannot be hard, give them a bean seed. If they say seeds can't be shiny, give them a corn seed. You might try to anticipate what they will say and have other seeds at hand as counter-examples.

This is likely to lead to a lot of good observation and thinking so that they will be ready for a general class discussion about the best ways to decide what is a seed and what is not. At first, they may suggest things like, "Look it up in a book;" "I could ask my mother." You may have to suggest that they think of things they can do to the little objects to find out which are seeds. Then they are likely to come up with a number of interesting suggestions. One idea that should come up is to plant them and to see which ones will grow. This is probably the best one to do first.

At this point, then, we are prepared with soil and a number of clear plastic sandwich boxes or other transparent containers. The best idea probably is to have one box for each kind of "seed" so that all the thirty corn seeds are put into one box, the lead shot in another, etc.

Summary of Advantages of Scientist-Educator Programs

The combination of professional scientists and educators for developing scope, sequence, and experiences in the elementary school science program present these advantages:

1. The development of new ideas and information in the science fields is so rapid that only professional scientists directly concerned with these developments can possibly hope to keep up-to-date.

2. Many of our previous concepts, facts, and viewpoints are partially or completely inaccurate; we must rely upon

experts to assist us in reviewing and revising our science concepts.

3. By presenting content on the basis of its crucial role in a scientific discipline, we can minimize or eliminate some of the ambiguity that may arise from a program that stresses only utility or facts in science. There could be a greater stress upon basic scientific principles and processes than some of our current gadget-type science programs.

4. The work of the scientist in fields of various disciplines can be utilized for having children gain insights into the significant problems that the scientists are encountering and the ways in which they are attempting to solve them. This is important for children to see and for the teacher to point out that scientists attack problems differently due to the uniqueness of their problems and their own personality; it is vital that teachers stress the fact that there is not any one scientific method.

5. We are presented with an excellent opportunity to present to children the occupational pursuits of different types of scientists, not as vocational training but as possible interest stimulation. It has been mentioned previously that because of the urgent need for an ever-increasing technical and scientifically trained populace, it is wise for education to present aspects of scientific jobs so that children may develop positive and even vocational attitudes about the work of these people.

6. An association of scientists and educators working on a joint scope and sequence of science concepts in many scientific fields will also perform an excellent public relations function by:

   a. bringing members of different disciplines together for an inter-disciplinary assignment.

   b. assisting members of the different disciplines in gaining a greater understanding and appreciation of the others' work.

   c. aiding in the off-set of accurate or inaccurate criticisms that our schools are not keeping up with the latest in science.

The scope and sequence of discovery procedures jointly prepared by professional scientists and educators can do much to up-date our science curriculum in the elementary school. In the experimental programs in which such cooperative work was done, it was found that content and discovery activities selected solely because of their crucial role in scientific discipline, as suggested by a professional scientist in that specific field, were exciting for children, and the comprehensions of such content by children in the normal intelligence range is truly surprising. At present, these joint programs are limited in number and are still somewhat experimental, but they are impressive. The list of basic science concepts and principles that are evolving may someday be used as the basis for many elementary school science programs, but it will take more work with children to refine them before they are ready for wide-spread adoption.

A Word of Caution

A planned and structured science education program should be tailor made for each school district. There should not be a single science education program for all school systems. Due to regional differences, the pace and level of instruction from school to school, even within a school district, vary in the quality of instructional materials as well as in their philosophical and psychological characteristics. Schools themselves are the only ones capable of determining the specific curricular organization into which their science education must fit. The authors will use the broad, basic concept areas recommended on page 164 by the AAAS

Feasibility Conferences for presenting actual discovery-type lesson plans in Part IV of this book. Teachers will find broad science content areas and discovery lessons as well as useful suggestions and explanations for preparing experiences for their children.

Summary

Science presents us with an accumulated and systematized body of basic concepts and principles surviving centuries of ceaseless testing and refinement. This is the product of science. The spirit of the endless testing of data and findings — the scientific attitudes and methods — are the chief contributions of science to man's quest for answers about himself and his universe. This is the process of science. Programs of science education, therefore, must use these elements of science in formulating their curriculums:

1. Science education for the elementary school should have a well-defined structure of basic science concepts and principles, so that there is an order and continuity to the program. Flexibility and variety are desirable within this structure.

2. Although a scope and sequence of science concepts is desirable as a guide, it should be recognized that no one knows the best order and selection from among all that might be taught; therefore, the teacher can be the only one to make the final decision of selection of specific items to be taught from suggested guides.

3. In order to be of greatest value, the preparation of instructional materials should be the joint efforts of scientists, classroom science teachers, and specialists in learning and teacher preparation.

4. Science education should emphasize the development of scientific principles and methodology instead of the memorization of facts. Teachers should employ the experimental or discovery approach to science with emphasis upon inductive learning, problem solving, and critical thinking.

Further Investigation and Study

1. Many well-qualified scientists and scholars have rejected the idea that there is a scientific method. Select from the following references and read about the ever-widening controversy over the scientific method and the question of the existence of one general method.

Ashford, Theodore Askounes. *From Atoms to Stars.* New York: Holt, Rinehart & Winston, Inc., 1960, Chapter 1.

Brandwein, Paul F., Fletcher G. Watson, and Paul E. Blackwood. *Teaching High School Science: A Book of Methods.* New York: Harcourt, Brace & World, Inc., 1958, Chapter 1.

Bridgman, P. W. "Prospect for Intelligence," *Yale Review,* No. 34 (1945), p. 450.

Cohen, I. Bernard. *Science, Servant of Man.* Boston: Little, Brown & Co., 1948, Chapters 2-5, 17, 18.

Conant, James B. *Science and Common Sense.* New Haven: Yale University Press, 1951, Chapters 1-3, 11-12.

_____. (ed.) *Harvard Case Histories in Experimental Science.* Cambridge, Massachusetts: Harvard University Press, 1957. (Introduction).

Kemeny, John G. A. *Philosopher Looks at Science.* Princeton: D. Van Nostrand Co., Inc., 1959, Chapters 5, 10.

Bright, Wilson E., Jr. *An Introduction to Scientific Research.* New York: McGraw-Hill Book Co., Inc., 1952, Chapter 3.

2. The hunch, brilliant flash of imagination, educated guess, or intuition all seem to have played some part in the mental processes of many research scientists. It would be profitable for you to read about these from research scientists themselves in the following, enjoyably written articles:

Beveridge, W. B. *The Art of Scientific Investigation.* New York: W. W. Norton & Company, Inc., 1957, Chapters 5, 6.

Conant, James B. *Science and Common Sense.* New Haven: Yale University Press, 1951, p. 48.

Sayvetz, Aaron. *Scientists at Work: Case Studies in the Physical Sciences.* Chicago: Center for the Study of Liberal Education for Adults, 1954.

Wolf, Abraham. "Scientific Method," Encyclopaedia Britannica (1955), pp. 125-31.

3. Select several everyday problems in your personal life from such areas as the economic, social, scholastic, or professional field. Analyze the processes by which you arrived at some solutions to these problems.

4. Analyze the Science Curriculum Guide for your school district, the State Curriculum Guide, or any other science curriculum guides that you can get, in terms of the areas suggested by the AAAS Feasibility Recommended Broad Scientific Concept Areas. Compare your guide with the Feasibility Recommendations as to differences and similar-

ities in content and language. You are urged to read the following for additional information: *Science,* 1331, No. 3469 (June 23, 1961), p. 2021.

5. Describe some of the factors shaping elementary school science.

6. A scientist discussing the scientific method said about cancer research:
    "What does *not* cure cancer is as much scientific as what cures cancer."
What did he mean?

7. What is the role of failure in science?

8. What are some misconceptions of scientists? What would you do to help children correct these misconceptions?

9. What checks does the scientific method contain for human frailty?

10. Why should the science program for the elementary school be structured?

Why Teach Science in the Elementary School?

Elementary schools in our country are faced with a formidable task of teaching more concepts today than ever before in our history. Elementary teachers naturally resist additions of new material to an already burdensome curriculum. It is, however, the responsibility of schools to prepare youth for the world of tomorrow. The world daily manifests scientific and technological developments. These shall continue and cause greater dislocations between the curriculum of the elementary school and our society. The citizens of the future, the elementary school students of today, will have to function in a complex society of rapid, scientific, and technological changes. They will need to be liberally educated with an extensive comprehension of scientific concepts, principles, attitudes, and modes of thought. It takes a long time to educate a person to be so qualified. A paramount task of the elementary teacher is to begin now to prepare children for a scientific and technical society. No elementary school can be meeting its responsibility unless it does encompass science instruction in its curriculum for the world of tomorrow.

THE CHALLENGE OF THE FUTURE

What will the world of tomorrow be like? What will today's first graders face in the future? Any elementary teacher must face this question in

23

order to formulate a modern curriculum. Truly the task of a curriculum builder in this decade is an unenviable one. The challenge is so great and our sight into the future so limited.

The Population Explosion Requires Better Science and Technology

All is not a mystery about the future. We know, for example, that the population growth of our country and world will continue to increase. The population in the United States is approaching the 200 million mark and will progress to 380 million by the year 2000. The United States population will more than double in the next forty years. This phenomenal growth is not only true for our country but for the world as well.

What does this growth mean for the generations ahead? It means fewer raw resources for more people to use. It means more of the earth's wealth will be gleaned from poorer resources. These increasing demands will require a more sophisticated technology with additional inventive minds. It is easy to mine the pure but hard to purify the mined. Waste in such a world cannot be tolerated. Conservation in the future will have to become a way of life, not just a phrase spoken by the wasteful. Included in conservation will be a more dynamic awareness of man's place in the ecological setting in which he operates. Man

must see the effects of his actions upon his environment. The future generations must be able to understand their place in the world and their interactions with it. They must realize that to destroy one facet of the environment may cause all to suffer. For example, to spray a community with insecticide to kill flies may result in the death of bees. Bees are necessary for their honey and pollination. Lack of pollination decreases seed production which, if continued, may lead to erosional problems.

Schools have a major responsibility to prepare citizens to cope with problems caused by increased population. Future citizens must be able to solve such problems intelligently and effectively. Certainly good science instruction on the elementary school level can help children learn skills that may aid them in solving these problems.

The Development of a Scientifically Literate Populace

Elementary school science must carry its share of the responsibility for helping to mold an intelligent citizenry. Scientific literacy and the development of mature attitudes toward national and international problems are as much the responsibility of science as social studies or citizenship education. The layman today is surrounded by scientific words: radio, electronics, penicillin, polio vaccine, missile, radiation, and isotope. He must make intelligent decisions based on his understanding of these words and concepts. An example of this decision-making on scientific matters by laymen can be seen in state and national political life. Most senators and representatives are trained as lawyers with only the barest necessities of science as part of their training. Yet, these politicians must sit in judgment of the value of expenditures for space flight research, public health, atomic energy, National Science Foundation expenditures, and military

HOW DOES RADIATION AFFECT THE GROWTH OF PLANTS?

GROWTH IN MILLIMETERS

RESULTS OF BARLEY SEED VARIOUS DOSAGE

preparedness programs. The wiseness of their decisions is dependent upon their understandings of science. Because of a continually accelerated growth of scientific knowledge and its influence on society, education for science literacy must start in the elementary grades. The truly educated man of the future will have to be scientifically literate.

Increased Population Mobility

A second, important aspect of the population explosion is the increased mobility of people. Population pressures cause people to move. Easy and inexpensive transportation facilitates rapid movement from one part of the country to another. In the United States very few individuals are born, live, and die in the same house, neighborhood, or state. Immigration in Los Angeles alone each week brings enough children into the city to build a school system the size of Rochester, New York. A child may be born in Iowa, raised in Kansas, New York, and California before he reaches high school age. This has far reaching implications for our national educational policies. Most science educators agree that there should be a kindergarten through twelfth grade science curriculum. Many school systems have actually organized such a curriculum. If all school systems had such an organization, children would face less difficulties when they transfer from one school to another. It must be extremely difficult for a child lacking any experience in science to enter a classroom of scientifically well-qualified children. He will undoubtedly feel insecure in the new subject because of his lack of experience compared to the rest of the class.

Donald, a fourth grader, is a case in point. He came from a small, rural school in the Mid-West where no science was taught. His folks moved West, and Donald entered a school where science was empha-

sized in the elementary grades. He seemed interested in the experiments the teacher did. However, during free time he never chose to do student experiments or to go to the science corner. When the teacher asked questions about a demonstration in class, he seldom showed enthusiasm to participate. Jane, Mack, and Anne, the children around him, had lived science experiences in the first, second, and third grades. They understood it, liked it, and most important, experienced success in their study of science. How long will it take Donald to catch up? Will he ever overcome a feeling of inadequacy in science? The shock of not being able to achieve well compared to the others in the class may cause him to dislike science. The cost of such a loss to science and to Donald cannot be assessed. A negative impression of science on a formative mind is not erased easily as the child passes from grade to grade. The truth is that it could have been prevented.

Prepare the Mind for Change

Increased population and technology require a mind more adjustable and more tolerant to change. It is not easy to train an individual to be prepared to live in a society complicated by myriads of technological gadgets. The stresses of the 1980's will be a far cry from the pastoral bliss of a Hopi or Tahitian community. The mind of the future must be prepared for rapid adjustments, greater insecurity, and acceptance of new and modern developments. Progress by its essence breeds insecurity because the traditional and orthodox patterns of life are changed. The price of progress may be high. Prevention of mental disease, therefore, will continue to be a challenge. Thus, the task of teachers is to insure that neurotics and psychotics are not nurtured by preparing children at an early age for the increasing changes and insecurities.

One important contribution a science program can make in helping children to achieve a sense of the dynamics of change is to show them that nothing is fixed and that the only constant in the universe is change. In a recent booklet by the Manufacturing Chemists Association, open-end experiments in

chemistry are presented for kindergarten through third grade so that the teacher can start even these young children to observe universal change and to become comfortable with it. In the brief sample of the following experiments, it can be seen that these activities can help five to seven year olds to see that change is not terrifying or unpredictable but orderly, rhythmical, and endless.

In what ways do things around us change?
Take your pupils on a hunt for change in the classroom, in and around the school building, and through the neighborhood.
Prepare them to look for signs of change when they are on trips and also when they are at home. Have the youngsters report any changes they observe. Record these observations on a chart for the whole class to see. Sample questions, with some of the possible observations given in parentheses, are the following:

What happens to a cut flower? (It wilts and decays.)
What happens to milk left out of the refrigerator? (It turns sour.)
What happens when you bend a wire back and forth? (It gets hot; it breaks.)

What happens to a puddle in the street? (It dries up.)
What happens to paint on some wood? (It peels.)
What happens to freshly poured cement? (It hardens.)
What happens to some wood when left in the earth? (It decays.)
What happens to a green tomato in sunlight? (It turns red as it ripens.)
What happens to colored paper in the sunlight? (It fades.)
What happens to unprotected iron? (It rusts.)
What happens when a potato is boiled? (It gets soft.)
What happens to an egg when it is boiled for ten minutes? (It gets hard.)
What happens to a mixture of gelatine and water? (It becomes a jelly-like substance.)
What happens to a sheet of newspaper when it gets old? (It yellows and loses some of its strength.)
What happens to an apple that has been bitten into? (It turns brown.)[1]

Additional evidences of change can be seen by children in the metamorphosis of a butterfly, seasonal changes, bird migrations, growth of their own bodies and abilities, and other changes in their immediate environment. These changes, however, are orderly and consistent changes which lawfully become apparent when children explore and discover for themselves through the teacher's guidance.

The Loss of Relatedness of People to Each Other and to Their Environment

It is not easy for people to feel that they have anything personally to do with conditions in the world especially if they do not feel affected directly. An example of this occurs in communities where people are not aware of the responsibility they have for the seemingly innocent, everyday hazards, such as, improper automobile carburetor adjust-

[1]*Matter, Energy, and Change* (New York: Holt, Rinehart & Winston, Inc., 1960), p. 8.

ment resulting in excessive air pollution, inadequately supervised and controlled trash burning resulting in fire and destruction of property and trees, shrubs and ground cover destroyed in making room for housing developments resulting in bare, unattractive land unprotected from erosion. Likewise, it is difficult for people to understand the physical environment in which they live and their interrelatedness to it. The psychological and emotional implications of the environment upon man were reviewed in the previous section. In the preceding discussion about the necessity of a planned, developmental program of science in the elementary school, it was pointed out that a child can be helped to see some order in the environment in which he lives. This is the beginning of a feeling of relatedness to the environment; through organization of this program, the feeling can be broadened and deepened.

A Part of the Total Program of the Elementary School

In an effort to help children see science in relationship to man and his environment, whenever possible, science should be a part of the total elementary school curriculum. This integration of science with other subject matter, as opposed to the separate subject approach where, for example, the geography of Long Island and the history of Jamestown were presented separately in the same morning, helps strengthen the bonds between science and the concepts and subject matter of other areas of the curriculum. By integrating science with other areas of the curriculum, it is not meant that science as a recognized subject should be lost; instead, time is organized and learning experiences are planned in the curriculum so that science enriches and is enriched by other curricular areas. When a science concept such as the transmission of electric (radio) waves through a vacuum (space) is presented in

conjunction with a social studies course on the international implications of space and space satellites, each subject profits from the other. By understanding the forces and properties of our universe a more meaningful comparison of the early explorers of America and the modern pilgrims or explorers into space is developed. Such common problems of spacemen and pilgrims stressing the closeness of the social studies and science are shown:

How did they get from one place to another? How did they steer their crafts?

What were their crafts made of? What aspects of our universe helped them? Hindered them?

What did they eat and how did they get their food?

How did they know where they were?

Why did they go?

Without the loss of any science material, studies can be prepared in order to provide for the integration of science with the other areas of the curriculum. In this way, the child can be helped to see by example and not by preaching that science helps man interpret and understand his environment from all aspects: health, safety, ways of making a living, ways of transporting, and communicating.

The Social Aspect of Science Should Be Stressed

Another implication is the necessity to look at science from the social or humanitarian aspects. By investigating man's past, children should be helped to view man's use of the contributions of science to control much of his environment. As man has learned more about the physical environment in which he lives, he has found ways in which to modify those elements most detrimental to his way of life. The scientist's role in the society should also be explored by elementary school children; scientists should be seen as part of the society rather than as an isolated segment. It should be pointed out that when correlating is forced or stereotyped, much of the value is lost. Most of the aspects of science in the elementary school lend themselves naturally to correlation and integration with other subject areas.

Science Instruction Can Lead to Better Use of Leisure Time

In spite of the demands of population growth, leisure time will undoubtedly gain in magnitude. Today a considerably shortened work week in many areas already indicates the labor trend. One can but wonder what workers will do with all their free time. Leisure to the Greeks meant time when citizens fulfilled their civic responsibilities and family duties, improved their minds, and recreated their souls. It was not a time only for play or licentiousness. The Greek concept of leisure is useful and culturally desirable. Citizens of the future should look upon leisure as a wonderful opportunity, a time to contribute to the cultural enrichment of community and family. Leisure should be a blessing and not a curse to be wasted later in life in drunken rivalry or simple diversions in hopes that "it too shall pass away." Science because of its investigatory quality offers a wealth of leisure activities. What boy or girl has not been fascinated with exploring a river, slough, or beach. What a thrill and what fun it is to discover some creature scurrying about its natural environment. Children are fascinated with crayfish, pollywogs, young frogs, mosquito larvae, cocoons, spiders, and burrowing animals. This is substantiated by the popularity of animated animals in cartoons. Children's love for adventure is bountiful. They enjoy collecting rocks, leaves, and flowers. Picture a fourth grade class visiting a pond to study its life. Jo Ann runs to the teacher, Mrs. Johnson, and shows her three leaves she collected from different plants near the water. Mark has captured a small insect that can walk on the surface of the water. He asks, "How can it walk on the water when I can't?" What fun it will be finding the answer to this question. Jerry has found some mosquito larvae and runs to the teacher and asks, "Why do they wiggle? Are they going to die?"

Mrs. Johnson is building a lasting foundation in kindling a thrill for inquiry. Her pupils will one day leave, but she has left an imprint, a love for exploring the world.

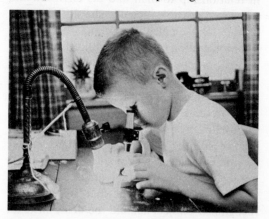

If these experiences are nurtured and reinforced in other grades, the children as adults will have the ability to use their leisure time wisely. They will be rock hounds, photographers, hikers, natural history addicts, readers, and collectors. For many children this will become a way of life. The leisure aspects of science are endless. Elementary teachers can open a world of excitement and adventure in leisure pursuits for their pupils and themselves.

Scientific and Technical Professions Present Great Opportunities

What will be the vocational world of the future? In what jobs will our pupils be employed? The scientific and engineering demands are the fastest growing areas of manpower supply.[2] The National Science Foundation estimates that by 1970 we will need 2.5 million scientists and engineers; whereas, in 1960 we only had 1.4 million. Needs in these fields increase on an average of six per cent per year. The demands for doctoral graduates in science and engineering will double by 1970. Growth of research and development expenditures over the past decade has accelerated. For example, expenditures have increased in the ten year period of 1950 to 1960 from 3.5 billion dollars to over 14 billion.[3] Who does this research and development? Obviously it requires highly trained technical and scientific manpower. Even today one has only to look at the want-ad section of a large metropolitan paper to realize how great the demand is for such people. It is reasonable to think that almost every citizen in the labor force in the next decade will work in some position involving technical tasks. The best employment opportunities in the future will be in the scientific and technical fields. The schools must prepare to take advantage of these opportunities. The elementary school has a significant role to play in preparing people for future vocations.

[2]National Science Foundation, *Investing in Scientific Progress, 1961-1970* (Washington, D. C.: U. S. Government Printing Office, 1961), p. 14.

[3]National Science Foundation, *11th Annual Report* (Washington, D. C.: U. S. Government Printing Office), p. 148.

Grin and Bear it   By Lichty

"No experience in electronics? . . . Great scott, miss, don't you realize this is an office? . . ."

More Women Will Enter Science Professions

Although proportionately fewer women are employed as scientists, engineers, and technicians today, more and more will be filling these capacities. Why shouldn't we expect women to be involved in technical pursuits? The American myth of masculine professional occupations must be changed. America no longer can afford to waste our women's intellectual pool. Failure to prepare women for tasks commensurate with their intelligence invites an indictment against the American school system.

Russians employ far more women in technical and professional fields than we do. In 1961 more than thirty-six per cent of Soviet engineering students were women, whereas, the United States enrolled less than .7 per cent in 1961.[4] Women in the future, because of increased efficiency in the home, will be able to devote more time to technical and professional activities. Elementary teachers are challenged to find and encourage those girls who have potential to become scientists,

[4]DeWitt, "Soviet Education: Newly Published Study Raises Some Disturbing Questions From the West," *Science,* January 19, 1962, p. 205.

engineers, or technicians. This potential is likely to manifest itself when girls are learning science in the elementary and junior high school. It is in the lower grades where outstanding future scientists are often caught in a web of interest which will later become their life work. It takes a long time to develop a scientist or engineer. Their training must of necessity begin early. A recent study of 384 high school students, finalists in the thirteenth National Science Fair, showed that many of them were stimulated toward thought of becoming a scientist while in the elementary grades.[5] Elementary teachers must help counsel girls with potential to think of science as a possible career. Imagine how you would feel if you had discovered a Madame Curie in the early grades and set her on her scientific career. Anne Roe[6] has suggested that teachers try to change the idea that some occupations are masculine and some feminine. Our culture tends to start early to build such an idea. Witness many parents' attitudes toward children's toys. Often mechanical toys or science kits are thought to be essentially masculine. Elementary teachers can correct such attitudes. By doing this, they insure that girls with scientific or intellectual potential are allowed to manifest their natural abilities.

Creative Minds in Science Must Be Discovered

Another future manpower problem is the development of highly creative individuals. American industry is built on competition which is not unique to the borders of continental United States. American products have to compete with foreign merchandise on world markets. Because of our standard of living and our labor costs, we cannot compete on a labor basis. Then, on what basis are we competing? We are selling our creative genius. We must always be on the frontier with newly developed industrial products. This requires very creative minds, minds that see and produce scientific and technical products not yet realized by foreign competitors. Maintenance of our standard of living depends upon nurturing creative individuals in our schools.

There is not a surplus supply of creative and gifted individuals in a labor force. We need far more than we presently have, and this need will accelerate. Instruction in elementary science can aid in meeting demands for the creative individuals in future generations.

Stimulate Science Career Interest

Although elementary school science education cannot be geared for training technicians, scientists, or other highly skilled scientific personnel, it can instill a desire in children to investigate the work of these people. Through studying science and the way a scientist works, children can be stimulated to think of science as a career. In the minds of children and adults, a scientist with a long white coat, flowing beard, and wild-eyed expression has too long been the image. Elementary science education can make children realize that scientists have challenging, worthwhile professions. Scientists are not weird individuals working in the realm of magic. By reading about scientists and their profession, children are better able to understand the role of scientists in society and to begin to build realistic impressions of the field of science.

It is an obligation of elementary teachers to expose children to descriptions and contributions of various scientific fields in the same manner that they discuss other professions. Instead of limiting the children's direct contact with the work of the fireman,

[5]DeWitt, "Science Interest Peak at Age 12," *Science Newsletter,* September 15, 1962, pp. 178-79.

[6]Paul Torrance, *Talent and Education* (Minneapolis: University of Minnesota Press), p. 68. (Paper presented at the 1958 Institute on Gifted Children.)

the policeman, and the farmer, the teacher should also present scientists at work. Have the children read about biochemists, physicists, laboratory and statistical technicians, and have them visit some of the laboratories in which they are employed. Almost every community has one electronics plant, biological or medical laboratory, hospital, and research facilities which can serve this purpose.

The greatest value gained by seeing scientists at work in their natural environment is that children see scientists not as radical extremists, but as methodical, searching, responsible people. By talking with them and their aides, children begin to see the importance of scientific work. Many scientific and commercial companies are devoting time to educating the public to the realistic nature of science. Publications are available for this purpose through pharmaceutical companies, medical supply houses, and government agencies. A partial list of such resources can be found at the end of this book and in science teacher journals. Before materials are used in the classroom, however, teachers must screen them for objectional or excessive advertising. Even six year olds can become as excited about a scientist as they do about a fireman. It is never too early to begin building realistic concepts of the scientific professions.

Summary

1. Science teaching in the elementary school carries the responsibility for developing children's attitudes and skills for making wise decisions concerning their future.

2. Children today live in a society characterized by a scientific and technological development. They are required to know and understand science in order to operate in society effectively.

3. Population increases and technological developments require more scientists, engineers, and technicians to maintain and improve our standard of living.

4. Population growth demands that individuals be better educated and more scientifically literate.

5. Children should be taught to accept change. They must recognize that nothing is fixed and that the only constant factor of our universe is change. They should expect change and the problems inherent with it. Science by nature evolves and can help to build a better understanding of the processes of change.

6. More attention must be given to leisure pursuits. Science instruction can help to build desirable uses of leisure time.

7. The occupations in the varied fields of science should be presented in order to stimulate children to think of them as possible future careers.

8. Great opportunities for employment and success in the future will be in scientific and technical fields.

9. Greater attention must be given to discovering and developing the scientific capabilities of girls. Those girls with ability and interest should be encouraged to study science. Women will play a more dynamic role in science and technology.

10. Science is creative. The American industrial complex is dependent upon the creative genius of our scientists and engineers. If we are to maintain our present standard of living and if we are to compete internationally, we must discover more creative minds.

11. Elementary school science is needed by all children. It is not only for those gifted in science. Pupils must understand the role science and scientists play in the democratic society. Our children, the citizens of tomorrow, need a realistic view of the scientist, his work, and research so they may make valid decisions relative to the scientific enterprise.

Further Investigation and Study

1. What is the challenge of the future?

2. Why is it hard to devise a curriculum which will have meaning for the elementary student ten to twelve years from now?

3. How will population pressures affect society?

4. Why should we have a scientifically literate populace?

5. How can science contribute to better use of leisure time?

6. What are the opportunities in the scientific and technical professions?

7. What will be the role of women in the sciences?

8. American labor is extremely costly compared to the rest of the world. How is it possible, then, for our industries to compete internationally?

9. Why should all children be required to have some science?

10. Why should elementary teachers spend part of their instructional time exposing children to scientific fields and professions?

The Nature of Science Teaching-Learning

3

Goals for a program of science education were presented in Chapter 1 and Chapter 2. A primary goal is the development of skills and attitudes for scientific investigation as well as scientific concepts and generalizations. In effect, we are concerned with developing sound patterns in our children's thinking, generally attributed to scientists as scientific thinking. It is, therefore, important for us as science teachers to look at what thinking is, the process by which it develops, the conditions by which it is facilitated, and finally what we as science teachers can do to nourish and direct it.

SCIENCE AND THINKING

Both Are Processes and Produce Products

Thinking is an extremely complex process. In many ways the processes of thinking resemble the *processes* of science as described in Chapter 1. For instance, instead of just one kind of thinking, there appear to be many just as there are many types of scientific processes or methods. Six types of thinking can readily be described: perceptive, associative, inductive-deductive, creative or imaginative, critical, and problem solving.[1] These types will be described later in depth.

Secondly, thinking is a process which produces a *product* as does science. The raw materials in thinking are sensations, percepts, concepts, and principles or generalizations which shape the *products* to be derived from the *processes* of thinking.

Thirdly, the *products* of thinking are varied. Among these are conclusions, opinions, thinking techniques, habits, and behavior or action. A brief look at raw materials and processes of thinking will give direction to the science education program.

Importance of Percepts

Briefly, percepts develop from impressions or awarenesses of sensations caused by an environmental stimulus which requires little interpretation. For example, the infant reacts to the sight of his nursing bottle — the visual sensation — with pleasure — the percept — that this is warm and good. Percepts are primary factors in thinking which often initiate train of thought. Concepts and later generalizations depend a great deal upon percepts for their formulation. Our senses shape and influence our perceptions. This process generally goes through a continuum of being aware of a total situation, breaking the situation down into separate parts, and then reconstructing these separate parts back into a clear pattern. This whole process may take only a matter of seconds, but it is extremely important in learning for four reasons:

1. Perception is the process by which most of the raw materials of thinking becomes available for use.
2. Perceptions are among the child's earliest learnings.

3. Perceptual learning merges into concept formation.
4. Perception is essential to learning by imitation.[2]

Children learn about things through their perceptions. Their readiness for new learning experiences depends to a great degree upon the type and accuracy of perceptions the child has had. Research has shown that our perceptions are influenced by many factors:

1. We tend to perceive what we have learned to perceive.
2. We tend to perceive what we want to perceive.
3. We tend to perceive accurately when our observations fit into a pattern that has meaning.
4. We tend to perceive what others perceive.
5. We can reduce but not entirely prevent perceptual error.[3]

Children should be exposed to as many first-hand or direct experiences as possible.

Thus, in order to develop, strengthen, or correct children's science perceptions, the school and the home must supply numerous opportunities for children to explore, inquire, manipulate, and play with toys, blocks, tools, and other equipment. Daily sensory experiences must be provided such as, feeling sandpaper and silk, tasting foods, handling toys, feeling the wind, hearing sounds of the street or woods, and smelling flowers. Many other first-hand experiences are vital and are found through trips to farms, fac-

---

[1] Much of the descriptions of the process and products of thinking can be found in depth in: David H. Russell, *Children's Thinking* (Boston: Ginn & Company, 1956).

[2] David H. Russell, "Concepts," *Encyclopedia of Educational Research,* C. W. Harris, ed. (New York: The Macmillan Company, 1960).

[3] Harry W. Sartain, "Percepts and Concepts," Papers of the 17th Annual Conference on Reading at the University of Pittsburgh, Donald L. Leland, ed. (Pittsburgh: University of Pittsburgh Press, 1961).

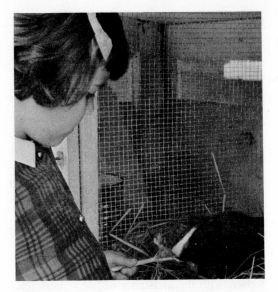

ality depends upon a type of thinking that slowly develops from the direct sensory experiences of children.[6] Sensory-motor experiences, such as manipulation, help the child construct and reconstruct percepts, concepts, generalizations, and other processes of thinking. This can be done on any level.

1. A young child believes a ball of clay changes weight when shape is changed. By changing shapes of clay he can experience that a long, thick, clay form can be the same weight as a short, thick one.
2. By trial and error primary grade children work out the relationships of weight and distance from the fulcrum on a teeter-totter. Later verbalization of the principle of inverse ratio of weight and distance will be possible.
3. The sixth grader who builds models of atoms with colored balls representing electrons, protons, and neutrons "sees" electrons gained and lost.

Each direct sensory activity then gives more fibers to the child upon which to weave the fabric of perception and thinking.

Science learning is improved by combining many senses.

Just as each active experience contributes to perception, each exerts an influence upon the other and reinforces it. By combining the five senses the learner is better able to reproduce for himself the experiences of real life situations which he encounters all

tories, and fields. Contrived experiences, such as pictures, books, television, films, and models, add to and enrich first-hand experiences. For instance, the young child who takes a trip to the harbor to see the tug boats perform is perceptually richer if by previous discussion, reading, and pictures he has developed a readiness and background for what he sees at the harbor. These early sensory experiences are very important; evidence shows that the bright student in physics and mathematics is more likely to have engaged in such sensory experiences as tinkering with toys, manipulating things, and inquiring through senses as a young child.[4] This also seems to be true for college freshmen whose differences in ability to learn science and mathematics have been partially traced to variances in the amount of their earlier direct sensory experiences.[5]

Piaget and his associates have gone even further with the relationship of direct sensory experiences to learning. They state that children's ability to deal with the broad concepts of space, time, matter, and caus-

[4]Celia B. Stendler, "Cognitive Development of Children and Readiness for High School Physics," *American Journal of Physics,* 12 (December, 1961), pp. 832-35.

[5]*Ibid.,* pp. 832-35.

[6]Jean Piaget and Inhelder Barbel, *The Growth of Logical Thinking* (New York: Basic Books, Inc., 1958), and Jean Piaget, *Les Mechanismes Perceptifs* (Paris: Presses Universitaires de France, 1961). An excellent interpretation of the works of Jean Piaget can be found in:
Mc V. Hunt, *Intelligence and Experiences* (New York: The Ronald Press Company, 1961), Chapters 5, 6, and 7.

the time. Our experiences give us impressions simultaneously through more sensory receptors than may be realized. We respond to temperature, odor, and taste in situations and not merely to sound or sight. Part of the sensory impact may be lost by relying only upon sight or sound.

By using many senses in combination, perceptions upon which new science learnings can be fashioned are built up and strengthened. Simple percepts are usually part of a pattern of percepts affected by all sensory experiences. An intersensory percept such as a rabbit may consist of feeling the soft, warm, furry body, smelling its odors, seeing the whiteness, darting eyes, twitching nose, and nibbling of food.

Contrast two teachers trying to present to city children the functions of the dairy farm. Teacher A relies upon reading and describing a dairy and may even improve upon the restriction of verbal communication by using pictures. Obviously much is lacking in the strong impact on the senses which the children may experience through an actual visit to a dairy with teacher B. As the children observe the cows being fed and milked at the dairy, they experience pleasant odors of good hay and feed in a clean barn, sounds of animals eating, shuffling, breathing; animal heat and smells on a cool autumn day; and the refreshment and enjoyment of fresh, iced milk in the storage area.

Another excellent example to illustrate the value of many senses concerns the development of the concept "water" by the blind, deaf, and mute child, Helen Keller, with the assistance of her remarkable teacher, Anne Sullivan. Although the accounts vary, the story reportedly follows these general lines:

Miss Sullivan took one of Helen's hands, put it in a bowl, and poured cold water over it while holding Helen's other hand to her own mouth repeating "Water, Water, Water, Water," over and over. After countless, painfully frustrating repetitions, Miss Keller finally uttered, "Water." Miss Keller relates that her concept of water at that moment was "cold" because the water was cold. The alert teacher sensed the partial concept formation and repeated the procedure substituting warm water for the cold. For a long time after that, Miss Keller had the feeling that water was anything liquid. In an attempt to broaden Helen's concept of water, Anne Sullivan began introducing other liquids to Helen such as oils and kerosene for comparison. Eventually using the multi-sensory technique and utilizing the senses available to them (unfortunately only smell, taste, and touch), Miss Keller and Anne Sullivan developed what to us is simple concept.

We all recognize that real, direct experiences with all situations may not always be possible for children. However, it is very desirable to consider any and all aids (sound, color movies, records, displays, experiments) to present fully each sensory approach and to combine as many sensory activities as possible in the learning situation. In this way, vicarious experiences are given added effectiveness in making learning more meaningful.

Use of Percepts for Concept Formation

When percepts are recalled at some later time without the use of external stimuli, images and memories have been formed. Percepts in the form of images and memories may develop into greater abstractions called concepts. The concept is usually organized as a result of many related sensations, percepts, and images with verbal symbols incorporated. When the child can distinguish dogs from other furry animals, whether the dogs are large or small, Collie or Beagle, black or brown, he has applied the word dog to a group of ideas and has developed a concept. The following chart indicates how experiences with salt led to concept formation and how verbal symbols are developed from these concepts as a result of further interrelated experiences and clarification. There is an ascending level of abstraction based upon concrete experiences and the assignment of words for the concepts that emerge.

Levels of Abstraction

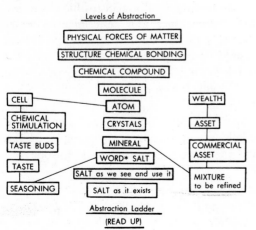

Abstraction Ladder
(READ UP)

Formation of Generalizations and Principles

Although the term concept is often limited to descriptive classes of things or events, such as dog, tree, and motion, there are other types of concepts. Generalizations and principles are concepts, but they differ from simple concepts in that they state some kind of relationship between two or more abstractions, objects, or events. Newton's Third Law, "For every action there is an equal and opposite reaction," is an example of a principle; the relationship between the concepts "action," "equal," and "opposite" is involved in this generalization.

The model illustrates the process and interrelationships of percepts, concepts, and generalizations.

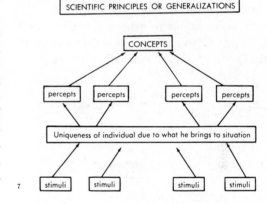

From this chart we summarize:

1. Persons screen and select stimuli.
2. Stimuli produce percepts.
3. Percepts form concepts.
4. Many concepts make principles or generalizations.

This process is often long and slow as is seen in the example of a child developing the

---
[7]Modified from chart in:
Charlotte Crabtree and Fannie Shaftel, "Fostering Thinking," *Curriculum for Today's Boys and Girls,* Robert S. Fleming, ed. (Columbus, Ohio: Charles E. Merrill Books, Inc., 1963), p. 259.

concept of a bottle and the generalizations of emptiness. A child sees one bottle and after a while many bottles of different sizes, shapes, colors, and contents. After many experiences, he begins to see that there is a certain amount of liquid in each. Eventually, he learns to distinguish empty bottles from full ones.

In summary, we have seen that the raw materials of thinking are sensations, percepts, concepts, and generalizations or principles.

Sensations develop an awareness of stimuli without much interpretation.

Percepts are what is known about an object, a quality, or a relationship as a result of sensations. Percepts are the fabric from which concepts are formed.

Images are previous percepts.

Concepts are abstractions which organize objects and events into categories.

Generalizations or principles are concepts involving relationships between two or more abstractions, objects, or events.

PROCESSES OF THINKING

Percepts, concepts, and generalizations are among the most important, raw materials in the process of thinking. By the very nature of the way in which they are formed, they make up the first three types of thinking — perceptual thinking, associative thinking, and inductive-deductive learning. Problem solving, critical thinking, and creative thinking — the next higher order of thinking which is commonly compared to scientific processes — depend upon the proper formulation of percepts, concepts, and generalizations for their foundation.

Problem solving differs from perceptual or associative thinking in requiring higher levels of choices to be made between possible actions. For example, if a child automatically knows the sum of five and three or which is the heavier of two equal volumes of differ-

ent materials, he engages in perceptual or associative thinking; however, if he must decide which present to buy with his five dollars or what are the causes of stream pollution in his community, a higher level of reasoning or thinking is necessary. Generally, the steps involved in solving these two latter problems are similar to the formal, scientific method. Many of us were exposed to such methods in high school or college science classes. Such thinking may be quite complicated and inventive because it includes the following:

Some form of recognition of problems
Selecting facts related to problems
Setting forth some tentative proposals for solving problems
Reaching some conclusions and trying them out

Critical Thinking

Critical thinking usually refers to appraising information in terms of a norm, standard, or value. In problem solving, critical thinking could apply to the third step, appraising the tentative proposals for the solution of the problem. Generally, though, science education has accepted critical thinking as a broadly desirable thinking activity which will hopefully permeate all of a person's thinking in all aspects of his life rather than just science. To be critical of statements, policies, and actions is good and should be encouraged so that we can minimize the number of people who go around with rigid, uncompromising minds. Critical thinking, however, does not imply rudeness or impertinence but rather calm, self-confident questioning. An example of this can be seen in this second grade episode:

Danny, a precocious boy whose parents encourage critical thinking and searching for information, visited the Hayden Planetarium in New York City and also read a great deal about planets. He discovered that the planet Uranus was pronounced *yoo' run us* at both the Hayden Planetarium and in his books, so he pronounced it that way in a discussion in school. His teacher immediately corrected him and said it is pronounced *u RA'-NUS*. After a short argument in which the child stated his sources of pronunciation, the teacher said, "After all Danny, I should know. I'm older than you."

In spite of his self-confidence and parental encouragement to seek answers, Danny was confused by the teacher's dogmatic approach. A better approach by the teacher might have been to explore the sources of the pronunciations and to point them out to Danny. As adults, we must guard against authoritarian behavior toward children who are struggling to exercise critical thinking. At the same time we must help children guard against being arrogant and impertinent.

Creative Thinking

In many ways creative thinking, involving spontaneity of the child, is the highest form of thinking. During this process new ideas are formed; whereas, in critical thinking reactions to the previously formed ideas of self and others are involved. The encouragement of creativity in science will be discussed in depth in Chapter 8. While critical thinking has been described as problem solving, a process involving isolated experiences being put into new combinations or patterns of thought, creative thinking seems to be more internal and emotional and involves greater intuition and imagination than problem solving.

In summary:

Thinking is built upon sensations, percepts, images, concepts, and generalizations.

The process by which the preceding are developed is through three types of thinking: perceptive, associative, and inductive deductions.

Problem solving, critical thinking, and creative thinking require sound percepts, concepts, images, and generalizations.

The processes by which thinking takes place are as desirable as the products.

We have looked at what thinking is and the processes by which it develops. Now it will be profitable for us to consider the conditions under which thinking is facilitated and what we as science teachers can do to nourish and direct it.

STIMULATING AND DEVELOPING THINKING SKILLS IN SCIENCE

Our basic job in science teaching is to help children develop sound raw materials, percepts, images, concepts, and generalizations to be used for stimulating and further developing thinking skills in solving problems. There are many things in our favor as we approach our task. Two aids to the science teacher are children's prior experiences in environments of science and, consequently, their interests in the field of science.

Children's Previous Science Experiences

For the five or six years before the child enters our classroom he has been involved in the interaction between himself and his environment. His experiences slowly help him perceive himself as a unique object different from other objects, such as his crib, his father, or his bottle. A prime element in this slow, determined process is the sensation registered to the children through touch, taste, smell, sight, and hearing. These sensations make deep impacts upon the child, the effects generally lasting throughout his life. The startling recognition of self is one of the first steps of the child's relationships with environment and helps him later with many explanations of his world.

At the same time that the child is learning about his newly acquired self, he is also developing concepts of the causation of events especially while viewing himself as the possible motivating force for events: the toy does not squeak until I squeeze it, the tall pile of blocks does not fall unless I push them over, Mother does not pick me up unless I cry. Repeated experiences with these types of activities assist him in becoming more aware that he is capable of producing effects in this world; later on he sees that other forces can also produce effects and that there is a cause and effect for events.[8] The child's constant experiences with gravity, rain, heat, cold, darkness, lightning, snow, and thirst as well as other physical and biological phenomena, solidify these causal relationships for him. All of these experiences have been an informal and perhaps chaotic approach to concept building requiring all of the child's senses and energies as well as many trial and error periods. As a result of these situations, he enters his classroom with a rich storehouse of uncountable experiences with science. The teacher should expect that the learner has been exposed to many elements and conditions in his environment although some of his ideas may require adjustment due to limited experiences or knowledge.

Children's Interest

Interest is a prime factor in teaching and learning science, and it is a natural outgrowth of the experiences of the learner. It is not difficult to develop interest even when the learner has not had contact with the

item to be learned. Curiosity may be aroused by the unfamiliar, and this curiosity may be used as a stepping stone to further interests. There is overwhelming evidence that children of all ages have deep and genuine interest in topics that fall into the science areas of study.[9]

General interest in aspects of science by the nation as a whole has added to the interest and attention of people. It is almost impossible to pick up a newspaper, listen to the radio, or watch television without some reference to scientific developments — space travel, cholesterol investigations, nuclear testing, electronics, and automation advancements — and this has a pronounced effect upon children. Even before the advent of mass communication, children were always interested in such areas of science as the change of their own bodies, the weather, plants and animals, rocks and soil, as well as other observable changes, such as rusting, burning, and breaking. Thus, through their past experiences and natural curiosity, chil-

[8]John G. Navarra, *The Development of Scientific Concepts in a Young Child: A Case Study* (New York: Teachers College, Columbia University, 1955); and Barbel Inhelder and Jean Piaget, *The Growth of Logical Thinking* (New York: Basic Books, Inc., 1958).

[9]Doris A. Young, "Factors Associated with Expressed Science Interests of a Selected Group of Intermediate Grade Children" (Doctoral dissertation, Northwestern University, 1956); and James Otis Morton, "Science Interests of Intermediate Grade Children" (Master's thesis, University of Utah, 1954).

dren are ready to continue the exploration of their scientific world with the teacher.

Other Conditions for Facilitating Thinking

To assist in selecting and organizing effective learning situations, the teacher must have a great deal of information about the ways in which children grow, think, and learn. Principles of learning give the teacher guides to possible influences upon the child's learning and suggestions for arranging his program. The following principles were extracted from specialists' summaries which have direct implications for the science teacher's selection and organization of learning experiences. Following each item of the list, there will be the specific implications of these principles for the program of science education in the elementary school:

PRINCIPLES OF LEARNING THAT
AFFECT TEACHING METHODS

1.   In the learning process, active participation by the learner is preferable to passivity, such as listening to a lecture or watching a motion picture. (ACTIVITY)

2.   The learning situations are dominated by purpose or goals set by the learner or accepted by him. (PURPOSE)

3.   The learning situation, to be of maximum value, must be realistic and meaningful to the learner and should take place within a rich and satisfying environment. (MEANING)

4.   Learning processes occur best through a wide variety of experiences and subject matter which are unified around a core of purpose. (VARIED EXPERIENCES AND UNIT APPROACH)

5.   The learner will persist through difficulties to the extent that he feels the objectives are worthwhile. (REWARD)

6.   Learning processes proceed most effectively when the experiences, materials, and

desired results are carefully adjusted to the maturity and background of the learner. (READINESS)

7.   Learning processes proceed most effectively under the type of instructional guidance which stimulates without dominating or coercing, which provides for successes rather than too many failures, which encourages rather than discourages. (POSITIVE ENCOURAGEMENT AND REINFORCEMENT)

8.   The products of the learning processes are socially useful patterns of action, values, meanings, attitudes, appreciation, abilities, and skills. (ADAPTABILITY)

9.   Transfer to new tasks will be better if, in learning, the learner can discover relationships for himself and if he has experience of applying the principles within a variety of tasks. (TRANSFERENCE AND APPLICATION)

10. The learning process and the achievement of results is materially related to individual differences among the learners. (INDIVIDUAL DIFFERENCES)[10]

IMPLICATIONS FOR SCIENCE TEACHING

Children's scientific curiosities are aroused by the home, mass communication, the school, and their own desires for answers to questions about their environment. These questions form the motivating force around which science teachers must devise teaching techniques. Finding answers to their questions demands that children develop problem solving skills. Science teachers have the responsibility for helping students improve

---

[10]Ernest R. Hilgard, *Theories of Learning* (New York: Appleton-Century-Crofts, 1958), pp. 485-87; and T. R. McConnel, "Reconciliation of Learning Theories," *Psychology of Learning* (Bloomington, Illinois: National Society for the Study of Education, Forty-first Yearbook, Part II, 1942); and William H. Burton, "Basic Principles in a Good Teaching-Learning Situation," *Phi Delta Kappan*, 39 (March, 1958), pp. 242-48.

their ability to solve problems through systematic and directed activities.[11] Which problems shall a teacher select for her science program? The teacher has many sources from which to choose her problems for study: current happenings in local, national, or world affairs, the textbook, the teacher's hobbies, a prescribed course for science study, or television programs available in the area.

Skill in science problem solving is increased through solving real problems.

If science in the elementary school is to help the individual understand common phenomena in his environment, to apply the habits of scientific thought to both personal and civic problems, and to appreciate the implications of scientific discoveries for human welfare, practice must be supplied under the teacher's guidance to children through experiences dealing with principles in common, everyday activities of home and school.

Sources of Science Study Problems

Since science is everywhere, many studies can and have been completed that suggest kinds of experiences which can assist children to identify problems of importance for study. Situations have been isolated for study in school that are a result of science advancements; suggested developmental science experiences are also available to help children meet these problems. Similarly, the needs of children in modern societies have been clarified, and ways in which the curriculum could be organized to meet these needs have been expounded. A most thorough coverage of scientific problem solving opportunities in the earth sciences (astronomy, meteorology, geology), the biological sciences (biology, ecology), and the physical sciences (chemistry, physics) is presented in one of the Science Manpower Project Monographs.[12]

Maxine Dunfee and Julian Greenlee summarized the importance of real life problem solving for fostering the development of scientific thinking in children:

If teachers are concerned with the needs and interests of children and if they encourage children to ask questions and to explore, they cannot plan a science program apart from the actual experiences of children.[13]

It should be pointed out that the source of the problem does not always have to be a real situation in the child's life. It is more desirable, however, especially in the primary grades to deal with the things with which children are most familiar. More time should be given to the more abstract problems as children develop greater science backgrounds. Problem areas then can be selected for science study from: 1) children's own questions: "Are there foods that are harmful?" 2) broad, planned, science areas of the curriculum such as principle sources of energy in their city; 3) correlation with other subjects such as foods and nutrition correlated with weights and measures, budg-

[11]These two studies, among many, found that teaching problem solving skills through direct activity results in greater skill development as well as science content development than does any other method:

Louise A. Neal, "Techniques for Developing Methods of Scientific Inquiry in Children in Grades 1-6" (Doctoral dissertation, Colorado State College, 1957); and

Regan Carpenter, "A Study of the Effectiveness of the Problem Solving Method and the Textbook Discussion Method in Elementary Science Introduction," (Doctoral dissertation, University of Colorado, 1958).

[12]Lester C. Mills and Peter M. Dean, *Problem Solving Methods in Science Teaching.* Science Manpower Project Monographs (New York: Bureau of Publications, Teachers College, Columbia University, 1960).

[13]Maxine Dunfee and Julian Greenlee, *Elementary School Science: Theory and Practice* (Washington, D. C.: Association for Supervision and Curriculum Development, 1957), p. 33.

ets, world food problems; and 4) individual interests and differences, such as personal or small group activities: building telescope for science fair projects or publishing science papers or journals.

Whatever the source of the problem, science teachers have a better chance of accomplishing their goals by organizing science learning experiences around the problem solving approach. The implications derived from using the problem solving program for curricular planning are varied and quite clear.

Efficiency in problem solving occurs most rapidly when the problems are related to the interests of students and are appropriate to their maturity level.

When pupils are involved with problems in which they are interested, they are happier, learn more easily, and present fewer disciplinary problems. However, before a child can become really interested in anything, he must become involved in real experiences. Teachers find that interest in areas of science can easily and quickly be developed in the classroom.

Interest is also aroused by the actual problem solving process itself. The involvement of the child in the actual planning, exploring, evaluating, observing, demonstrating, and experimenting provides much in-

terest and motivation. The excitement and suspense that can be so much a part of the process of problem solving provides an almost detective-like or discovery approach to learning often missing in other classroom procedures. A brief treatment has been given to the role and importance of interests because it is so apparent in the nature of teaching.

The climate, atmosphere, or environment in which problem solving operates is highly important.

The classroom is a physical and intellectual environment for children as well as a closely interrelated social and emotional environment. As such, the teacher concerned with developing problem solving skills should use these elements of the environment to best advantage. Suggestions for organizing and using the classroom climate have been supplied to science teachers from such psychologically oriented fields as brainwashing and psychotherapy. These two fields have presented the teachers with much information about ways of stimulating children's sensory perceptions as well as ways of creating a climate that fosters open-

mindedness, encourages thinking, and respects children's efforts at thinking.[14] Specific helps to the teacher in providing stimulating physical and intellectual environments are presented in the next chapter.

If children are to develop skills necessary for solving problems that they meet in everyday life, they must be given the opportunity to formulate suggestions for ways of answering their own questions. What better way is

[14]The following present results of extensive research on effects of physical environment upon the individuals' perceptions:
O. Hebb, "The Motivating Effects of Exteroceptive Stimulation," *American Psychologists,* 13 (1958), pp. 109-13; and W. Heron, B. K. Dean, and T. H. Scott, "Visual Disturbances after Prolonged Isolation," *Canadian Journal of Psychology,* 10 (1958), pp. 13-18; J. Vernon, E. McGill, and H. Schiffman, "Visual Hallucinations During Perceptual Isolation," *Canadian Journal of Psychology,* 12 (1958), pp. 31-34; and Ira J. Gordon, "Brainwashing-Perception and the Task of the Teacher," *Childhood Education,* November, 1958, p. 122.

there for growth in this area than to have children engage in the solution of problems in school under the able guidance of the

Problem solving skills are developed through cooperative pupil-teacher planning.

teacher. If children are to develop initiative and resourcefulness in actually working through problems, they must have concrete experiences with real problems and must be given opportunities for suggesting directions and solutions for these problems. Cooperative planning does much to guide the child in problem solving while it does not inhibit his creativity if the classroom is run in a democratic fashion. It is established that democratic climates produce children who are more cooperative, more courteous, and more responsible than children from authoritarian environments.

Summary

Skills necessary in problem solving are stimulated and developed through the problem solving approach to science teaching. The individual learns best by solving problems. When the problems are real and meaningful to the learner, his progress increases. Cooperative pupil-teacher planning assists the development of problem solving skills.

Further Investigation and Study

1. Select an article from the following areas of sources of problems for science unit studies. Indicate the ways in which the selected study could be adapted for use in your local community. Problem solving opportunities are stimulated by:

Scientific advancements:

Stratemeyer, Florence B., H. L. Forkner, and Margaret G. McKim. *Developing a Curriculum for Modern Living.* New York: Bureau of Publications, Teachers College, Columbia University, 1948.

Children's needs and interests:

Jersild, Arthur, *et al. Child Development and the Curriculum.* New York: Bureau of Publications, Teachers College, Columbia University, 1946.

Subject matter fields:

Mills, Lester C. and Peter M. Dean. *Problem Solving Methods in Science Teaching.* Science Manpower Project Monographs. New York: Bureau of Publications, Teachers College, Columbia University, 1960.

World events and depletion of natural resources:

Brown, H. Emmett. "The Influence of World Events on Science Experiments in the Elementary School," *Science Education,* 29 (December, 1945), pp. 244-49.

Enders, Abbie C. "Bunnies, Buns and Babies," *Childhood Education,* 23 (April, 1947), pp. 370-72.

Harding, L. W. "Building Values in a Problem-centered Curriculum," *Progressive Education,* 26 (October, 1948), pp. 19-22.

Kitching, Eugene. "A Classroom Teacher Looks at Unit Teaching," *Clearing House,* 17 (March, 1943), pp. 416-19.

Ross, Helen B. "Conservation Education in the Elementary Schools," *The Science Teacher,* 18 (February, 1951), pp. 31-34.

Wong, Herbert. "The Use of an Integrated Elementary Science Program and Cooperative Procedures of Learning and Teaching Natural Science, Ecological Relationships and Conservation," Unpublished thesis, San Jose College, 1956.

2. Evaluate your classroom climate for science teaching-learning. What are your attitudes concerning science teaching and the scientific attitudes and methods? How do your children see the classroom and your role in this scientific atmosphere? For help you may wish to refer to an enjoyable and informative description of the role of climate in problem solving by:

Fleming, Robert S. (ed.) *Curriculum for Today's Boys and Girls.* Chapter 9, "Promoting Intellectual Development Through Problem Solving," written by Fannie Shaftel and Charlotte Crabtree. Columbus, Ohio: Charles E. Merrill Books, Inc., 1963.

The effects of teacher attitudes on children:

Bexler, James Edward. "The Effect of Teacher Attitude on Elementary Children's Science Information and Science Attitudes." Unpublished dissertation for Ph.D., Stanford University, 1957.

The effects of self-perception on children:

Carin, Arthur. "Children's Perceptions of Selected Teaching Acts." Unpublished doctoral dissertation, University of Utah, 1959.

3.   Cooperative pupil-teacher planning is vital to science problem solving, but it is very difficult to do properly. If you would like to know more about pupil-teaching planning and its vital role in the science problem solving program, read:

Association for Supervision and Curriculum Development, *Group Planning in Education*. Washington, D. C.: National Education Association, 1945. Pp. 156.
Greenlee, Julian. *Better Teaching Through Elementary Science*. Dubuque, Iowa: William C. Brown Company, Publishers, 1954. Pp. 204.
Hurley, Beatrice J. "Science Experiences for Nines to Twelves," *Childhood Education,* 26 (March, 1950), pp. 300-303.
Shaftel, F., C. Crabtree, and V. Rushworth. "Problem Solving in the Elementary School," Chapter 3 in the *Problems Approach to the Social Studies*. Curriculum Series No. 9 (Rev. ed.). National Council for the Social Studies, 1960.
Suchman, J. Rochard. "Inquiry Training in the Elementary School," *Science Teacher.* No. 27 (November, 1960), pp. 42-47.
Webb, Ruth K. "All Children Think and Plan," *Childhood Education,* 23 (March, 1947), pp. 315-21.

4.   Plan a lesson using the discovery approach to science problem solving. Do you know the difference between question solving and problem solving? Do you feel adequate with the questioning that is necessary in this type of approach? For help with this read:

Anderson, U. H. (ed.). "Creativity and Problem-solving," *Creativity and Its Cultivation*. New York: Harper & Row, Publishers, 1959.
Bruner, Jerome. "The Functions of Teaching," *The Rhode Island College Journal,* I. No. 2 (March, 1960), p. 39.
McDonald, Frederick J. *Educational Psychology*. Chapter 10. San Francisco: Wadsworth Publishing Co., 1959.

See the example discovery lessons in Part IV of this book.

5.   Look at the Pictorial Riddles of Science in Part IV of this book. Think of some scientific concept you would like to teach. Draw a diagram which can be used as a riddle to bring out this concept through class discussion.

6.   Can you explain the meaning of the following in your own words: sensations, perceptions, concept, generalization or principle, thinking processes.

Organizing and Planning for Teaching Science

Part 2

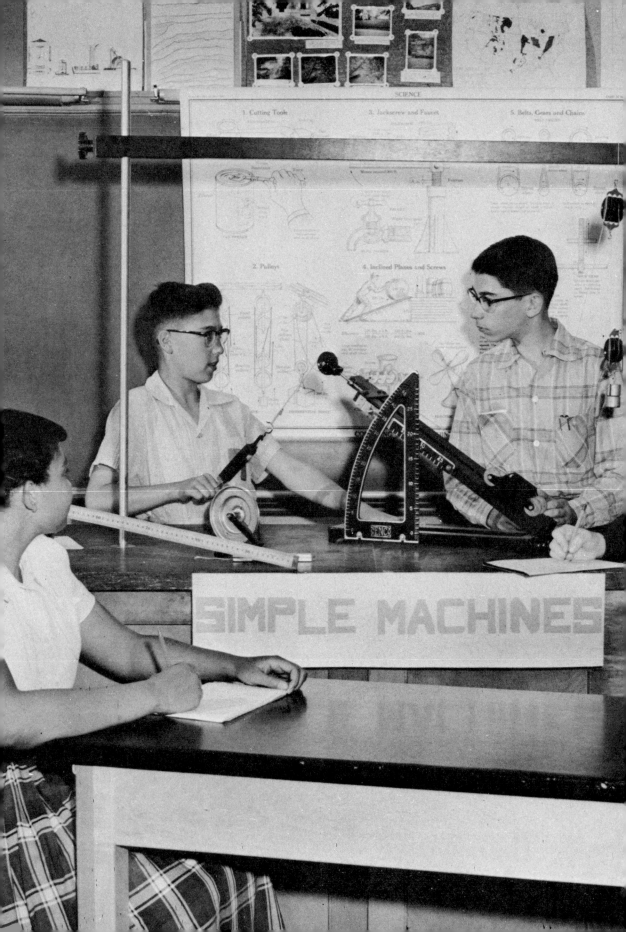

Unit Approach to Science Teaching

4

There are many ways to organize science teaching in the elementary schools. By using the processes of science presented in Chapter 1 and by applying them to the ways in which children learn from Chapter 3, however, a specific organization is most applicable. This organization is called the unit approach to science teaching.

The unit approach to teaching has long been established in the elementary schools. It parallels problem solving processes by being organized around a central problem or several problems in which answers to many questions must be discovered. Organizing and finding these answers form the backbone of this approach rather than teaching fragmentary, isolated science lessons.

ADVANTAGES OF THE UNIT APPROACH

Science units help develop the percepts, images, concepts, and generalizations so necessary for critical thinking and problem solving skills. It was found that critical thinking skill improvement and content development were enhanced through the science unit approach.[1] Children also find the unit approach more interesting and challenging than separate, unrelated science lessons.[2] They seem to learn more and are better able to see interrelationships between phenomena when working in the unit approach to science teaching.

---

[1]John Mason, "Experimental Study in the Direct Teaching of Critical Thinking" (Unpublished thesis, 1961).

[2]Victor E. Marrone, " A Comparison of the Social Living Approach with the Separate Subject Approach to Social Studies and Science" (Unpublished thesis, West Virginia, 1957).

Perhaps the paramount value of science units is the abundant opportunity for exciting and challenging teaching-learning experiences for teacher and pupil. Science lessons are not limited to sporadic, single, science lessons, nor are they bound in by the textbook. Teachers are limited only by their own backgrounds, their courage to try something new, and their willingness to find out how to improve. The following format for the science unit can give some direction for the teacher who has never attempted this approach with children.

SCIENCE UNIT FORMAT

The format of the science unit, although unique to each problem and teaching situation, is very similar to the ways in which scientists go about attempting to solve their problems. Teaching techniques which reflect the unit approach are those in which students spend a great deal of time planning, defining, investigating, reworking, trying out, making judgments, organizing, evaluating, interpreting, applying, devising, cross-checking, observing, demonstrating, and experimenting.

Although the following format is not prescribed in a rigid fashion, it does offer the teacher some directions for setting up a unit in her classroom:

SCIENCE UNIT FORMAT

1. Stimulate interest in the children through the physical and intellectual environment of the classroom.

2. Formulate interesting questions arising from the stimulation. They must be genuine concerns of the children to be of maximum value.

3. Participate in suggesting methods by which information pertinent to their questions can be found. This should be done jointly by teacher and children.

4. Gather information from as diversified sources as can profitably be used, including books, experiments, trips, television, movies, pictures, people, etc.

5. Encourage suggestions for tentative solutions to their problems as a result of this initial information.

6. Test these tentative solutions and gather and test any needed additional information.

7. Summarize the information gathered and devise methods of presentation.

8. Consider carefully the use to which the findings will be put.

Teachers may not necessarily follow this format each time in exactly the sequential arrangement given. If they know what the general format and goals of the science unit are, however, they can intelligently depart from it whenever circumstances so warrant. Let us now examine the teacher's role in implementing this format for teaching science through units.

THE ROLE OF THE TEACHER IN THE SCIENCE UNIT

Stimulating Interest and Raising Questions

Many children do not come from home environments which stimulate interest in problem solving or encourage critical thinking. Many homes physically do not include articles for manipulation and experimentation necessary for stimulation with the exception of a few commercial toys. It, therefore, profits the teacher to scrutinize his classroom to see if he has included the items with which he wants his students to have personal contact and to which they should be reacting. Four simple devices the teacher can employ to stimulate interest in science and to arouse questions in children's minds are bulletin boards, collections, displays, and science corners.

Bulletin Boards

Attractively presented materials and thought-provoking questions can stimulate interest. Bulletin boards offer this aid to teachers. A type of bulletin board is shown that can raise science questions and that can arouse the interest of children in knowing more about the answers to these questions.

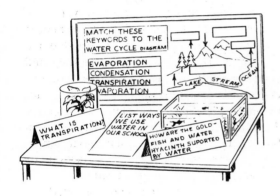

Vessel and Wong, *Water — A Resource,* Fearon Science Education Series (San Francisco, 1960), p. 1.

Collections

Collections provide a means of bringing children into direct contact with the tangible objects of the environment. The teacher should welcome the children's collections and provide space for them to share their collections with others. Children will become collectors with little encouragement and will bring to school everything from nests, insects, and animals to dolls, gifts, and plants. A simple table can serve as a place for displaying collections, but the teacher must be sincere about making use of it. He cannot say, "Oh, put it on the science table," for a way of disposing of the object from discussion and then after many weeks say: "I think it is time to clean up our science table and take home the things that have been around for a long while." The teacher who does this will soon wonder why children do not bring in their collections anymore. The teacher should be alert to the time at which the collection brought in for sharing with others has accomplished its purpose, however, and should encourage children to take collections home at that time. In this way, collections can be used actively within the science unit and then removed without discouraging the continued participation of the children.

Displays

Displays set up by the teacher with materials for investigation are worthwhile. The display can stimulate interest in the area to be studied by encouraging children to tinker with the materials that are set out. An example of such a display is shown.

Science Corners

A science corner in which an assortment of materials is available for experimentation as well as a shop bench and materials for the construction of things, such as cages, models, demonstrations, and experiments, is an important element in teaching science by discovery. A work area of this kind can be simply two desks pushed together, or it can be a commercially prepared section containing materials and a work bench. Storage space should be provided so that tools, equipment, and other materials can be put away when not being used. Free time must also be provided for activity in the science corner; assigned times for individuals or small groups can be arranged as part of the current work in science or other curricular areas. A list of the equipment, supplies, and materials that are useful for such an area are presented in the Appendix. One example of a science corner is included.

In the classroom, areas should be set up which provide the children with stimulation and give them opportunities for actual participation and experimentation with a variety of materials necessary for them to experience for themselves. Some of these areas of stimulation such as bulletin boards, collec-

tions, displays, and science corners have been mentioned here to show the purposes of these devices as a part of the science unit. Chapter 9 will deal in greater length with the construction and arrangement of these areas.

Sharpening Children's Observation

Another way in which the teacher may sharpen children's appetites for new and interesting challenges is by encouraging the children to observe the everyday wonders around them that they may not even have known existed. It seems difficult to believe that it is necessary to develop observational techniques as a method for stimulating and encouraging inquiry, but adults are perfect examples of how people can become immune to the stimuli of their environment. Adults often become so unconcerned with the familiar aspects of their environment that, unless an occurrence is startling or catastrophic, they go unnoticed.

Several well prepared and presented experiences can do much to stimulate those children who may not have been introduced to the phenomena of the world in the same

way that the alert teacher can do. The impact of so many of these experiences loom large in the memories of many present day scientists, who recall with fondness the day in class when they took a nature walk around the school grounds seeing many interesting things never noticed before. For many of us some particular experience stands out from the thousands that we have experienced in school; and yet, experiences in the area of science seem to have a much greater impact upon many.

The teacher who consciously plans experiences for developing observational techniques is doing much to keep inquiry alive in children. Even simple games can be used to increase children's awareness of their surroundings. A few such games are:

> Identifying objects while blindfolded by feeling, smelling, tasting, and hearing.
> Trying to remember objects on a table (apple, pencil, paper clip, etc.) by closing the eyes and identifying the object removed.
> Locating missing parts of animals, houses, etc. Much of the reading readiness materials contain elements of observational techniques.

The physical environment then can stimulate the development of perceptions, and eventually, through teacher directed questioning, direct concepts and generalizations will follow. These generalizations and principles can then be used in developing the procedures and skills needed for adequate problem solving.

An encouraging classroom climate aids in the development of problem solving skills.

Not only is science problem solving a set of procedures and skills dependent upon adequate development of science percepts, concepts, and generalizations, but it is also an attitude. The attitude is an openness to search, a willingness to explore, to make guesses, to try out an idea, to make mistakes, to back up and start over again. The procedures and skills in science problem solving can only be developed in classrooms where searching is encouraged, creative thinking is respected, and where it is safe to investigate, try out ideas, and even make mistakes.

Teacher Attitudes

One of the most important aspects of the problem solving approach to children's development in scientific thinking is the teacher's attitude. The teacher is the person who can make the emphasis in elementary science one of inquisitiveness and eagerness for finding answers instead of merely collecting isolated bits of information. His approach should be teaching science with a question mark instead of with an exclamation point, as a renowned science educator urged.[3] The acceptance of and quest for unique solutions for the problems that the class is investigating should be a guiding principle in the teacher's approach to his program of science. This approach also takes the pressure off the teacher for being an authority with all the answers, because the entire class can possibly find diverse ways of finding answers to the same problems. By planning with children, many suggestions can be developed that might not have been thought of by the teacher, for it has been shown many times that we underestimate the potentials of children.

Feelings are facts to people, and the way in which they feel about something colors the ways in which they see the facts. This means that teachers must develop sensitivities to children and to the meanings of their behaviors. The teacher must ask himself, "I wonder how the child sees the lightning we are having now? I wonder how the child

---

[3]Nathan Washton in a paper presented at the Thirty-Second Annual Meeting of the National Association for Research in Science Teaching, Atlantic City, New Jersey, in conjunction with the Council of Elementary Science International, February 21, 1959.

feels when I introduce this snake that Charlie brought in? How does the child feel when she turns over the decayed log in the woods on our trip?" The teacher must be aware of feelings and use these feelings for preparing experiences for his children that help them toward desirable goals.[4]

The encouragement of creativity among the children with whom the teacher is working does much also to help children develop resourcefulness and initiative with which to attack future problems. Teachers should be ready to accept any suggestion for the solution of problems regardless of how irrelevant it may seem to him, for this is really the true spirit of scientific problem solving. Only by testing these ideas can we help the child see that perhaps his suggestion was not in accord with the available information. In this way, however, we can show that this failure gets us that much closer to the correct solution by eliminating one possibility from the many offered by the problem.

In order to avoid the temptation at all times to tell the right answer to save time, the teacher must be convinced of the fact that the road to scientific thinking takes time. Children should never be exposed to ridicule for their suggestions of possible solutions to the problems or they will show a strong tendency to stop suggestions except in the most aggressive or gregarious cases. Fishing for the right answer also defeats an atmosphere conducive to sticking your neck out, for very few of us want to be forced to chance defeat before our peers. We should welcome breaking with convention when it comes to a solution to problems.

Another more subtle influence that the teacher has in stimulating and nurturing children's scientific inquisitiveness is the teacher's reactions to many everyday occur-

rences. By welcoming and providing ample facilities for keeping and displaying items that children collect from their immediate environment, the teacher also does much to encourage the inquiring mind. It is not necessary nor even advisable to launch into an extended study of each object brought in. The purpose would be worthwhile enough to simply convey to children that their inquisitiveness is not only appreciated but welcomed in the classroom.

Helping Children Discover Answers to Their Questions

The next job for the teacher, after getting children stimulated and interested in seeking answers to their questions, is to help them find those answers. The unit approach to science teaching helps the teacher here because there are a variety of activities and sources of information available to the teacher. Among the most important activities for children to use in gathering information in science units are experimenting, reading, discussing, observing, and visiting. Each of these activities aids the child in finding solutions to his science problems, and each activity is an integral part of the unit approach to science teaching.

Experimenting to Find Answers and Try Ideas

To almost everyone — especially children — experiments and science are synonymous. Once an idea occurs to a scientist he immediately thinks in terms of ways of trying out his ideas to see if he is correct. Trying to confirm or disprove something, or simply to test an idea, is the backbone of the experiment. Experiments start with questions in order to find answers, solve problems, clarify ideas, or just to see what happens. Experimenting should be part of the elementary school science program as an aid to helping children find solutions to science problems as

[4]The reader is referred to this unpublished doctoral thesis for a comprehensive review of the effects of self-perception, its development, and interrelationships with common classroom situations:
Arthur Carin, "Children's Perceptions of Selected Teaching Acts" (University of Utah, 1959).

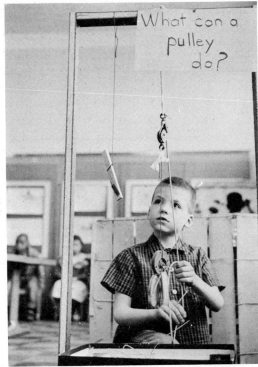

well as for helping them to develop appreciation and understanding for one of the basic tools of science.

Whenever the question of how to find an answer for the solution of science problems arises, the children can be helped to see that there are many times when experiments provide appropriate methods of solving problems. The more approaches children have for problem solving the better chance they will have for obtaining satisfactory solutions. Too often children think only in terms of an authority — textbooks, teachers, television — for finding their answers.[5]

Science teachers should encourage more direct experimentation by children in order to help children broaden their range of fact finding skills beyond the 3 T's — teacher, textbook, television — and to help them evaluate the validity of the information de-

rived by these means. Children need more opportunities to solve problems in experimental ways.

It is vital that there be a real purpose for doing an experiment. One excellent rule to follow is to ask yourself this question in regard to the appropriateness of selecting an experiment for the class:

> Can our problem be solved better by doing this experiment than by reading, explaining, or showing?

The teacher can assist the children in defining the problems for experimentation by careful questioning. The problem to be explored can be as simple as "Why do corks float?" Through questioning, the children can begin to analyze and clarify the problem: "What do we mean by corks floating? Can you think of ways for finding out why things float?" From these guided questions, children can set up tentative procedures or ways of doing the actual experimenting. (See

---

[5]Catharine Bergen, *Some Sources of Children's Science Information* (New York: Bureau of Publications, Teachers College, Columbia University, 1943).

the discussion of thought provoking questions in Part IV — Discovery Lesson Plans.) Also from these procedures the materials that are needed to conduct the experiments can be listed. "What do we mean that corks float?" From this question we can see that we will need corks, a basin, and water. Out of purpose and procedures grow the necessary materials for experimentation.

An important part of all experimenting, especially among children who are building skill and confidence in these areas, is the encouragement of guessing or hypothesizing what will happen in each experiment and why they think it will happen. These guesses should be recorded so that they can be checked for accuracy and validity. One way of checking accuracy and validity is by careful observation; later on, further checks can be made by science reference books and further experimentation.

Importance of Careful Observation in Experimenting

A good observer has been described as a person who has learned to use his senses of touch, sight, smell, hearing, and taste in an intelligent and alert manner. The value of careful observation has been discussed as a way of keeping scientific curiosity and inquiry alive for children. By being aware of the phenomena of his world, the child finds new and challenging questions. By the same process of careful observation that stimulated him to new questions, the child can develop answers to his questions. Early in their schooling, children can be helped in developing accurate observations and the habit of checking to be sure they are correct. If a child says that the stone is floating in the water, the teacher should ask the child to observe again and to redefine the term floating. Such a simple thing as observing just what is happening occurs in other areas of the curriculum, such as the language arts. Teachers in the primary grades spend much time helping young children develop skill in being able to recall and relate stories in sequence and accuracy of detail.

As children mature, they should be assisted in developing skill in comparisons of observations over longer periods of time. This development introduces the need and advisability for keeping records. Having children check each other on their observations helps them develop accuracy as well as an understanding of the advisability of checking the authenticity of information from more than one source. This habit of checking will also carry over into other activities including reading.

Children also have difficulty in separating their observations from their explanations. Teachers must help them distinguish between

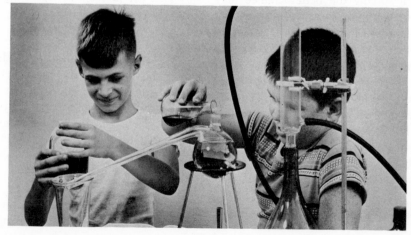

the two. We want children to observe what happens in experiments and to have ample opportunities to state their observations accurately. We also want them to try to explain what happens in reference to their problem, but we want to make certain there is a separation between observation and generalizations and conclusions. Their conclusions should be drawn very cautiously and should always be looked upon as tentative. Further observations, experiments, and reading are needed in order to verify what seems to be true. We are violating the true spirit of science if we allow children to generalize from one experiment or observation.

The following steps are generally accepted as valuable in developing and concluding science experiments with children:

1. Write the problems to be solved in simple words so that everyone understands.

2. Make a list of activities that will be used to solve problems, such as experiments, demonstrations, and educational trips.

3. Gather materials necessary for conducting experiments.

4. Work out with children a format of the steps in the order of procedure so that everyone knows what is to be done. Always list precautions that seem necessary. Reminder: Allow for creativity in format of experiments.

5. The teacher should always try the experiment himself to become acquainted with the equipment and procedure.

6. Record the findings in ways commensurate with the maturity level and purposes of the student. Avoid the fetish of the old science notebook of former days and the unnecessary writing at the conclusion of the experiment.

7. Assist children in making generalizations from conclusions only after sufficient evidence and experiences. Avoid making incomplete judgments and hasty conclusions.

If an experiment does its job, it accomplishes much more than answering the questions or solving the problem, for it also assists the child in building kinds of questioning and problem solving techniques that will be useful in answering other questions he will have about the world. Unless the experiment does this, the teacher might as well tell the answer to the children or read it to them from a book. It should be remembered that teachers cannot learn for their pupils; the pupils must be given opportunities to try out their intellectual wings by being given an active part in the learning process. In summary, the children can gain the following ideas from carefully planned experiments:

1. Experiments are one way of finding or checking answers to problems.

2. Careful observation is vital in experiments.

3. Authoritative sources should be used to check findings in experiments for validity and accuracy.

4. Generalizations and conclusions should be withheld until there is sufficient evidence to warrant such conclusions.

It is thoroughly accepted that success is greater with experiments in elementary schools if they start with a real purpose, are simply done with uncomplicated apparatus, are done by children under the careful direction of the teacher, and help the children think and draw valid, tentative conclusions.

Reading and Solving Science Problems

Effective teaching of science problem skills requires effective teaching of science reading. Although children learn best by engaging in first-hand experimental inquiry, reading is a vital and necessary appendage to science experiences.[6] In the primary grades, written symbols become more meaningful to the children as a result of first-hand science experiences. Experience charts can be used very effectively to summarize the discussions about the science problems studied, the procedures used in experiments, the observations and the results of these experiments, and the interpretations and applications of the results. There are also many additional values for the use of experience charts in the higher grades.

[6]Esther Pauline Roossinck, "Purposeful Reading of Science Materials by Scientists and Children" (Unpublished doctoral dissertation, Urbana: University of Illinois, 1961).

In the upper grades, reading takes on additional purposes and forms. Children could use reading to find and verify the information observed in their experiments. In the event that the experiment "does not work," reading should help give the children clues as to what went wrong and why. The elementary school science program should also guide the student in the development of skills to read science information and science literature with the proper perspective. Instruction should be given on understanding and interpreting science materials read. There is an urgent need in our scientific age for citizens who read science materials intelligently and accurately. Programs of science in the junior and senior high schools depend upon the elementary schools sending them students that are scientifically literate.

Besides factual checking, children's reading could lead to recreational enjoyment in the area of science literature: the lives and works of famous scientists and the technology that has arisen from them. The creative and occupational values of such reading are quite apparent.

As each science unit unfolds and the many science experiences give meaning to words, special vocabulary develops from these experiences. The meanings of the science words grow from the experiences as well as dictionaries, encyclopedias, and science books. The

questioning approach and emphasis of the teacher in the experiments stresses the correct meanings of the science words used and developed. The science teacher also provides for other reading activities which include reading to locate specific information, organizing the science readings for presentations, assisting children with skills for recall of science information, and following directions for science activities such as experimentation.

In an effort to avoid excessive reading about science, the teacher should use these suggestions for science reading:

1. Science reading — unless recreational — should be done for a specific reason, such as to verify conclusions, answer questions, solve problems, find information, learn how to do experiments.

2. Science reading should be done from several sources so that sources may supplement one another and present varying points of view.

3. Science reading may be the initial activity from which other activities originate.

4. Science reading materials may be selected by teacher and pupils.

5. Science reading should provide experiences for such skills as the use of table of contents, index, and other reading references.

6. Science reading materials should be of many levels of reading difficulty if they are to be useful.

7. Science recreational reading and science information reading should be made clear to children; both should be stressed as serving a valid purpose, but children should develop a clear understanding and differentiation of them.

Individualizing Science Reading Materials and Activities

If the teacher allows and even encourages individuals to branch out from the main unit of study according to their interests and abilities, he must be ready to guide them into a variety of materials and activities. The single science textbook will not suffice especially since it has been discovered that many of the textbooks are too difficult for many of the children for whom they were intended; in fact, some textbooks are difficult for children on all grade levels.[7] By shifting the textbooks around from class to class, teachers have a range of reading levels from the easiest to the most difficult. In this way the teacher will be able to direct the book to the appropriate reading level of individual students enabling all students to have a science book that they can read.[8] Basic readers, social studies books, science trade books, pamphlets and magazines, weekly children's newspapers, and other commercially prepared science materials are becoming abundantly available and should be placed in the classroom. Some teachers have children bring in books from home for use in the class library, and many parents are very cooperative in supplying magazines with much science content.

[7]George G. Mallinson, Harold E. Sturm, and Robert E. Patton, "The Reading Difficulty of Textbooks in Elementary Science," *Elementary School Journal*, 50 (April, 1950), pp. 460-63.

[8]The following are some of the low vocabulary-high interest science books: *What Is It Series*, Chicago: Benefic Press; *All About Books*, New York: Random House, Inc.; *Webster Classroom Science Series — Let's Read About*, St. Louis: Webster Publishing Company; *About Book Series*, Chicago: Melmont Publishers.

Local libraries generally loan books to teachers if they know sufficiently in advance the topic, age, and reading levels of the children and the length of time the materials will be needed. Commercial companies and the federal and state governments prepare special materials in science for the classroom. Teacher-prepared materials are extremely valuable. During the individual projects, the teacher can rewrite difficult materials at a level that will be useful for a student having difficulty with reading. There are unlimited opportunities for reading materials for individual needs and interests, and the teacher should be able to secure these from many sources. Two excellent sources for obtaining free and inexpensive materials available to teachers are listed below.[9]

Discussion in Science

Another language area important in the science unit is discussion. Opportunities are unlimited during discussion times for the teacher to find out much about her class as well as for the children to understand each other and the teacher. Aside from getting clues about interests for unit studies, the

[9]Muriel Beuschlein, *Free and Inexpensive Teaching Aids for Science Education* (Compiled as a supplement to the *Chicago Schools Journal,* October, 1950). *Free and Inexpensive Learning Materials,* 12th ed. (Nashville: George Peabody College for Teachers, Division of Surveys and Field Services, 1964).

teacher is able to evaluate quickly the concepts and misconceptions possessed by the children. After children have spent some time experimenting or reading, the teacher can profitably use the discussion time for an informal evaluation time which can provide him with information which will help him plan further learning activities for individual children.

There are times when it is very desirable for children to share their newly-found information with each other; the discussion periods allow for this type of activity. After a study of the effects of atomic testing, a group of children could present a panel discussion to the class on the pro's and con's of atomic testing. A group of children exploring an area of science by themselves could then be encouraged to share their information with others.

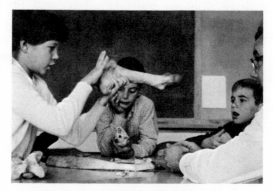

When there is freedom in discussion periods for the children and the teacher to express ideas, an excellent working environment develops for finding answers to questions. It is also during discussion times that procedures and methods of working are established. Many studies emphasize that growth is perceptively apparent in children's abilities to question, speculate, recognize relationships, and draw conclusions when there is ample time for them to have science discussions.[10] The abilities mentioned here are

[10]Katherine E. Hill, *Children's Contributions in Science Discussions* (New York: Bureau of Publications, Teachers College, Columbia University, 1947), p. 97.

essential for development of scientific attitudes and methods of working. Thus, discussion groups deserve a part in the science
program for the elementary school.

Educational Trips

All trips that are taken in the science
program should have a purpose that is definite and clearly understood by the children
who are to participate. There are times
when the purpose of the trip will be explora-
tory and will offer many specific areas for
further study. These educational trips are
more than outings or relief from the classroom although they may offer enjoyment different from the routine of the school day.
When carefully planned and carried out,
these educational trips can bring nature and
scientific facts together for a broader and
more inclusive program. Studies indicate that
school educational trips help expand children's interests in the subjects being explored
in the classroom; there is also evidence that
development of scientific attitudes and methods of working are furthered through well
planned and conducted educational field
trips.

These trips need not be very extensive in
either distance covered or time involved. The
school grounds and the immediate surround-
ing area offer countless possibilities for
useful trips even in the largest and most
industrialized cities. Erosion of soil from
the bank of the playground, the change of
trees and shrubs on and around the school
grounds, power lines carrying electricity to
the school, the construction of buildings,
and the florist's greenhouse down the street
all have possibilities for a short, worthwhile trip. For descriptions of the potential
science-learning experiences available
through trips to the immediate environment,
the reader is encouraged to investigate several descriptive studies which include many
useful teaching suggestions at the end of this
chapter under the section, Further Investigation and Study.

The teacher who knows his community readily sees the potentials for including educational trips in his science program. By planning with the children, the people involved at the place of the trip, and others, such as parents that might assist with the trip, success will be greatly enhanced and the expected results will probably be achieved.

Through an intelligent use of educational trips, the teacher can also help his children see that science takes place everywhere, not only in school. If he is alert to the world around him, the child begins to see that answers to questions are everywhere if he will only look for them and become aware of what the answers are when he sees them. Hence, this is another reason for the development of observational skills. The teacher can also assist children with their learning by organizing the educational trip so that it will be physically located at the primary source of information. Much of this primary information cannot be learned in the same way through any other source.

Summary

The unit approach to science teaching offers many advantages for both children and teachers. Critical thinking and problem solving skills are developed through units. Children are more interested and learn more by units than through isolated science lessons. Units offer more flexibility for individualizing science teaching. Units offer greater challenge and opportunities for exciting teaching-learning.

The format for the science unit parallels the ways in which scientists go about finding answers to their questions. Opportunities are abundant for stimulating questions in children and then guiding them to find answers to these questions. Of prime importance in units is the atmosphere of inquiry that the teacher must establish in the classroom. The physical and intellectual environment should be conducive to experimentation by the children. Units should include the following activities so that children can be helped to discover answers to their questions: experimenting, reading, observing, and visiting.

Further Investigation and Study

1.   Design a bulletin board display to illustrate some scientific concepts or scientific principles.

2.   Plan a trip for your class. Are you familiar with some of the possibilities for the trip and procedures that are valuable for conducting trips? You may find help by reading:

Clark, Ella C. "An Experimental Evaluation of the School Excursion," *Journal of Experimental Education,* 12 (September, 1943), pp. 10-19.

Curtis, Dwight K. "The Contributions of the Excursions to Understanding," *Journal of Educational Research,* 38 (November, 1944), pp. 201-12.

Josephson, Ruth Annis. "A Study of the Value of Field Trips for the Teaching of Natural History in the First Grade Curriculum of the Fox Point-Bayside School," Fox Point, Wisconsin (Master's essay, Ithaca, New York, Cornell University, 1952), Pp. 104.

Barnett, Sue Malone. "A Study of Our Marine Environment as a Florida Resource to be Used in the Elementary Science Program," (Graduate Study for M.A. Degree, Tallahassee, Florida, Florida State University, 1953), Pp. 72.

Shirling, A. E. "Experience in Natural Science, Childhood Environment Resources for the Teaching of Science in the Primary Grades," (Original research paper, Muncie, Indiana, Ball State Teachers College, 1954), Pp. 63.

Operation New York, Board of Education of the City of New York, 1960.

3.   How would you teach children so that they would become more observant?

Selecting and Planning
Science Studies

5

INTRODUCTION

There are unlimited possibilities in the elementary school classroom for selecting and planning science studies. Where does Miss Jones, a third grade teacher, begin to make her decisions about the specific studies for her particular class? In many respects, the processes by which Miss Jones does this selecting and planning parallel the scientific processes described in Chapter 1. These practical problems of Miss Jones, typical of all teachers who are beginning to establish the science content for their teaching, start the scientific processes in motion:

> Which science content areas shall I select? How do I plan for these science studies? Which activities are best for my class with its limited classroom space and science equipment? How do I learn and begin to feel adequate with science concepts myself? Where do I get the necessary materials, printed matter, and equipment? How do I know if my students are really benefiting from my science program?

Like all real problems, solutions are not easily obtained; they require careful, diligent work and constant evaluation and reconstruction. What to teach varies for each individual teacher and class. Just as a doctor cannot prescribe the same pill for every person, a principal, teacher, or author cannot prescribe the same science program for all teachers. There are not any formulas for selecting and planning for science studies in individual classrooms.

The teacher, being a professional person, gathers as much reliable information as is available, evaluates it, and then makes a wise decision based upon the information. Perhaps the reader may become aware of possible ways of proceeding with the selection and planning of science studies for her own classroom by observing the ways in which Miss Jones attacked her problems. Although Miss Jones' approaches and solutions to science study and planning are not a remedy for everyone's problems in this area, possible directions for solving some of the common problems in elementary science may become apparent.

SELECTION OF SCIENCE PROBLEM AREAS

Miss Jones agrees that science teaching in the elementary school should originate from and be organized around problems in broad units. Sources for these problems are numerous. It has been previously mentioned that broad science problem areas are desirable for giving structure and continuity to programs of science in the elementary school. Teach fewer science areas and teach them in depth rather than more areas in isolated fragments.

The following science concept areas have been recommended for studies in each elementary grade:

cosmology
evolution
ecology
structure and function
reproduction and development
structure of matter
energy interrelations
change of state of matter

Part IV of this book includes lesson plans organized around these broad science concept areas. Although terminology may differ slightly, similar broad science concept areas are recommended in all state, local, and commercial science curriculum guides for the elementary teacher. Regardless of the thoroughness of these guides, they should be used only as guides. Miss Jones must still make final decisions for the specifics to be selected for her class, and they should be based upon these considerations.

CHILDREN: What are my children like? What is the science background of my children and how is it manifest in their behavior, their information, misconcepts, half-truths, superstitions, fears, and anxieties?

COMMUNITY: What is unique about my community's physical environment and climate, occupations and industries, general level of education and cultural opportunities available to children and adults?

CURRICULUM GUIDES: Are there local and/or state curriculum guides for science content in my school? If so, what interpretations do the administration and supervision attach to these guides and to what extent do they restrict me? For instance, am I literally required to follow the guide or am I encouraged to deviate whenever I find it necessary?

AVAILABLE RESOURCES: What materials, equipment, and people are available to me in my school, by the children from home, from the community, or from other sources?

TEACHER: What are the strengths and weaknesses in my own science background? Is my class well organized and controlled? Do I feel adequately prepared in my other subject fields?

Miss Jones discussed her problems of selection of science studies with fellow teachers in one of her courses at a nearby college.

She discovered that four teachers arrived at different decisions on what to teach to their specific classes. Here is a brief description of their decision making:

1. THE USE OF THE SCIENCE TEXTBOOK AND CHILDREN'S BACKGROUNDS AND INTERESTS

A fifth grade teacher in a large city had many children whose fathers were in the electric and electronic fields. The school system had adopted one science textbook series, and the teacher was moving through the book topic by topic. As she got to the part of the book that was assigned to the study of electricity, she found that most of her class had concepts that were well beyond those presented in the textbook for that particular grade. By observing and listening to her children, the teacher was able to discover their abilities and interests. The teacher was also able to find out that the parents could contribute to this study, and she lost no time in involving them in the program by persuading them to supply needed materials, information, and encouragement. Several fathers came to class and gave demonstrations and brought in and explained pieces of electrical and electronic equip-

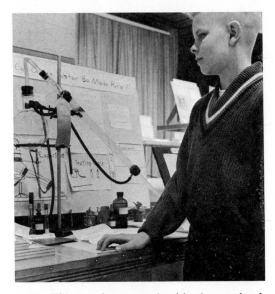

ment. This teacher started with the textbook and the unit of study suggested by it as the source of the science content and activities, but modified the study to meet the unique background of the children and their parents.

2. UTILIZING THE SOCIAL STUDIES UNIT AND COMMUNITY NEEDS

One first grade teacher from a small suburb related that she was in the midst of a social studies unit — Living in Our Community — when she decided upon a specific science study for her class. It was June and the swimming season was beginning for this community. The local newspaper had carried a series of articles about the deplorable conditions of the beaches, and the health department after investigation had decided to close the beaches to public use because of the pollution and other possible health dangers. Although the teacher at first felt that the children in her class were too young to appreciate the situation, she became very interested as the children's discussions constantly referred to the topic of the beaches and how it would not be any fun this summer without swimming. Much resentment and hostility was generated towards "that mean old health department."

The teacher decided to launch a study of bacteria, pollution, its causes, and the relationship of the health department to the community's health and safety. With the help of several local community services (health department, hospital, and a medical laboratory) plus the help of the school nurse, the class became familiar with bacteria, conditions that affect bacteria breeding, and how the beaches became polluted.

These six-year-olds through the guidance of their teacher actually sent several letters to local industries that were causing the pollution by the dumping of their waste materials into the stream that feeds into the beaches. Thus a social studies unit, coupled with what the teacher felt was a community need, supplied the source for teacher selection of science content and appropriate activities.

3. THE INFLUENCE OF CURRENT EVENTS IN SELECTING SCIENCE UNITS

Mr. Hart had decided that his third grade class should be exposed to a study of weather sometime during the year. His decision was based upon the reading he had done in the science curriculum guide of a neighboring community which was reported to have an outstanding science guide. Mr. Hart's school district did not have a science curriculum guide, and lacking teaching experience, he wanted some direction for possible science areas from which he could plan his year's science program. Science areas were selected as the skeletal framework for the total year, but they were not in any fixed length of studies, priority or order of studies, or specific science concepts or activities. The science areas were merely yearly goals. As the children returned from a particularly severe snowstorm on the weekend, interest and apprehensions of the severity of the storm were at a high pitch. This was the time for the study of the weather. The children related many of the experiences that they had had as a result of the storm, such as isolation due to crippled

communication and transportation. The teacher recorded both the accurate and inaccurate information for use in structuring and guiding the direction of the unit on weather. By the

teacher cooperating with the children, they were able to structure a unit of study that attempted to answer their particular needs and interests. The curriculum guide of the neighboring school district supplied Mr. Hart with suggestions for science content and activities for this unit of weather. It is not wise to gear the entire science education program to such events, or the science program will be haphazard; however, teachers should be alert to the times when these events make certain science studies very desirable and meaningful to children.

4. TEACHER INTEREST, HOBBIES, AND SCIENCE BACKGROUND INFLUENCE UNIT SELECTION

Teaching for the first time can leave one full of apprehension, and this was true for Mr. Charles, a sixth grade teacher, who had never taught before and whose school district did not have any curriculum guides. He was convinced that science education was important and decided to include science units of study in his curriculum. In his last year at college, Mr. Charles had taken a course in biology in which many field trips into the community were taken. As his interest and liking for these trips grew, Mr. Charles made many attractive collections of leaves and wild flowers. His interests in nature had been stimulated beyond mere fulfillment of the requirements of the course. He brought the collections to school and attractively displayed them in his classroom with an accompanying bulletin board. Interest was generated spontaneously, and his children started bringing their own collections. Before long, the class's first science study — Living Things in Our Community — was started with enthusiasm.

This teacher's interest and enjoyment in the aspects of nature proved to be the source for the selection of content and activities for a study in science with his children. Teachers have many other areas of interest that can be sources for science studies. A few of these areas include lovely plants, souvenirs from trips, and collections of all kinds.

Four teachers with four different classes used four different sources for their science units. Miss Jones found that other teachers used the following sources for units of related science study:

The holidays such as Halloween (pumpkin food preservation, seeds) or Christmas (knowledge of electrical safety with trains and tree lights) provide problem areas for study.

Children's pets and hobbies furnish possibilities for science studies.

Occupations of parents of children in the class often stimulate science interests.

Educational and recreational television provides much stimulation for science interests in children.

Teacher-prepared science corners, displays, and bulletin boards can spark interests.

Whatever the source, arriving at "what to study" leads to many further questions. Foremost among these questions is how to plan and prepare for helping children learn the scientific concepts, attitudes, and processes valuable in the unit selected.

LONG-RANGE PLANNING FOR TEACHING SCIENCE

Miss Jones found out early in her teaching career that probably there is not any one thing that helps more for getting good results

in teaching than to have everything planned down to the last detail. This is as true for science teaching as it is for math, social studies, art, or music. She may change or modify her plans from day to day according to the situations that arise, but she likes the security of knowing what she is specifically trying to accomplish with her class. Experience has shown that elementary school teachers have better success in teaching science if they plan basically in three ways: long-range resource unit planning; weekly planning; and daily, discovery-type lesson planning. Methods for all three types of planning will be discussed.

SCIENCE RESOURCE UNIT PLANNING

A science resource unit is a preplanning device used by teachers prior to initiating and carrying out a study with children. It is a large collection of ideas, concepts, materials, and experiences focusing upon a specific topic, area, or problem; it also includes a general, flexible organization which a teacher can use in planning and developing a science unit with her class. A resource unit differs from a teaching unit in that the former usually contains much more than will ever be used in a teaching unit. While the resource unit is a suggestive preparation for the teacher, teaching units take their direction from the teacher and children and, after the study, are actual records of the unique ways in which the class pursued answers to their questions.

Some teachers never use a science resource unit because they prefer to rely upon their extensive understandings of the science concepts as well as of the activities for helping children learn. Other teachers use the resource unit as a standard to be applied to their class, and in time these units become actual teaching units. Both extremes miss something. Those teachers who never use resource units may miss important sources of learning while the others may take all the discovery and spontaneity out by their rigidity. For the teacher who avoids either of these extremes, the science resource unit can perform several functions and can contain these traits:

1. Science resource units are written for and by teachers for use in preplanning science studies with their children.

2. Science resource units are broad areas or topics organized in such fashion that they are easy for teachers to use flexibly.

3. Science resource units contain more materials, activities, and resources than can generally be used by any one group of children.

4. Science resource units present a wide variety of possible experiences for children for achieving the desired goals.

Sources of Science Resource Units

The fact that teachers are pressed for finding time for planning as a result of committee meetings, grade level meetings, faculty meetings, parent-teacher conferences, PTA meetings, in-service courses, and mountains of paper work is commonly known; and yet, science resource planning does get done. There are many helps for the teacher's planning; she can reduce the actual amount of writing for resource units by obtaining resource units from a variety of sources. Almost every state department of education is publishing science resource units. School districts have been writing and accumulating resource units which are beginning to become readily available to teachers. Commercial and philanthropic organizations are releasing science resource units. For the con-

venience of the reader, a list of books and other sources containing numerous specific science content resource units is included in the Appendix. The teacher should send a brief letter to the places listed, preferably using school stationery, to indicate that she is a teacher. In return the teacher will receive detailed information and resource units. The listed books, in addition to the many resource units, contain comprehensive bibliographies of additional sources for resource units and related information. The teacher will find that this list will yield other valuable resources including printed materials, pictures, exhibits, and other audio-visual teaching aids.

Teachers Write Resource Units

It is most valuable if scientists and educators jointly write resource units. Unfortunately, this is not very common as yet; therefore, teachers are frequently responsible for compiling their own resource units. It can save much time if several teachers on the same grade level divide the areas to be studied for the year leaving only two or three resource units for each to plan. In this way a file of resource units is quickly and quite easily planned for a whole year of studies. Each year additions and revisions are made to the file so that in several years a very comprehensive resource unit file is made. Miss Jones agrees upon the value of resource planning and asks, "How does a beginner go about setting up a resource unit?"

Format and Procedure for Planning Resource Units

The planning of resource units can be as unique and individualistic as are the people writing them; the following format, however, is probably broad enough to include most of the items of importance in preplanning for teaching science. Terminology and organization may, of course, vary somewhat.

SUGGESTED FORMAT FOR SCIENCE
CONTENT RESOURCE UNITS

I.   Introduction of desired goals
II. Developing science concepts and generalizations
  A. Anticipating children's questions and problems
  B. Relating science principles and content
III. Suggested science activities
  A. Initiating and raising questions
  B. Seeking answers
  C. Enriching
  D. Culminating
  E. Evaluating
IV. Science bibliography
  A. Reading materials for teacher
  B. Reading materials for children
V.   Science materials and equipment
  A. Science equipment and supplies
  B. Other audio-visual aids

Miss Jones Plans Resource Unit

Let us look over Miss Jones' shoulder as she plans a resource unit for a study of weather for the primary grades K-3. Her third grade is not on the average level due to their lack of science background. She, therefore, prepares for a variety of age differences giving wider choices of things to do when she actually goes into the study with her class. She selects the area of weather from the broad area of ecology, the interrelationship of man and his environment, because it is an area of interest to the children as well as quite applicable to many stages of student advancement.

As Miss Jones starts planning her resource unit, she finds that much of the work has already been done for her. The desired goals as well as science concepts and generalizations are well presented in the teacher's guides of the children's textbooks which Miss Jones uses as they are in most of the professional teacher books in elementary science in her library. Miss Jones adds a few more of her own goals or principles that she hopes to have her children accomplish in her unit on weather. In the Appendix are references that will be useful in planning for desired outcomes, concepts, and generalizations for science resource units:

  A. General teacher reference books
  B. Suggestions for organizing science progress (pamphlets)
  C. Sources of science concept charts (published)

These sources can help the teacher feel more adequately informed. The teacher should realize, however, that she must keep up with the latest in science subject matter. Periodicals are an enjoyable and informative way of doing so.

Miss Jones now has the science subject matter of what to teach as well as the goals desired; now she must determine the methods used to teach a variety of experiences to children. She has discovered that Part III of this book presents experiences for specific content areas. She recognizes, however, that no one book could contain all the possible teaching-learning experiences, so she also investigates the experiment, demonstration, and construction references for teachers and children listed in the Appendix.

Supplies and Equipment

Miss Jones knows that she must be aware of the supplies and equipment needed for the activities in her resource unit. She realizes that it would be foolish to plan for an activity only to find out that it is impossible to get the necessary materials. This happened to the teacher in the next room to Miss Jones. Mr. Simon had his class construct a cinder cone volcano in order to show lava flow patterns. When he was unable to get the needed ammonium dichromate, he discarded the volcano to the dismay of his thirty children. If he had known that he could get the chemical from a photographic processing lab, it could have been a very worthwhile experience. From this misfortune Miss Jones learned the importance of finding sources for supplies. Three such sources are the school, the home, and the community.

Although most elementary schools are beginning to stock supplies and equipment for teaching science, there is a noticeable shortage of useful items. Very often expensive, technical, and complex equipment has been purchased that is not commonly used. There is also a tendency for items to be consumed, broken, or misplaced as a result of uncoordinated use of available items and a failure to restock. These conditions will improve as science teaching increases in the elementary school. In the meantime, the elementary school teacher will have to rely upon two other sources, the home and the community, for the bulk of her supplies and equipment.

Home

Often supplies and equipment not available in school can be obtained quickly by asking children to bring items into class. Miss Jones recalls her experience in asking her children to bring in empty frozen juice cans. After two days she had more juice cans than she could use in a lifetime. She had excellent success in getting needed items for science by sending this note to parents:

Dear Parents:

Our class is investigating the area of weather in science. We would appreciate it if you could help.

There are pieces of equipment that we will need, and you may have them available at home. If you could loan us some of the items below, it would help us. Please put your name on each item, and we will be sure to return them to you when we are finished. If you have quantities of the same items, we would welcome them.

We all thank you for helping us explore weather.

> Sincerely,
> Miss Jones and her Third Grade

Supplies and Equipment Needed

tea kettle, sheet of glass, pie tins, adhesive tape, thermometers, milk bottles, table salt, large feathers, coffee cans, rags, balloons, soda straws, gallon jugs, empty jars, empty cans.

Although a large stock of supplies were accumulated by this letter, some items were still short. Miss Jones and her children then turned to the other community sources for the remaining items.

Other Community Sources

Miss Jones and her children scoured the town and found many places and people that were potential suppliers of items needed in their science program. Merchants and parents in business were anxious to contribute to the school program. In discussing parents' occupations, Miss Jones discovered a rich source of potential science items from such a variety of positions as the manufacture of men's shirts to garbage removal. Miss Jones found out after a while that getting materials was not the problem; it was tactfully stopping the flood of supplies. In the Appendix there is a list of excellent sources of free and inexpensive science items.

Example of a Science Resource Unit

As a result of the work indicated above, Miss Jones prepared the following science resource unit on weather for primary grades. Other teachers saw it, and after some discussion, the eight primary grade teachers decided to do the same for different broad science areas and then to share their resource units. In a short time, a collection was made for grades K-8.

MISS JONES'
RESOURCE UNIT ON WEATHER FOR PRIMARY
GRADES (K-3)

I. *Introduction and desired outcomes*

A study of weather is well suited to the elementary school, especially the primary grades, since young children experience and generally enjoy the daily elements of weather. The child should be assisted in developing concepts of the nature of air, moisture in all its variations, and winds in order to be able to observe and discuss the daily weather intelligently.

Influences of weather upon man should be stressed. Children are increasingly exposed to radio and television weather broadcasts and they should be helped to observe, report, and understand these weather reports. Fears, anxieties, and superstitions should be explored and removed when possible, for children should be aided in living with these feelings without undue worry.

II. *Concepts to be developed*

A. *Anticipated questions and problems of children*

SUN

1. How can we keep the sunlight out of our classroom?
2. Why do certain things feel hotter than others in the sunshine?
3. Why is it cooler in the shade on a hot, sunny day?
4. Why is it cooler when a cloud covers the sun?
5. Why should we wear light-colored clothes on a bright sunny day?
6. Why do people hang wet clothes in the sunshine?
7. How can we keep cool on a very hot day?
8. How do people know how hot it is besides just feeling hot?

WINDS

9. What is wind?
10. How do we know which way the wind is blowing?
11. How do we know how strong the wind is?
12. Do winds do things to help people?
13. Do winds do things to harm people?

CLOUDS AND FOG

14. What are clouds and how are they made?
15. Can we make a cloud?
16. How are clouds different?
17. Is fog a cloud?
18. How do clouds move?
19. Why can't we see in fog?
20. Why does everything we touch feel wet in a fog?
21. Do clouds help us?
22. Do clouds harm us?

MOISTURE: RAIN

23. What is rain and how is it made?
24. Why does the sky look so funny on rainy days?

25. Why does rain soak into some things and not into others?
26. Why do we wear raincoats when it rains?
27. How can we collect rain?
28. Why are sounds on a rainy day different from those when it is not raining?
29. Is rain helpful or harmful?
30. Can we make rain?
31. What happens to the puddles of water after a rain?

MOISTURE AND TEMPERATURE: ICE AND SNOW

32. Why does ice form on the puddles after a rain on a cold day?
33. Why does the windowpane feel cold on winter mornings?
34. Why do icicles melt when we bring them inside our classroom?
35. Why does the red liquid in the thermometer go down on cold days?
36. Why are the handlebars of your bike colder than the grips on a cold day?
37. Why is the classroom so much warmer than the outdoors on a cold day?
38. Why do we wear heavy clothes on a cold day?
39. Why do the radiators in our room warm us?
40. Why does snow melt into water?
41. Why does your father put salt on the ice on your front steps?
42. Why does your father put chains on his car when there is ice or snow?
43. Why does snow get so black after a few days?
44. Does snow help us in any way?

B. *Related science principles and content*

1. The sun gives the earth its heat and light.
2. The sun helps dry wet objects.
3. When something blocks the sun, shade or a shadow is made.
4. A thermometer shows how hot or cold the air around us is.

5. Moving air is called wind.
6. Wind pushes things.
7. Wind is able to lift and move some things.
8. Wind helps things dry.
9. Winds can cause damage.
10. Wind blows on water and makes waves.
11. A cloud is composed of tiny drops of water or crystals of ice.
12. Clouds are in the air.
13. Some clouds are very high in the sky; some are much closer to us.
14. Clouds are different from each other in size, shape, and color.
15. Clouds are moved around by wind.
16. Clouds are like fog.
17. Fog is a cloud near the ground.
18. It is hard to see in fog.
19. It is wet in fog.
20. Sometimes water comes from the clouds as rain.
21. Rain soaks into some things and not into others.
22. Some rainwater goes back into the air.
23. Water may freeze and become ice on very cold days.
24. We know when it is very cold because the liquid in a thermometer goes down.
25. On cold days ice forms on ponds and other outside places.
26. On cold days snow may fall from the clouds.
27. Snowflakes have many interesting shapes.
28. Sometimes snow gets very icy.
29. Salt helps melt ice.
30. Radiators help warm us.

III. *Suggested activities*

A. *Initiating and question-raising activities*

1. Take trips outdoors
   a. Observe the nature of the sky outside the building where children can see in all directions. Raise such questions as:

1) Is the day clear, partly cloudy, or cloudy? How do you know?

2) What do you notice about the color of the sky, brightness (light), visibility, warmth (temperature), movement of wind? How do you know?

3) How do the clouds compare in size, shape, distance, color, etc. What do some of the shapes remind you of?

4) If the day is cloudy, look for patches of brightness and visibility in different directions. Why is it clear? Are the clouds moving? How do you know? Will it rain? How do you know?

5) Compare the sky at several times during the day and ask the preceding questions.

b. On a bright sunny day have the children go outside and feel and compare the degree of warmth (temperature) of different objects in direct sunlight. Such objects might be cars, soil, grass, concrete, brick, cloth, bare metal, etc. Which are warmer? Why?

c. Have the children compare how it feels standing in direct sunlight and then in shade. Which is warmer? Why?

d. On a windy day look for things that the wind is moving and the directions they are being moved. Why are they moved and in what direction?

e. Take children outside on a foggy day and have them touch many different objects. How do the things feel? Why? Why don't they all feel the same?

f. Dress the children in rain gear and take them outside on a rainy day. Observe what is happening and why? Ask for sensory reactions to rain; such as, is the rain warm or cool on the face? Does the air smell any different during or after a rain? Why?

g. After the rain storm, walk around the school grounds and look for evidences of what the rain has done. Make a list and then probe into why the things happened.

h. On a cold day open the classroom windows for a few minutes and ask children to note what happens. Why?

2. Try experiments

a. Have class observe water boiling in a tea kettle. (Caution: it is safer if the teacher conducts this activity involving the children only in the questioning.) Bring the condensing steam to the attention of the class if they miss it. Raise questions as to what it is, how it is formed, etc. Place a cold sheet of glass in path of the steam. Observe. Raise questions.

b. As soon as the class is settled in the morning on a freezing day, place a pan of water on the window sill inside the room and another pan with water outside the room. At intervals during the day (11 A. M., 1 P. M., and 3 P. M.) observe the conditions of both pans. If there is any difference between the pans, explain.

c. Mark the level of water in an uncovered aquarium by placing a strip of adhesive tape on the level. The next morning observe the level and compare to the tape. Is there any difference? Why? Is there anything we can do to prevent it? How?

3. Show films and filmstrips

Use any or all of the following to stimulate interest and raise questions, but avoid telling too much except where it will speed the movement of thought in the the desired directions. It may be necessary and desirable to provide background for the children so that the films and filmstrips have more meaning.

FILMS

Blow, Wind, Blow — 11 minutes — Coronet Films — suitable for grades K-2. This story relates the wind to man through the helpful and destructive aspects of the wind.

Snowflakes — 10 minutes — Moody Institute Films — suitable for grades K-3. Not only is the beauty of snow portrayed, but the use of snow for play (recreation) and work (irrigation) is well presented.

FILMSTRIPS

People Get Ready For Winter — Jam Handy — suitable for all grades from K-6. This has universal appeal in raising questions of why we change clothing in fall, why it gets windy, why shadows get longer, why leaves change color, and other aspects of seasonal changes.

Air, Wind, and Weather — Eye Gate House — suitable for grades K-2. Excellent stimulation for discussions about the importance of air and the interrelationship between air, winds, and weather.

4. Read one or more of these books about weather to the children to stimulate interest and reawaken their own past sensory experiences with the weather elements.

Bendick, Jeanne. *All Around You.* New York: Whittlesey House, 1951. 48pp. The physical environment and its weather is examined in a charming fashion. Interest level — K-2.

Blough, Glenn O. *Not Only for Ducks.* New York: Whittlesey House, 1950. 48pp. Using a child as an investigator, the cycle of weather is examined simply enough so even the youngest child can understand. Interest level — K-3.

Gallant, Kathryn. *Jonathan Plays with the Wind.* New York: Coward-McCann, 1950. 51pp. A young child has sensory experiences with the wind. Enjoyable for grades K-3.

Pine, Tillie and Joseph Levine. *Water All Around You.* New York: Whittlesey House, 1959. 48pp. Water in several forms is presented with simple experiments that can be done by teacher and/or children. Interest level — K-2.

5. Play records or play the music for the following again using the sensory experiences that children have for stimulating interest in weather and air and winds.

Pitts, Lilla Belle and others (eds). *First Grade Book About Winds and Weather.* pp. 120-42.

Perkins, Clella Lester. *How to Teach Music to Children.* New York: Hall and McCreary Co., 1946.

————. Cloud, p. 114.

————. Cold's the Wind, p. 129.

————. First Snow, p. 120.

————. Good Morning Merry Sunshine, p. 150.

————. In September, p. 101.

————. Old March Winds, p. 109.

————. Snowflakes Race, p. 106.

————. Wind, p. 119.

————. Windmill, p. 110.

Any of the activities mentioned in this section may also be used in the next section, Answer-seeking activities, the difference being the approach the teacher uses with them. Here the teacher is stimulating interest while in the next section children will have a distinct need for specific information for answering their questions.

B. *Answer-seeking activities*

1. Keep record of weather each day on the calendar of the month using such symbols as a sun for sunny day, umbrella for rainy day, a cloud for cloudy day, snowflakes for snowy day, kite for windy day, etc.

2. By using smoke blowing from chimney or scattering of leaves from trees, keep a record of the wind direction and speed, with such words as: no wind, slight breeze, or strong wind.

3. Observe the differences in the thermometer at regular intervals during the day and record the differences with such words as: the liquid has gone up, down, or stayed the same. Reading of the actual numbers should be delayed until there is adequate number concept development.

4. Take two identical wet rags. Place one in direct sunlight and the other in the shade. Have children feel the difference between the two after a sufficient time has elapsed. Stress the accurate observation and reporting of their test.

5. Have children place two sheets, one of white and the other of black construction paper, on the window sill on a very bright, sunny day. After ten minutes have the children touch each of the papers and report differences.

6. Blow up a balloon and tie a string around the middle of it. Put the balloon in the bright sunlight (or heat over radiator) and observe the difference in the balloon.

7. Have children suggest ways of cooling the classroom after they have had some experiences with heat conduction.

8. Place two tablespoons of water in each of two pie tins. Put one pie tin in the direct sunlight and the other in the shade. Observe any differences after one hour. The same experiment can be done by placing one pie tin on a source of heat while the other remains unheated.

9. Have several children paint on the chalkboard with water.

What happens to the water?

10. Have two children wet a square foot of blackboard drawn with chalk by the teacher as far apart as possible. When the squares are soaking wet, one child fans his square. What happens?

11. Take rags and wet. Hang one up so that it gets a lot of wind. Place the other in the teacher's desk drawer or other sheltered spot. Compare the two rags after an hour.

12. Each child is given a soda straw and a milk container half full of water. Children are asked to blow through the straw onto the water. What happens? Why? Have the children increase the strength of blowing. Observe.

13. On a very cold day have children go outside and breathe out hard through their mouths. What happens? Why?

14. Boil water and pour slowly into a milk bottle. Extreme care should be taken so that the bottle does not break. Spill out most of the water leaving a half inch of water. Hold the bottle up to strong sunlight or light from slide or movie projector. A fog or cloud should form.

15. For a variation of No. 14, clean a gallon jug and put two tablespoons of water in it. Pump as much air into the jug as possible. (Bicycle pump works very well.) Quickly release the air and observe the fog or cloud. Why?

16. Get several icicles and ice cubes Have class compare them and then allow them to stay at room temperature for an hour. Now observe and compare.

17. Take two shiny empty tin cans and fill with ice cubes. Have children hold both cans wearing a glove on one hand. Observe and record the different sensory reactions. Why are there different feelings?

18. Have the custodian take children on a tour of the heating room, and explain the function of the heating equipment and the transfer of heat to various parts of the building.

19. The whole class listens to a radio weather forecast or watches a television weather report, and together they discuss its meaning.

20. After a particularly hard rain, have the children go outdoors and have them outline in chalk a few large puddles on the hard surfaced areas. At intervals of an hour each, have children observe the puddles and report to the class any changes in puddles. What eventually happens to the water? Why?

21. Put ice cubes in two jars and sprinkle salt over one jar of cubes. After some time, examine the difference between the two jars of cubes.

22. Place enough black construction paper in the freezer for every two children in your class. During a snowfall, take class outside and have them catch snowflakes on cold paper and observe the shapes with magnifying glasses. Two children working together makes it easier to do.

23. Immediately after a snowfall, place a piece of oaktag over the new-fallen snow in a protected area such as a window sill or untraveled area under the windows. Compare the snow under the oaktag with the snow around after a few days and observe the difference in whiteness. Why?

24. To further show that dust falls on snow and blackens it, place snow under oaktag and uncovered snow in jars. Bring both jars into the room and allow to melt. Compare the differences noticing especially the dust content.

25. Make wind vanes. Give each child a soda straw, a large feather, a straight pin, and a pencil with an eraser. Have children put the feather into soda straw with the feathers sticking out like an arrow. Balance the soda straw and feather on finger and place straight pin through straw at the point of balance. Attach pin to eraser of pencil and hold up to mouth. Blow straw and observe what happens.

C. *Enrichment activities*

Any of the previous activities can be used for enrichment just as any of the following enrichment activities can be utilized as initiating or answer-seeking activities with any of the children.

1. Construct a rain gauge by placing a coffee can in an unsheltered spot and measuring the water after a rainstorm. Report to class.

2. Make a shadow stick. Put a stick in the ground out in the open and mark the length of shadows at different times during the day and from week to week. Report finding of shadow differences to class.

3. Have children interview their parents to discover if the weather affects the work mother and father do. The same can be done with the postman, milkman, fireman, policeman, pilot, or any other occupation available for interview.

4. Construct a simple barometer. Stretch a balloon across the mouth of a jar and tie tightly. Glue a long soda straw to the middle of the stretched balloon, and allow to dry thoroughly. Place barometer against a wall with a sheet of paper attached to it. Mark the place where the soda straw touches the wall. Ob-

serve the straw's position daily and mark each spot. The difference in the position of the straw is due to fluctuations in air pressure.

5. A scrapbook can be kept of pictures from magazines showing activities that people generally engage in on warm and sunny, rainy, snowy, or foggy days.

6. Observe vapor trails of cars, trains, and planes on cold days. Report to class.

7. Children can draw pictures to show how the same scene would look on different weather days (hot, sunny, rainy, snowy, foggy) as well as different seasons.

8. Have children find out the places at home where they can find dew forming naturally (water pipes, windows, bathroom mirrors, eyeglasses, walls, automobile windows on rainy days, etc.)

9. Make a record of observations of clouds and cloud patterns and discuss with the class.

10. Put an empty gallon mayonnaise jar in a refrigerator overnight. The next morning leave the uncovered jar at room temperature for a few minutes and then cover tightly. Observe the dew that forms inside the jar.

11. Visit a local weather station, usually at an airport, with parents and report back to the class. This may precipitate a trip for the whole class.

12. Make a simple anemometer. Nail two small flat cans (tuna fish cans are fine) to the ends of each of two flat pieces of wood approximately 1″ x 12″. Make a cross of the two pieces of wood with the cans attached. Make a hole in the exact center of the crossed sticks. Get a strong broom handle and nail the crossed sticks to it through the hole in the center of the sticks. Make certain that the crossed sticks swing freely. Place this anemometer in the ground in a place where the wind blows unobstructed.

13. Make a large outline map of the United States. Have the children keep a national picture of the weather as a result of their radio and television programs. Symbols similar to those in No. 1 of the Answer-seeking activities on page 80 may be used, or appropriate pictures of weather conditions may be used.

14. Have the children collect as many thermometers as possible, including bath thermometer, oven thermometer for baking, candy or icing thermometer, rectal thermometer, outdoor thermometer, etc.

15. Make a model of a thermometer. Cut a rectangle out of cardboard approximately 6″ x 24″ with slots at each end about one inch from the side. Get the widest red and white ribbon available (at least 2 to 3 inches wide) in lengths a little more than 24″. Slip a length of white ribbon through the slots, so that it extends around through to the back. Sew a length of red ribbon to the length of white ribbon so that it forms an endless belt through the slots. This will simulate the mercury in the thermometer and can be moved up or down, the red indicating the temperature. Share with class.

16. Many of the reading references that follow can be used by capable children for further learning and for acquiring additional activities of their own.

D. *Culminating activities*

1. Conduct an exhibit of the experiments and demonstrations that children were exposed to

during their study. Children can stand next to their exhibits and act as guides or experts to answer questions. Parents and other children should be invited.

2. Present original dramatization using the principles learned. Possible theme could tie in man's concern with understanding and in the future possible controlling of the weather.

3. Reports can be given, enriched by displays and experiments, by children in class to share information found. Excellent outlet for the capable youngsters is provided.

4. Set up a weather station for the class or school, and post vital information daily in a conspicuous spot in the school. (temperature, wind direction, speed, etc.)

5. Take a trip to the weather station to see first hand how professional weather men conduct their studies of weather conditions.

6. Make a weather bulletin board where information gleaned from radio, television, newspapers, and other sources can be kept. A map of the United States or the world can be used to pinpoint origins of weather and different kinds of weather appearing daily in the world.

E. *Evaluating activities*

For this age group, mostly observation by the teacher or oral evaluation can be used. A possible guide for such evaluation might be:

1. At what height was the enthusiasm? High? Average? Low? Why?

2. What was the degree of participation by the children? High? Average? Low? Why?

3. Was there growth in the children's abilities to communicate accurately what they saw and experienced?

4. Did the children complete work started and did they accomplish what they intended?

5. Were the children's attitudes and ideas developed along the lines expected or desired?

Objective-type tests (see Chapter 10) can be devised by the teacher, but it is advised that they be used sparingly, if at all; if they are used, they could be given orally in the form of a game. The more capable or interested child could be helpful in devising some of the questions to be used.

IV. *Bibliography*

TEACHERS

Adler, Ruth and Robert Irving. *Hurricane and Twisters*. New York: Alfred A. Knopf, Inc., 1955.

Bates, David Robert. *Earth and Its Atmosphere*. New York: Basic Books, Inc., 1958.

Blair, Thomas. *Weather Elements*. Englewood Cliffs, New Jersey: Prentice-Hall, Inc., 1937.

Bolton, Joe. *The Wind and the Weather*. New York: The Crowel-Collier Publishing Co., 1957.

Brands, G. *Meteorology*. New York: McGraw-Hill Book Co., Inc., 1944.

Brooks, Charles F. *Why the Weather?* New York: Harcourt, Brace & World, Inc., 1935.

Chapin, Henry and F. G. Walton Smith. *The Ocean River*. New York: Charles Scribner's Sons, 1952.

Donn, William L. *Meteorology*. New York: McGraw-Hill Book Co., Inc., 1951.

Forrester, Frank. *1001 Questions Answered About the Weather*. New York: Dodd, Mead & Co., 1957.

Gallant, Roy A. *Exploring the Weather*. Garden City, New York: Doubleday & Company, Inc., 1957.

Houghton, Henry. *Atmospheric Explorations*. New York: John Wiley & Sons, Inc., 1958.

Humphreys, E. J. *Map of the Weather*. New

York: The Ronald Press Company., 1942.

Kimble, George H. *Our American Weather.* New York: McGraw-Hill Book Co., Inc., 1955.

Junior Aviation Meteorology. Albany: University of the State of New York, State Education Department, 1949.

Lehr, P. E. *et al. Weather.* New York: Simon and Schuster, Inc., 1957.

Longstreth, Morris S. *Knowing the Weather.* New York: The Macmillan Company, 1953.

Milgrom, Harry. *The Adventure Book of Weather.* New York: Capitol Publishing Co., Inc., 1959.

Miller, Denning. *Wind, Storm and Rain.* New York: Coward-McCann, Inc., 1952.

Namowitz, Samuel N. and Donald B. Stone. *Earth Science: The World We Live In.* Princeton, New Jersey: Van Nostrand Co., Inc., 1960.

Sloane, Eric. *The Book of Storms.* New York: Duell, Sloan & Pearce, Inc., 1957.

Snow, Frost and Ice. Cornell Rural School Leaflet, Vol. 41, No. 3 (Winter 1948).

Spar, Jerome. *The Way of the Weather.* Mankato, Minnesota: Creative Educational Society, 1957.

Taylor, George. *Elementary Meteorology.* Englewood Cliffs, New Jersey: Prentice-Hall, Inc., 1954.

Any professional books previously listed.

CHILDREN

Bell, Thelma. *Snow.* New York: The Viking Press, Inc., 1954. (3-6).

Benedick, Jeanne. *All Around You.* New York: Whittlesey House, 1951. (K-2).

Black, Irma. *Busy Water.* New York: Holiday House, 1959. (2-4).

Friskey, Margaret R. *The True Book of the Air Around Us.* Chicago: Children's Press, Inc., 1953. (K-3).

Marino, Dorothy. *Good-Bye Thunderstorm.* Philadelphia: J. B. Lippincott Co., 1958. (1-3).

Norling, Jo and Earnest. *The First Book of*

Water. New York: Franklin Watts, Inc., 1952. (3-6).

Podendorf, Illa. *The True Book of Seasons.* Chicago: Children's Press, Inc., 1955. (K-2).

Reed, William Maxwell. *And That's Why.* New York: Harcourt, Brace & World, Inc., 1932. (3-5).

Tresselt, Alvin R. *Follow the Wind.* New York: Lothrop, Lee & Shepard Co., Inc., 1950. (K-2).

Walsh, Mary. *Water, Water, Everywhere.* Nashville: Abingdon Press, 1953. (3-6).

Zolotow, Charlotte. *The Storm Book.* New York: Harper & Row, Publishers, 1952. (K-3).

V.   *Materials and equipment*

    A.   *Science supplies*

        tea kettle
        sheet of glass
        pie tins
        adhesive tape
        an aquarium or large glass dish
        thermometers, assorted types
        milk bottles
        ice cubes
        table salt
        large feathers
        rags or handkerchiefs
        construction paper (white and black)
        balloons
        paint brushes
        soda straws
        empty milk cartons
        gallon jugs
        empty shiny tin cans
        empty jars, assorted sizes
        straight pins
        wide-mouthed gallon jars
        coffee cans

    B.   *Films*

        Air All Around Us, Young America, 10 min.
        Air in Action, Coronet, 10 min.
        Animals in Winter, EBF, 11 min.
        Children in Autumn, EBF, 11 min.

Children in Spring
Children in Summer
Children in Winter
How Weather Helps Us, Coronet, 11 min.
Nothing But Air, EBF, 11 min.
One Rainy Day, Coronet, 11 min.
Weather, Gateway, 11 min.

C. *Filmstrips*

The Air, EBF
Air, Wind, and Weather, Eye Gate
All My Seasons, McGraw-Hill
Autumn Is Here, Jam Handy
Foggy and Windy Day, McGraw-Hill

How Does Water Get Into the Air?
Jam Handy
Our Weather, EBF
We Learn About the Weather, L. W. Singer
What is Weather? Jam Handy
What is Wind? Jam Handy
What Makes Rain? Young America
What Makes Things Dry Faster? Jam Handy
Where Do Clouds Come From? Jam Handy
Winter in the Country, Society for Visual Education
Winter is Here, Society for Visual Education

Summary

One of the better ways that a teacher can prepare herself for teaching a particular science content field in a minimum of time and with relative ease is the science content resource unit. By systematically organizing procedures, the teacher gets an overall view of the possibilities of such a study as well as a background and reserve of science content: facts, concepts, ideas, and understandings. Along with this background the teacher is presented with possible activities for starting, guiding, and finally culminating and evaluating the unit of study. These science resource units can be written by the teacher or obtained from textbooks or other commercially prepared materials. The science resource units guide the teacher in his preplanning for teaching a unit before entering the classroom. More materials of all kinds are included in the science content resource unit than a teacher can use with any one class; therefore, the units are only suggestive and can be used with flexibility. Many schools have prepared these resource units for the teacher. Other school systems have encouraged several teachers to work together on making resource units.

After the teacher has fortified herself with science information and activities, she is ready to enter the classroom for organizing and conducting the science unit with children. The next chapter will deal with the actual planning and presentation of the materials to children and with the arrangement of the classroom for a program of science education in the elementary school.

Further Investigation and Study

1. Using the format for a science resource unit on page 75, construct a resource unit from any of the suggested A.A.A.S. Feasibility Study broad areas. (See page 10 for these areas.)

2. Compile a collection of science resource units from the list of sources of science content resource units in the Appendix.

3. Frequently the social studies present many opportunities for potential science content studies. Select from the following references and organize a science content resource unit around a social studies content area:

California State Department of Instruction, *Science in the Elementary School.* Sacramento, California, 1954.

Hanna, Labone A., Gladys L. Potter, and Neva Hagaman. *Unit Teaching in the Elementary School.* New York: Holt, Rinehart & Winston, Inc., 1959.

Lee, J. Murray and Doris May Lee. *The Child and His Curriculum.* New York: Appleton-Century-Crofts, 1950.

Merritt, Edith P. *Working with Children in Social Studies.* San Francisco: Wadsworth Publishing Co., Inc., 1961.

4. Survey your community, and compile a list of the available materials useful in science for the elementary school. Indicate the source of the supplies such as home, dime store, gas station, drugstore, etc.

Working Your Plans

6

It has been said that teachers should plan their work and then go ahead and work their plans. Once the teacher has planned her science resource unit, she is ready to prepare for the actual teaching of portions of this unit to her class. Because the resource unit is so large and usually comprises much more than can actually be used, more definite planning must take place. Weekly planning and daily, individual lesson plans eliminate some broad concepts for the teacher, and yet, supply more details for other areas. For this reason, the teacher must plan for time allotments within weekly and daily schedules. The structure and use of these plans are discussed later in this chapter.

WEEKLY LESSON PLANS

A weekly plan offers the teacher opportunities for blocking out portions of her resource unit into manageable pieces. In this way, Miss Jones can plan experiences for her class on a flexible basis. In her weekly plan for the study of the nature of air and air pressure, she has provided approximate estimates of work necessary and profitable for each particular day. There is the possibility that she planned too much or too little for each individual day and must, therefore, modify the plan and play each day by ear. She alone can determine the specific course of each day, but for the sake of planning a program she must estimate the time she feels will be needed to accomplish each step of the way in her children's understanding of air and air pressure. The two-headed arrow (↔) at the left side between the days in the following weekly plan is an attempt to indicate that each day's estimate may be revised up or down, depending on the rapidity with which the children learn the materials.

Miss Jones' Weekly Plan: Air and Air Pressure

First Day: Review what children know about air and air pressure by presenting several simple experiments for stimulation. Children should be aided in seeing that:

> Air is real and occupies space.
> Air exerts pressure.
> Air is all around us.
> Air is colorless, tasteless, and odorless.
> Living things need air.

Arrange time for the children to perform the simple experiments and to make their evaluations and generalizations. This will help in planning tomorrow's work. Total time probably 1½ hours, includes discussion, class participation in experiments, evaluation and generalization, and clean-up.

Second Day: Move on to further characteristics of air, such as:

> Air pressure can do work for man.
> Air is a mixture of gases.
> Air is elastic and can expand.
> Air expands when it is heated.
> Air contracts when it is cooled.

Make certain that children understand the previous points and that they are not just verbalizing. The teacher should perform some of the experiments dealing with the heating of things. Children can be helped in writing up the experiments in simple form. (Note: The fetish of meticulous notebooks can ruin this important skill in recording.) The class might write together on a large chart and keep a class experiment book. Children should be helped to record accurately. Total time is about one hour, 45 minutes for teacher-performed experiments

and discussion and 15 minutes for the writing of an experiment for the class experiment book. The writing can be continued during language arts time, and vocabulary lists can be obtained from the experiments.

Third Day: Slow down and review previous concepts through the use of film (*Air is All Around Us* by Young American Films) or filmstrip (*Air and Its Properties* by Young American Films). After previewing the film, make a list of possible questions needed to evaluate children's understanding of previous work. Total time is 30 minutes.

Fourth Day: If the children are ready and further work on previous concepts is not necessary, try to guide the children to an understanding of the causes of winds as a motivation or lead-in for a study of weather. Build upon previous concepts to show that:

> Wind is moving air.
> Warm air expands.
> Cold air contracts.
> Warm air is lighter than cold air and rises.

Stress the safety factors to the class when using heat, and, when possible, use electric hotplates or other flameless sources of heat. Allow time for all the children to get a chance to do all the experiments. Total time is one hour.

Fifth and Sixth Days: The children should be quite aware of the ways in which air functions under heat and cold and can now move into the relationship of the previous concepts to their local winds. Here are some of the concepts they will need to know in interpreting winds:

> Air is heated chiefly by contact with the earth.
> Substances differ in their abilities to absorb heat from the sun.
> Local winds are caused by the unequal

heating of the ground in different places.

The wind shifts its direction from day to day, and even from minute to minute.

Winds are named for the direction from which they blow.

These concepts might take several days to develop and should not be rushed. Play it by ear.

Some teachers may react to Miss Jones' weekly plan with "My gosh, my class could never handle so many concepts in one week." Others might find that they would be running out of material before the end of the week. It all depends upon the individual class and teacher. Even in the best prepared plans, the teacher must be atuned to the background and interest of her particular class and each day modify her plans accordingly. It would be valuable now to look at our last type of planning, the individual "discovery-type" lesson plan.

Learning by discovery in problem solving is more enduring, meaningful, and useful than learning that has come about by telling.

There is great emphasis being put upon the discovery approach to science teaching as a result of the work of people in varied learning-process fields.[1] The fundamental purpose of discovery learning is to get students to approach their problem solving with facts, materials, and events, to put them together in their own ways, and to come out

with relationships upon which to build generalizations or principles. This process of discovery relies heavily upon *questioning* as opposed to *telling* children either by direct teacher explanation or textbook explanation. Science teachers are using the discovery method in problem solving with much success by conducting experiments and demonstrations in which they help students discover the scientific principles by asking a series of questions.

Through such questioning during the process of doing a demonstration or experiment, the teacher is able to direct students' reactions to the whole problem solving process: analyzing problems, making hypotheses, recalling pertinent and previously learned knowledge, making tentative conclusions, testing these tentative conclusions, and finally coming away with a tentatively final conclusion based upon the available data. As an important side effect of this discovery approach, the student is aided in visualizing and taking part in the process by which scientists discover facts and relationships about the environment. Students, thereby, not only learn science concepts but also one of the major methods of problem solving — inductive reasoning or putting things together in their meaningful relationships.

DEVELOPING INDUCTIVE THINKING THROUGH QUESTIONING

Science as practiced by scientists is a creative, intellectual activity requiring active participation of the scientist. Teachers who tell students answers and continually lecture to their class allow little opportunity for their students to develop intellectual activity and creativity. In fact, the only mental demands placed upon the students by such teachers is memorization.

In doing demonstrations or experiments, a good rule to follow for getting students

[1]The authors are indebted to the following for their fine work in the fields of learning dealing with the discovery approach:
Jerome Bruner, *The Process of Education* (Cambridge: Harvard University Press, 1961).
Laura Zirbes, *Spurs to Creative Teaching* (New York: G. P. Putnam's Sons, 1959).
Robert S. Fleming, ed., *Curriculum for Today's Boys and Girls,* Chapter 9, "Promoting Intellectual Development Through Problem Solving," written by Fannie Shaftel and Charlotte Crabtree (Columbus, Ohio: Charles E. Merrill Books, Inc., 1963).

actively involved is: ASK — DON'T TELL. By asking questions you require students to be active participants in the learning process. In answering your questions the students have to analyze what you ask and call upon their past and present experiences to make hypotheses before, during, and after the actual experiment. As they gather information from their observation of the experiment or demonstration, they are guided to check their hypotheses; questions guide them in synthesizing their tentative conclusions.

Several examples of questioning techniques used in experiments and demonstrations to develop skills in inductive thinking will now be discussed.

Questions and Pictures

In one investigation children are presented with twenty-one picture cards of which three are of ducks, four are of birds but are not ducks, four are of animals that fly but are not birds, seven are of animals that do not fly, and three are of inanimate objects. Children are asked to arrange the picture cards in piles so that the animals that resemble each other are in the same pile.

Now the children are asked the following specific questions:

Suppose we were to put the cards into these three envelopes, each with its own label. This label says birds. Could we put this pile (ducks), and this pile (other birds) in the same envelope, and still keep this label?

Now this label says animals. Could we put these (birds) in with these (animals that do not fly), and still keep the label, animals?

Could we put these (animals that do not fly) in with these (birds other than ducks), and use the same label?

Next the children were asked:

If all the ducks were killed, would there be any birds left?

If all the birds were killed, would there be any ducks left?

If all the animals were killed, would there be any birds left?[2]

The teacher asks the children to justify their responses after each question. For instance, if a child rejects the bird label for ducks, he is asked: "Aren't ducks birds?" If a child rejects the animal label for birds, the teacher asks: "Are not birds animals?"

Each time the teacher probes with "Why not?" not only can the children benefit by being actively involved, but the science teacher can learn much more about how the children are thinking about a problem and what specific difficulties they are having with a concept.

Experiments and Thought-provoking Questions

Another example of questioning in the discovery approach to science in the elementary class can be observed through a teacher's work with a Galileo or air ther-

[2]Jean Piaget and Babel Inhelder, *The Growth of Logical Thinking* (New York: Basic Books, Inc., 1958).

mometer. After setting up a thin-walled, flat-sided, medicine bottle with a long glass tube attached and inverted in a small glass of colored water, the teacher's questions might proceed in this way:*

What do you think will happen if I heat the bottle with my hands? Let's watch and see. (The teacher warms bottle with hands.)

What did you observe happening? (Many bubbles move out of the end of the straw into liquid below.) Why did this happen? (The air inside bottle expands when heated and moves out of straw into water.)

What do you guess will happen when I take my hands away from the bottle and let it stand for about 15 minutes? Let's put it aside and see it. (After 15 minutes it is observed that a small column of colored water has risen in the tube.)

Why did the water rise in the tube? (It takes the place of the air bubbles that were forced out.)

What may happen when I put this ice cube on the bottle? All right, let's try it. (The liquid rises up the straw quite rapidly.)

Why did the colored water rise in the straw? (The air inside the bottle contracts, and the air pressure on the outside of the liquid forces the water up the tube.)

In this situation visualize how another teacher might have approached the same learning experience. At the point when the bottle cools and water rises in the tube, the teacher could quite easily tell the students: "When the bottle was heated, the air in it expanded and some of it rushed out of the bottle, down the tube, and into the classroom. When the tube cooled, the gas or air contracted producing a partial vacuum in the bottle."

By telling, what has the teacher done? The students may have learned the prin-

*See Discovery Lesson on page 338.

ciple of a gas expanding when heated plus certain other things about pressure, but the teacher robbed the children of the thrill of discovering for themselves. More important, the children were not allowed to become actively involved in thinking and formulating relationships between the particular phenomena witnessed and possible reasons for the happenings. They did not have a chance to exercise their inductive thinking processes.

Children Ask the Questions

A third example of the importance of questioning in the development of scientific discovery has a rather unique procedure which has been proven to give excellent results. Instead of the teacher questioning students, students question the teacher. In this investigation short films of physics demonstrations raise problems of cause and effect. Children are encouraged to solve these problems by asking their teacher questions after the films. The teacher's answers to the children's questions furnish the children with data, help them identify variables and determine their relevancy to the problem, and formulate hypotheses of cause and effect that are tried experimentally. No data is supplied except through children's observations and from their teacher's direct answers. Here is a portion of the type of sessions the children would have after seeing a film. This session dealt with the film, *Ball and Ring Demonstration,* in which a brass ball just fitting through a brass ring is heated. An attempt is then made to pass the ball through the ring.

PUPIL: Were the ball and ring at room temperature to begin with?

TEACHER: Yes.

PUPIL: Would the ball go through the ring at first?

TEACHER: Yes.

PUPIL: After the ball was held over the fire, it did not go through the ring?

TEACHER:	No.
PUPIL:	If the ring had been heated instead of the ball, would the results have been the same?
TEACHER:	No.
PUPIL:	If both had been heated would the ball have gone through then?
TEACHER:	That all depends.
PUPIL:	If they both had been heated to the same temperature, would the ball have gone through?
TEACHER:	Yes.
PUPIL:	Would the ball be the same size after it was heated as it was before?
TEACHER:	No.
PUPIL:	Could the same experiment have been done if the ball and ring were made out of some other metal?
TEACHER:	Yes.[3]

To these children, science is becoming the discovery of new relationships. They are being helped to discover cause and effect relationships through their own initiative and control not by the explanations and interpretations of teachers or other adults. This program is attempting to make pupils more independent, systematic, and empirical.

These three examples have shown the ways in which questioning benefits and enhances the children's development of inductive thinking through discovery. Perhaps, though, the greatest advantage of the discovery approach in science is that it increases interest on the part of the student and the teacher and most of all allows the student to experience the rewards of discovery.

[3]Richard J. Suchman, "Inquiry Training in the Elementary School," *Science Teacher,* No. 27 (November, 1960), p. 42.

DAILY DISCOVERY-TYPE LESSON PLANS

The daily lesson plan is used to focus upon ways of achieving specific purposes within a given block of time with specific, carefully chosen teaching-learning experiences and materials from all the possible ones in the Resource Unit on pages 77-86. Types of daily lesson plans used currently vary greatly, and they should if the science education program is to avoid boredom and non-productivity. The way in which the teacher plans reflects his personality, training and background, and to varying degrees upon the administrative and supervisory requirements of his school. Some teachers keep commercially prepared plan books covering all subject areas in brief outline form for each day while others keep a running log or devote a card or form for each curricular area. Regardless of the form used, most teachers feel a need for some sort of outline guide to follow in planning the specifics of the individual lesson. Rarely, if ever, is teaching constantly at a level of excellence without some sort of planning by the teacher.

A plan offers the teacher the opportunity to select actual methods, techniques, and procedures as well as to think out the possible ways of teaching that will be advisable for her class. It also allows the teacher to make some provision for the materials that will be needed for the study and to formulate very carefully what he hopes his children will accomplish while being exposed to this study. Without a plan he will try to adlib his way through lessons, and while some of them may be good, a teacher must have a plan for building the backgrounds of his children.

The actual writing down of plans and the amount of detail depends a great deal upon the teacher's preferences and experience with planning. In most carefully planned lessons, however, these parts are included:

SUGGESTED FORMAT FOR SCIENCE
DISCOVERY-TYPE LESSON PLAN

Purposes: First find out how much of the material your children already know and then include a brief list of what you are hoping to have your class accomplish. Be specific and make your purposes realistic and attainable for your particular class.

Materials: Include all materials to be used by both teacher and children. The teacher should have used all materials, equipment, film, etc. before so that he will be thoroughly familiar with them and see the possible uses for each. Make certain that all materials and equipment are available and in good working condition before listing them for use in the lesson. Never count on anything being there ready for use unless you get it yourself and try it.

Procedures: List specific ways needed to arouse and maintain interest and include questions to be used for this purpose. Include specific activities to be done by the children themselves. Give somewhat of a sequential arrangement of the activities and make provisions for specific directions for individual and group activities. Provide opportunities for children who

need special help. *Include thought-provoking questions to stimulate discovery-learning.*

Scheduling of Time: Include time estimates for the introduction and for the activities of the pupils including the evaluation and conclusions or generalizations. It is imperative that time be given to clean-up as this type of activity is more prevalent in science education studies. It can also develop responsibility in children.

Summary and Evaluation: Questions and activities for finding out if the children know what you have been teaching should be included in this section. Many of these items may appear under the other sections, especially procedures, because summarizing and evaluating are constantly going on during a lesson as a part of teaching.

The following example shows how Miss Jones used this basic form for planning a daily lesson for her third grade from her unit on weather. Note that the plan is practical, specific, and easy to follow. Attention throughout the lesson plan is given to concrete experiments to be done with children. Stress is put upon assisting the children in discovering concepts and relationships through careful, thought-provoking questions and direct sensory experiences for the children. Thought-provoking questions and answers are presented here and in the Discovery Type lesson plan in Part IV for emphasis and ease of use by teachers.

MISS JONES' DAILY LESSON PLAN:
AIR IS REAL AND OCCUPIES SPACE

Purposes

1. Acquaint children with these scientific phenomena:
    a. Air is real and occupies space.
    b. Air is colorless, tasteless, and odorless.
    c. Air is all around us.
    d. Living things need air.

2. Help children develop an understanding of living things and their dependence upon air.

3. Guide children's thinking through actual experimentation with simple materials and observation under the teacher's direction.

4. Provide supervised opportunities for children to have independent work which can teach self-responsibility and methods of working with people in groups.

Materials

Enough of the following for each child except glass pans of which six will be enough: polyethylene plastic bags (from shirts, food, etc.) water glass, handkerchief, glass pan, safety matches, soda straws.

Procedures

1. For motivation and introduction, flatten an empty polyethylene plastic bag. Now fill the bag with apples and ask the children what is in it. How do you know there is something in it? (Examples of answers: It bulges, you can feel it, etc.) Empty apples and fill bag with water. Again ask: Is anything in the bag now? How do you know?
    Empty water, open the bag wide, and move it through the air. Close the mouth of the bag by twisting after the bag has bulged. Now ask: What is in the bag? (Children of this age should answer air, but if not the teacher should suggest it.) Make it a point to establish what is real and how we can know if something is real. Although we cannot see, smell, or feel air, how are some other ways we might show that air is real and occupies space?
    If no suggestions come forth, the teacher can present the following experiments:

2. Turn a glass upside down and push the mouth as far as it will go in a pan of water. Why is the level of water in the glass lower than the water level in the pan? Why does more water not go into the glass? Tip the glass so one edge is

above the water. Observe what happens. Why? (AIR OCCUPIES SPACE)

3. Have children put a clean dry handkerchief in a drinking glass and invert into pan of water used in the preceding experiment. When the glass is removed, will the handkerchief be wet or dry? Why? (Note: The same experiment can be used by placing a safety match in the handkerchief before inverting it in the water and then striking the dry match after removing it from the glass. The teacher should strike the match. (AIR IS REAL AND OCCUPIES SPACE)

4. Capture air in the polyethylene bag and twist the mouth shut. Make sure air is staying in the bag. (Hint: If the air is coming out of small holes, just apply cellophane tape to the hole and it will seal immediately.) Place several heavy objects (such as books or pieces of wood) on the bag and be aware of what happens. Does the bag hold up the weight? Why? Ask if this knowledge has been put to any use for man's benefit. (Children's bicycle tire, inflatable rubber rafts, car tires, etc.) (AIR SUPPORTS OBJECTS)

5. Fill glass with water to overflowing and quickly place a piece of cardboard over it. Invert glass. What happens? Why? (Caution: Always perform this experiment over a pan or sink.)

6. Each child holds his finger over one end of a soda straw and immerses it in water. Water does not rise in straw. Why? Remove your finger and the water rises. Why? Put your finger back on the straw and move the straw out of the water. Why doesn't the water fall out? (AIR OCCUPIES SPACE AND EXERTS PRESSURE IN ALL DIRECTIONS)

7. After working the simple experiments and demonstrations himself with children taking part in the questioning and observing, the teacher will outline the procedure that will be used for children's participation. The teacher has set up six areas with materials at each for the performance of the experiments. The teacher

has selected groups that will work together, and then he goes over the rules
and regulations they all feel are necessary
for conducting the experiments. When
groups begin to work, a teacher should
move about quieting, reassuring, and
helping her students. Directions given
must be very clear and must be checked
to see if they are understood.

8. Clean up quickly and quietly.

Evaluating

1. Discuss experiments and observations.

2. A report does not necessarily have to be
   devised so that children's observations
   can be shared and verified and checked,
   but there should be stress placed upon
   accuracy of observation.

3. Clues for future planning for the study
   can be obtained from the children either
   through direct questioning or as a result
   of the other evaluation techniques employed.

4. Evaluation of the group activities should
   be done to make sure that the time was
   well spent and to obtain suggestions for
   improving them next time.

Scheduling of Approximate Time (Total — one
hour)

1. Introduction and motivation — 5 minutes.

2. Teacher-conducted experiments and directions for group work — 15 minutes.

3. Children-conducted experiments in
   groups at separate tables — 20 minutes.

4. Cleaning up and replacing furniture
   — 10 minutes.

5. Questioning and evaluation — 10
   minutes.

Note: Although the total lesson runs one hour
which is long for young children, the children
engage in active physical participation after
twenty minutes of passivity. Miss Jones set up
the six activity areas before children arrived

in the morning and started her science lesson as
the first activity for the day.

ARRANGING TIME FOR SCIENCE TEACHING

For many reasons, it becomes impossible
and undesirable to prescribe to the teacher
exact amounts of daily or weekly time for
science education. As a bare minimum, however, it is recommended that at least 150
minutes a week be set aside for science content studies. The patterns by which time is
designated for daily time allotments vary
considerably.

The choice of how the time allotment for
science is arranged is usually determined by
the teacher. The teacher's decision for a
pattern of time utilization is affected by her
curriculum preferences, science as a separate
subject or integrated with others; by the
school policy and interpretation of the teacher's immediate supervisor, required science
daily or by a flexible weekly arrangement; or
by the type of science program conducted:
self-contained classroom or science specialists on a regularly scheduled time basis.

Generally, it appears more desirable for
science to be taught in large, flexible blocks
of time two or three times a week rather
than daily in short blocks of time. Large
blocks of time offer teachers and children
advantages especially in a science education
program that stresses experimentation and
discovery. Anyone who knows children well
realizes that it takes time to stimulate children to work on something; then it is
detrimental to the learning process to stop
activities in the middle because the time is
gone. In addition, it usually takes such a
long time to take out and put back materials
used in science that all the time would
be used in just the passage of supplies and
materials. It takes more time for a teacher
and his class to set up and have partici-

pation in the activities peculiar to science education than it does in a more sedentary reading or listening program. There are times, of course, when such sedentary activities as reading and listening are appropriate in science study, and for this reason, it would be unwise to arbitrarily set science periods

in which this flexible time pattern can be arranged is seen in Miss Jones' time allotments for several days.

By looking at the time schedule for the day in which she presented the preceding lesson, the reader can see how Miss Jones planned for a one hour lesson.

Time	Subject-matter Area	Minutes
9-10	Science Content Lesson (Air is Real and Occupies Space) (Groups working on experiments at 6 tables set up by teacher before school opened)	60
10-10:20	Clean-up	20
10:20-11	Reading (skill teaching)	40
11-11:30	Physical Education in gym	30
11:30-12	Music	30
12-1	Lunch	60
1-1:30	Arithmetic	30
1:30-2:10	Language Arts (spelling and sentence structure)	40
2:10-2:40	Art	30
2:40-3	Clean-up and planning for next day	20

for five thirty-minute periods a week. The total of 150 minutes could be more efficiently used in more flexible patterns dictated by the needs of the activity selected as appropriate for that particular time. If it is necessary for the teacher to schedule one hour for setting up, performing, and discussing experiments with the children, it should not be necessary to cancel all other science for the week because the arbitrary allotment of time was consumed. How much better it is to be able to rearrange the time to best advantage. An example of the way

The one hour was actually a larger block of time because the teacher used the half-hour before school opened to set up the six tables for simple experiments that the children could perform themselves. This lesson was an outgrowth of the previous day's work, and the teacher thought it necessary to follow up immediately with the children's active participation. There are times, however, when even a bigger block of time is necessary; this is the way the same teacher scheduled science for another day and another type of science activity.

Time	Subject-matter Area	Minutes
9-9:30	Planning for nature walk, what to bring, what to look for, how not to destroy living things, etc.	30
9:30-10:30	Reading skills	60
10:30-10:45	Recess	15
10:45-11:15	Arithmetic	30
11:15-12	Language Arts	45
12-1	Lunch	60
1-2:45	Science — nature walk around school grounds and immediate area for collection of leaves, insects, etc.	105
2:45-3	Brief evaluation of trip and housing collected materials properly	15

Still another plan might use the entire day for science content work where all or most of the subjects might be related to the present science unit study. Although the science patterns used here consumed a whole day's work, they reinforced all other skills taught in the academic and aesthetic curriculum. The schedule for Miss Jones' third grade would look like this:

Time	Activity	Minutes
9-9:30	Plan for the total day and give specific assignments to individuals and committees.	30
9:30-10:30	Reading skills — read books on weather obtained by teacher for different levels.	60
	Specific assignments are to find weather instruments and directions for building.	
10:30-10:45	Recess	15
10:45-11:45	Work in committees for setting up a weather station — each group investigates different weather instruments from information found in books from reading time.	60
11:45-12	Read and correct each others letters of thank you to the weather station for the trip they took.	15
12-1	Lunch	60
1-1:30	See and discuss a motion picture about weather instruments, their use, construction, and weather forecasting.	30
1:30-2	Music (not necessarily integrated)	30
2-2:30	Total class plans together and makes rough draft of an outline for an original dramatization on weather to be presented in assembly for parents and other students.	30
2:30-3	Make list of supplies that will be needed for constructing weather instruments. Make lists of new vocabulary words in science unit. Tomorrow put them into vocabulary books and find proper meaning and usage. Clean-up.	30

Summary

Planning takes organization and time, but the educational returns are beneficial. Short cuts and increased confidence in the field of science education decrease some of the time consuming work. Once the teacher has taught one or two science content studies, he usually finds that he enjoys them as much as the children do. The teacher also finds that the time needed for finding ideas, information, and needed materials is decreased as the material becomes repetitious. There is no substitute for a well-planned lesson in science education if the teacher is alert enough to alter the plan when it is necessary. Use flexible, large blocks of time for scheduling science activities. Here are some other suggestions that teachers have found worthwhile in planning and teaching science.

1. *Proceed with Caution*

It is wise to go slowly in each lesson, not to attempt to cover too much territory, and to check constantly to see if children are learning what it is you are trying to teach. Never assume that because you have done or said something that it was understood by the children in the way you intended. Rushing over materials to cover the syllabus usually ends in vague and fragmented learnings. REMEMBER: it takes time to learn. Make it a practice to provide for constant review in your lessons not only as a reinforcement of learning but also as an evaluation technique. This advice is not limited to children who have difficulties with learning, for the most capable children need time to reflect upon what has been taught. Opportunities should also be made available for a variety of experience so that there are not only class presentations; this is very important for the children who need additional teacher time for learning. Do not be so busy teaching that you forget that children learn at their own rate and in their own patterns. We can accomplish most by presenting flexible and stimulating experiences in which children are genuinely active and interested in the planning.

2. *Include Children in Planning*

Teachers should allow ample opportunity in each lesson plan for children to take an active part in some of the direction of the lessons and for them to develop the ability to think independently. Just because the teacher has spent time in making a plan does not mean that he should ramrod his plan through regardless of worthwhile alternatives that his students might have to offer. Children can do much in giving direction to lessons if given the opportunity. This planning is vital to meaningful experiences for children especially in science education where critical thinking and problem solving is stressed. Too often we underestimate our children's abilities and knowledge.

There are times during the day when children can contribute to future planning. At the beginning of the day or of the lesson children usually can suggest things, as a result of the previous day's work, by bringing from home needed supplies and equipment or by reminding the teacher that today is the day the first grade invited their class to see their aquarium. Before a lesson there are also many times when children establish the goals although they may be completely different from the ones the teacher planned for this purpose. For instance, some children might remember that the class did not get a chance to discuss the nature walk from yesterday because they had a fire drill. Other children might volunteer the suggestion for taking care of the insects and small animals seen on the nature walk. These contributions may have been forgotten from the previous day or may have been an essential part of the current day's schedule, but the teacher should be glad to share the responsibility of selective planning with the children. The teacher will fill in the gaps in the children's comments and guide the lesson from there, but much of the planning and the impetus comes from the children. During small workshop sessions, committees might stop their own work to tell the teacher that they need additional information before their weather instruments can be constructed. The teacher would then take this into consideration for planning the next day's work. This is a further example of the daily modification of plans according to the needs and interest of the children within a class. At the end of a lesson, children might be able to summarize what the teacher had attempted to teach especially through adept questioning by the teacher.

3. *Do Not Work Alone*

Teachers find that working together on an informal or planned, grade-level or school-wide, basis is helpful to their science teaching. The division of the science curriculum among teachers in a school for planning resource units provides a large and rich storehouse of potential learning experiences for children. The sharing of existing equipment by teachers increases the possibilities for teaching. Collective planning for new supplies and materials is valuable for avoiding unnecessary duplication or omission of needed items. Combining of classes on a team-teaching basis can be profitable and can increase the competence of the teachers who cooperate in this manner. Having the principal, science consultant, or other personnel assist the teacher is helpful. Utilizing parents in the science program increases the possibilities for the classroom teacher. Custodians very often are excellent resource people for teachers to use in their science programs. In other words, do not work alone; opportunities for worthwhile contributions are many, and these additions can greatly enhance your science teaching.

Further Investigation and Study

1. Select one of the science content areas from the Feasibility Conferences listed on page 10 and write a science resource unit. Use all the items included in the format for Science Resource Units on page 75.

2. Listed below are some sources for commercially prepared science resource units. Select one and plan a weekly plan and five individual lesson plans for that weekly plan.

Ballard, Katherine L. "A Study of the Sea," *The Instructor,* April, 1961.

Branley, Franklyn M. "Air and Outer Space," *Grade Teacher,* April, 1959.

Foracci, Henry J. and Theodore Huff. "Science Unit on Rocks and Minerals," *The Science Teacher,* March, 1961.

Leonard, Naomi A. "The Water Problem," *The Instructor,* April, 1963.

Facilities and Materials for Teaching Science

7

If science studies are to progress beyond the planning stages, the elementary schools should contain adequate facilities and materials. Science teaching requires its own particular facilities and materials; this is especially true if science is to be more than a mere "read and discuss" type of program. We would not think of having art, music, or map instruction without the materials unique to each of these fields. For too long a time we have expected elementary school teachers to scavenge for necessary science materials. It is true that many items can be made or obtained from home or local stores; however, substitutions for some items are hard to find. It is recommended that the planning, purchasing, and constructing of science facilities and materials be done on a total school or school district basis. Then some items can be stored in a central school facility, servicing everyone, while other items can be placed in each individual classroom. Obviously, the patterns will differ according to whether science is conducted in a self-contained classroom by the classroom teacher, by specialists in the regular classroom, or by specialists in a special science room. There are advantages and disadvantages for any of these three patterns.[1] The predominant pattern in American elementary schools, however, is that the classroom teacher present the science in her regular classroom. Nevertheless, consideration for the teacher using materials and facilities for the total school as well as the individual classroom will be explored.

---

[1] For excellent presentation (including examples of instructional practices and recommended supplies and equipment) of science programs conducted by science specialists and by team teaching in elementary schools see:
Joseph Zafforoni and Edith Selberg, eds., *New Developments in Elementary School Science* (Washington, D.C.: National Science Teachers Association, 1963). Albert Piltz, "Getting the Most from the Equipment Dollar," *The Instructor,* No. 73 (January, 1964).

SCIENCE FACILITIES AND MATERIALS FOR THE TOTAL SCHOOL

Special Science Room

A special room set aside for science facilities and materials is very desirable in an elementary school even where a self-contained program is conducted. This room can be specially planned in a new building, an unused classroom, part of an art or shop room, or any other available space. This room can be used for special science projects, science equipment and supply storage, school greenhouse, science fairs, and ex-

hibits. The room should contain the following if possible: running water, electrical outlets, working tables, a source of heat, work bench with assorted hand tools, several rolling carts for distribution of science materials, and ample storage facilities.

Pieces of equipment that are more expensive or delicate should be stored in this room. Microscopes and microprojectors, models, galvanometers, telescopes, and other equipment could be made available on a school-wide basis from this room. Some

pieces of special equipment will only be needed for a short time. Many items, such as Geiger counters, may be borrowed from the high school, a local lab, or industry; these could be housed temporarily in the science room and loaned to teachers in the school for the time needed for their study. Locked storage cabinets in this room could handle such equipment as well as items not to be handled by anyone but the teacher such as acids, sharp dissecting tools, or combustible materials.

This room could also serve as a supply depot for items necessary for the science program. Responsibility for ordering, replenishing, delivering, maintaining, and housekeeping should be carefully worked out. This can be the work of a science specialist, the librarian, an audio-visual co-ordinator, a classroom teacher, the school secretary or clerk, the principal, a competent custodian, or a committee of trained

and responsible, older children. Lists should be kept of materials, and periodically replacements should be made of worn, damaged, or consumed items. Unless this is carefully done, supplies become depleted and unavailable for classroom use. All teachers should be supplied with an up-to-date list of supplies and equipment in the science room. Supplies and equipment can be scheduled by teachers and used in the science rooms or delivered to the classrooms. Schools have found cafeteria or supermarket carts valuable for delivery purposes. Commercially prepared science kits and mobile science labs are also available. These science kits and mobile labs can also be stored in the science room and scheduled for use in the regular classroom. Although they are rather expensive, these kits and mobile labs are becoming more popular in large elementary schools or even among several schools.

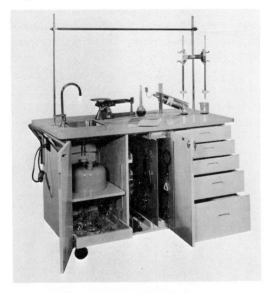

Due to the profusion of science materials on the market today, extreme care should be used in selecting and buying kits. See this excellent pamphlet for information concerning practical considerations in selecting and using kits in science teaching:

Albert Piltz and William J. Gruver, *Science Equipment and Materials: Science Kits* (Washington, D.C.: U.S. Government Printing Office, 1963).

There is also a list of commercial suppliers of kits in the Appendix of this book. By having many classes share the kits and mobile labs, cost per class is cut down. Pictures of these types of portable units follow.

CLASSROOM SCIENCE FACILITIES AND MATERIALS

In many cases, the elementary classroom must serve the total elementary curriculum. Therefore, the physical arrangement, equipment, and materials within the classroom must be used flexibly. The nature of the elementary science program as suggested in previous chapters necessitates that plans be made in the regular classroom for these science areas: activity areas, storage areas, research and library areas, conference areas, and display areas.

Activity Areas

Most modern elementary classrooms contain much movable furniture. The center of the room usually houses the movable desks or tables and chairs. The wall-space areas provide opportunities for more stationary equipment and facilities. Science facilities should be grouped as much as possible in one general area of the room. The needed equipment, supplies, and other facilities should be readily and easily available for making, assembling, experimenting, and demonstrating in science. This area should be well-lighted, should contain running water if possible, electrical outlets, and a source of heat. Because of the stress on experimentation, the work area should be given thoughtful consideration.

In active, pupil performance there must be adequate space to work. Even in small and crowded classrooms, experiments, demonstrations, constructions, and the other activity parts of the science education program can be performed. When the room arrangements for such work do not allow for a workbench or table, this work can be done right on the desks. Of course, the desk

tops should be protected by laying sheets of cardboard, Masonite, or other suitable materials in the designated manner.

Storage Areas

To teachers, inexperienced in science in the elementary school, the problem of storage of all the supplies may present problems. It need not, however. As previously mentioned, some schools provide a central storage closet for the entire school in which those items that are not needed frequently or are dangerous, expensive, or delicate may be kept. A class, usually the highest grade of the school, can be placed in charge of dispensing and keeping track of the supplies in this room. Requests are then sent to this class, and the children handle the requests

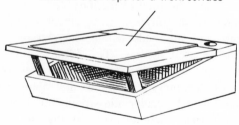

Tempered masonite — 1/8" or 1/4" thick used on desk tops for a work surface

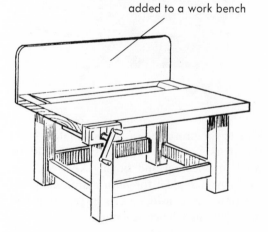

3/4" plywood tool panel added to a work bench

Tables can also serve as work areas by the same treatment.

Temporary work areas, which are preferable in most self-contained elementary school classrooms, can be improvised by putting boards or plywood across two wooden boxes or sawhorses. Having a workbench, however, is very desirable in an active science education program. Schools can purchase stand-

ard workbenches in any size to fit the age and size of the children who will use them. These work benches are generally used for preparation of materials for other areas of the curriculum as well as science. Saws, hammers, screw drivers, pliers, and other hand tools are needed for use in these areas. Since other materials are also needed, storage facilities are required.

FACILITIES AND MATERIALS FOR TEACHING SCIENCE

with a minimum of teacher supervision. Pupils from this class help in keeping the room in good order and even help in purchasing supplies that have been depleted. The central storage cabinet alleviates the burdening of each teacher to store seldom-used or bulky materials in each classroom. For equipment and materials used frequently by teachers, storage within the classroom should be provided.

Work Area Storage

By simply enclosing the bottom of a workbench, considerable storage area is made for construction supplies and hand tools. The following diagram will illustrate how much space is gained by the enclosure. Another attempt by some schools to alleviate the storage problem in science has been the portable laboratory table or work bench that can be moved from room to room. Any table around school, preferably one at least six feet square, can be mounted on wheels. The lower level of the table can be used for the storage of supplies and equipment. The pictured shopbench could serve the same

Same bench made more useful by boxing in the ends and back and adding a shelf or two inside

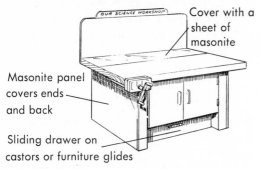

Cover with a sheet of masonite

Masonite panel covers ends and back

Sliding drawer on castors or furniture glides

purpose. Having one of these for each two rooms is extremely useful since they can be moved out of the way when the space is needed. The custodian in the school could probably make a portable table within a couple of hours. The cost of converting such a table would be very little since the basic

table would be available in the school. Occasionally parents can be asked to help with such projects.

Making Storage Cabinets

Storage space for a science program can be improvised by using orange crates or other partitioned wooden boxes. Besides being either free or extremely inexpensive,

From crates or boxes   Supply cabinets

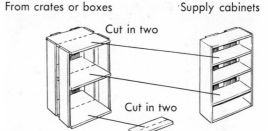

Cut in two

Cut in two

Make door battens from one-half of center section

Two crate slats   Large cardboard disc — lettered to suit

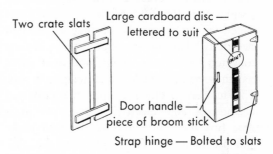

Door handle — piece of broom stick

Strap hinge — Bolted to slats

the crates are easy to use as is shown. These boxes can be arranged side by side in a row along the wall in the science area. Casters could be attached to the bottom of the crates so that they could be moved around the room or from room to room. A piece of plywood attached to the back and extending over the top of the crate can supply display space. The possibilities for a variety of uses for these crates is limited only by the ingenuity of the children and teachers.

Shoe Box Collection Storage

Shoe boxes provide devices for collecting and storing the readily available science ma-

Care for Living Things

Provisions must be made for caring for all types of living things in the classroom. In order to encourage children to bring in animals and plants, the classroom must have a variety of suitable containers for housing them. The wise teacher will always have the following containers available in her classroom: insect cages, small animal cages, aquariums, and terrariums.

Insects

Use small cake pans, coffee cans, or covers from ice cream cartons for cover and base. Roll wire screening into cylinder to fit base and lace together with strand of wire.

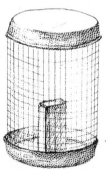

ticular science area. For instance, let us assume that the fifth grade has just completed a science study of magnetism and electricity. During the study the children collected bits of wire, bells, and light sockets; they made switches and telegraph sets. The teacher decided to put the collected magnetism and electricity materials in a shoe box with directions on how to make and use them as well as questions the children asked or solved. The teacher with the children's help did the same for other science curricular areas and eventually had many kits of materials for teaching science. Shoe boxes limit the amount of materials collected which makes the teacher more discriminating in selecting and storing materials. Plastic trays can be substituted for the shoe boxes; either can be stored satisfactorily in the crates previously described.

Cut windows in paper coffee container, oatmeal box, or shoe box. Glue Saran, cellophane, silk, or nylon stocking over windows.

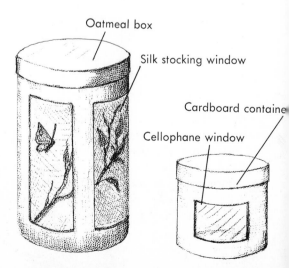

Oatmeal box

Silk stocking window

Cardboard container

Cellophane window

[2]Additional information for kit construction can be found in these practical articles:
Robert L. Gantert, "Science Kits As Classroom Aids," *Laboratories in the Classroom* (New York: Science Materials Center, 220 East 23rd Street, 1960), pp. 87-88. Erwin F. Lange and K. E. Payne, "Science Kits in Elementary Science Teaching," *The Science Teacher*, 25, No. 6 (October, 1958), pp. 321-23. "New Line of Classroom Kits to Aid Teachers Without Science Training," *Teacher Topics*, I, No. 1 (Spring, 1962), pp. 1-3.

FACILITIES AND MATERIALS FOR TEACHING SCIENCE

Fill wide-mouthed quart or gallon pickle jar with soil to within two inches of top of jar. Cover jar with nylon stocking and place jar in pan of water. Can be used for ants, termites, worms, etc. Cover jar with black construction paper after putting in insects.

A cage for a larger animal can be made from wire screening. Cut the wire screening as shown. Fold where dotted lines are shown. Tack or staple three sides to a wooden base. Hook one side to enable easy cleaning.

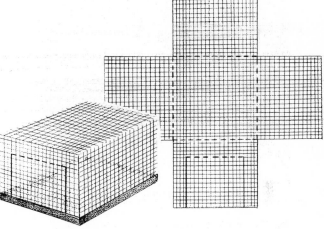

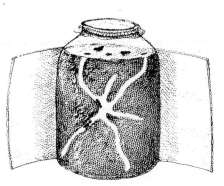

Animals

Some of the insect containers can also be used for small animals. Larger animals can be housed in these easily constructed cages.

Here are some suggestions for housing some of the more commonly used animals in the elementary school.

TERRARIUM

Get six pieces of glass any size (custodian can be of assistance here) and place as follows: arrange glass according to diagram using wooden matches for spacing. Use tape one inch wide (plastic or adhesive) on joints and rub very hard to insure good adhesion. Remove matches. Turn over and put tape on other side in same manner. Place tape on lid according to diagram and another piece for a handle. Place glass terrarium in cookie or cake pan.

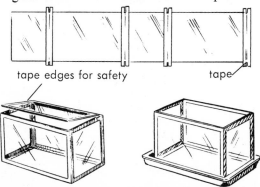

tape edges for safety   tape

HOUSING

Wooden box or crate about 24 in. x 16 in. x 12 in. with door added.

Metal or wire mesh (gnaw through wood); removable solid bottom for cleaning; woodshavings, sawdust, or strips of paper on floor of cage, bottle with one hole stopper and tube for water.

Wire screen home; woodshavings, sawdust, strips of newspaper; water bottle mentioned previously.

Should be wire mesh as rabbits need a great deal of ventilation; use type of wire cage as shown but enlarge to at least 3 ft. x 2 ft. x 2 ft; floor should be perforated.

Depends on variety; some need aquarium; some woodland terrarium; some combination of two; escape easily so place tight cover on them.

Wire mesh; wooden branch for support; must be solid with tight cover as snakes escape easily.

Aquarium

Terrarium with land and water.

Classroom Research Corner

An area should be set aside for research from textbooks, charts, pamphlets, encyclopedias, and other reference books. A study area should be well-lighted, provided with adequate furniture — tables, chairs, bookshelves — and well-stocked with many kinds of supplementary science materials. Efforts should be made to include as wide a range as possible of reading levels and interests and areas of science. It should be a place where children can go in order to find answers to some of their scientific questions. Encouragement should be given by the teacher in order to stimulate the use of this area. The teacher can also point out to children that scientists, especially in large laboratories, also require great amounts of reading from these materials. Directions for use of the area should be worked out cooperatively between the teacher and the students. Stress should be made on the use of many references and not upon just one source of information. The children can be encouraged to bring in science reading materials to add to the ever-growing science research corner.

Conference Area

There is very often need for the teacher and children to hold small conferences or carry on group planning in the science program. An area can be set aside for such a purpose. Often a table and six chairs is satisfactory if it is placed away from distracting influences. Occasionally the classroom research area serves as the conference area. Other times it merely means moving six chairs to the back of the room. However it is done, the conference area should allow small groups to confer and plan quietly without being disturbed or disturbing others.

Display Area

Bulletin boards and displays are essential tools for teaching science. They can arouse curiosity, stimulate interests, and raise questions. By doing so, these devices involve children in planning and developing the content and activities of the particular science study. Bulletin boards and displays also provide all children with materials that may not be available in sufficient quantity. It can easily be seen that classrooms presenting science bulletin boards and displays place value and emphasis upon science. This in itself is stimulating for children.

Construction of science displays and bulletin boards is the same as for any curricular area. By planning for such displays in advance, children and teachers can collect pictures, charts, models, and other materials long before they are needed. Children, after working with the teacher, can assume much of the responsibility for the planning, collecting, and arranging of such displays and bulletin boards.

1. Microscope	10. Dropper	19. Amoeba proteus	28. Hotplate
2. Toothpicks	11. Iodine stain	20. Calcium chloride	29. Yeast
3. Tweezers	12. Methylene blue	21. Sugar	30. Measuring cup
4. Optical lens	13. Rosin	22. Calcium chloride	31. Meas. spoons
5. Euglena	14. Kosher salt	23. Straws	32. Vegetables
6. Microscope slides	15. Brown sugar	24. Empty bottle	33. Spoon
7. Test tube rack	16. Pond water culture	25. Molasses	34. Knife
8. Jar	17. Paramecium caudatum	26. Vinegar	35. Weeds
9. Cover glass	18. Soda straw balance	27. Coffee tin lid	36. Test tubes
			37. Bottle brush

Summary

Consideration should be given to careful planning of facilities and materials for the science program. Although patterns for teaching science varies, teaching is usually done by the classroom teacher in her own regular room. It is desirable for elementary schools to have a science room even though science is taught in a self-contained classroom. Total school science facilities and materials should be coordinated to service the self-contained classroom. Portable equipment should be used for this purpose as much as is feasible. The elementary classroom space, equipment, and materials must be used flexibly in order to carry on the broad curriculum. Adequate attention should be given within the classroom for these necessary science areas: activity space, storage, research, and library space, conference area, and display and bulletin board area. The classroom must be organized properly for an actively working science program.

Further Investigation and Study

1.   You have been selected as coordinator for materials and equipment for five teachers of your grade level. Assuming that very few science materials or equipment are now available in your school, make a list of essential items you would recommend for purchase or construction within a $300 budget. Indicate the name of the equipment, quantity, price, and source of supply. Some sources of such materials are listed in the Appendix.

2.   Draw a floor plan for your classroom and arrange the room for these science areas: activity, research and library, storage, conference, display and bulletin boards.

3.   Devise furniture innovations in your room which would allow for the areas in No. 2. Provide multiple uses for as much furniture as possible.

4.   Organize and collect materials for several shoe box collections in science areas of your choice. Include as much equipment as is possible in each box along with sufficient information for conducting the experiences.

5.   Construct several small cages for insects or animals.

6.   Set up and maintain an aquarium or terrarium. Once established, add a small animal or animals.

7.   Sketch out bulletin board and display layouts for six science areas. List materials needed for each of the displays and bulletin boards.

Methods of Teaching to Meet Individual Differences
Encouragement of Creativity in Science
Evaluation as a Teaching-Learning Science Experience

Enrichment Activities for Science Teaching-Learning

Part 3

Methods of Teaching Science to Meet Individual Differences

INDIVIDUAL DIFFERENCES MAKE TEACHING DIFFICULT

Teacher education has traditionally emphasized the importance of individual differences and the existence of wide variations among the individuals of each class. Each student learns at a different rate and in a different way. Teachers often profess that they adjust their teaching to meet the individual differences, but this usually means that they occasionally give an exceptional student some extra reading. Good teachers of science certainly endeavor to motivate their students to achieve in accordance with their potential; this, however, requires that the teacher be well prepared and extremely sophisticated in his teaching techniques. Although teachers are usually aware of the desirability of organizing their class according to individual differences, they seldom adjust their instruction enough to accomplish complete motivation of all students. Some of the reasons are:

1. A classroom organized for individual differences allows each student to progress at his own rate. This requires more teacher preparation and can lead to discipline problems if the teacher has not carefully introduced children to this type of class pattern. Pupils coming from traditional classes may mistake such class organization as favoritism by the teacher or a recreation time for individual students.

2. The teacher must have more ingenuity to think of different activities in science for varied capabilities.

3. The instructor must be better organized and more aware of science materials and teaching techniques in order to follow the students' performance at varied activities and at different rates.

4. A greater variety of equipment and resources are required for students performing different tasks. These may not be easily available. A teacher must be able to improvise when the occasion demands it. This individual attention to supplies also calls upon the ingenuity of the teacher.

5. To adjust teaching to individual differences the teacher has to be more alert to the children's interests, needs, and levels of scientific concept formation. She will also have to keep records of the progress of each student. Evaluation of this kind is discussed in considerable detail in Chapter 10.

Because of these difficulties some teachers fall back to the easy way of teaching and eventually rationalize themselves into thinking they are doing a good job. Nevertheless, a classroom organized for individual progress in learning science is one in which there is greater learning and excitement. The following fifth grade class demonstrates this point. Mary is working on a report about butterflies; Terry, Mack, and Ralph are busy wiring a small doll house. Martin is doing one of the new programs on space flight. Alice, John, Margaret, and Jim are making a replica of a museum scene of the desert they saw in a magazine. The little Pegler boy is doing one of the chemistry experiments from the teacher's book on elementary science. Johnny is reading about animals in a book easier than the text. Bobby is trying to find out how birds fly.

In this situation the teacher has to be organized. How easy it would be to have all thirty children doing the same thing at the same time. But would it be profitable? Would the children be as thrilled with science and their experiences? Would the teacher be having such a terrific time? She is learning a considerable amount of science from her children. She said, "It's work to teach this way, but I would have it no other way. I come alive, and teaching is exciting when children are involved in varied science experiences. The time just flies by. We never seem to have enough time to do all we want!"

In studying science at their own speed, children can progress amazingly when allowed certain degrees of freedom under the teacher's direction. Some pupils motivated by freedom have accomplished in six months the equivalent of a year's work in science. Children encouraged to do experiments, work on projects, and do special assignments at their own rate often surprise the less experienced teacher with their capabilities and proficiency. Good class organization allows for rapid individual progress. A pupil's progress should not be restrained because it is easier for a teacher to keep all students together. Ease of method should never be the ultimate criterion for class organization. Good teaching is hard work, and it is difficult. To truly teach for individual differences is not an easy assignment, particularly in science. The rewards, however, are great, immediately observable, and very satisfying.

HOW TO TEACH FOR INDIVIDUAL DIFFERENCES

The following list makes some suggestions on how to give better individual attention to learning science. The list is by no means exhaustive. A wise teacher aware of teaching for maximum learning and not afraid to experiment in his approaches to teaching science will undoubtedly discover many more.

For the upper elementary grades make an extra-credit file for each student and allow him to contribute summaries of all types of science activities in which he participates. This is one way to keep records on the progress and interest of the pupil. For each project the student should place a note about what he learned in the folder. The following activities might be included:

1. Write a report about taking a programmed science lesson. These could be commercially produced or teacher-made. They might involve some type of teaching machines.

2. Make a science book report. Credit should also be given for reading only portions of books.

3. Write a science report on some special problem or give a talk in front of the class about some science topic.

4. Finish a science notebook.

5. Complete a collection of rocks, leaves, or insects. The children should label their specimens and display them.

6. Perform demonstrations in front of the class.

7. Make reports on all other special experiments performed. Many experiments can be carried on in the home. Children love to raise plants, care for animals, study the effects of fertilizer, watch spiders, insects, and pond life. All of these can be done at home. "Show and Tell Time" can be used occasionally for the purpose of evaluating these experiences.

8. Take trips to museums, planetariums, observatories, and parks; then make reports or drawings of some of the things seen. Parents should be encouraged to take their children to these places. Trips of this nature provide enriching experiences which often stimulate children in ways seldom possible in a classroom.

9. Watch a television science program and write a summary of it.

10. Go to a science movie.

11. Complete a science project. These should be special assignments, original and experimental. Books helpful for such projects are: *Project Ideas for Young Scientists,* by J. Taylor, P. Knipling, and S. Falcones, Joint Board of Science Education, 1530 P. Street, N. W., Washington 5, D. C., 1960. Also see, *Science Project Handbook,* Science Service, 1719 N. Street, N. W., Washington 6, D. C., 1960.

12. Finish an assigned task such as caring for a rock garden, bird house, bird bath, aquarium, or terrarium; raising animals or plants; or setting up a science display.

13. Participate in science nights or science fairs where project work is on display. Parents like to see what children do in science.

14. Do a study of the natural areas near the school. The children should find out what types of rocks, plants, and animals are present. The environment of the community might provide a pond, forest, seashore, or desert for further study of other organisms and their relationship to the community.

Have the children report on 3″ x 5″ cards the things they found such as the following:

Place of our trip _____ Date _____
Name of the young scientist _____
What did you find?
Where did you find them?
What things really interested you?

How to Help the Science Gifted

A visit to a fifth grade class revealed a teacher doing a demonstration using levers. He asked several questions about the lever as he moved the lever arm and varied the weights. The pupils in the process of answering the questions soon discovered principles the teacher wished them to learn. They were attentive and interested in figuring out the riddle of how the lever could lift heavy objects. During the demonstration, one student who seldom volunteered information gave very advanced answers. This was Richard, a gifted child and one the teacher said loved science. The teacher decided Richard had been bored with school since he had seldom been given any special work. School was drudgery because he was not being challenged.

Teachers often have difficulty helping gifted students. This is especially true in science because the elementary teacher seldom has studied much science. If taught properly, gifted science students can be a great aid to the teacher. They love to do experiments and work on science projects. If an instructor does not know very much about science, this should not stop him from having gifted students do science projects. He can learn with them. Children like to have their teacher learn with them, and they enjoy seeing the teacher get excited about the results from some experiment. This approach certainly motivates gifted children and often makes the learning process come alive. The important point to remember in working with these children is that individual attention must be a rule rather than an exception. But what projects and experiments can be done to stimulate these students? Many of the activities already mentioned will also work with gifted students. Some additional suggestions are outlined as follows:

1. Let them make science kits. A science kit contains the directions, all the materials, and apparatus necessary to do a demonstration or experiment. Shoe boxes serve for the container. The name of the experiment can be labeled on the outside of the kit. When a pupil has time, he can get a kit, take it to his desk or the science work area, and do it without disturbing the teacher. The gifted have fun assembling kits while others enjoy doing the experiments. Some teachers call the kits "surprise boxes" because of the discoveries made in science when the children do the experiments.

2. Assign gifted children to do research problems. They could consult with a scientist or engineer in the community on a problem. Local museums, zoos, botanical gardens, and hospitals have resource people who will often help.

3. Have the gifted in the upper elementary level go to some of the lower grades and demonstrate a scientific principle or explain a science project. They can also be helpful in working with other members of their class. They can often explain things better to their fellow students because they speak on the same language level.

4. Encourage them to enter the school or district science fair.

5. Obtain special equipment for them to use. The federal government has supported through the National Defense Education Act (NDEA) extensive purchase of such equipment. These expenditures are likely to continue in the future. Local laboratories, such as those in hospitals, high schools, or industry, will often give or loan equipment and chemicals to elementary teachers for special project work.

6. Encourage the parents to obtain books and toy science kits for their children and to discuss science with them. Often desirable science-learning situations arise when the family takes vacations. In your talks with parents at PTA and other activities emphasize how they can utilize their opportunities to reinforce the school science program. Stress the importance of the parent buying supplemental booklets such as the "How and Why Wonder Books" and the "Golden Books." Explain the desirability of motivating the gifted, and clarify any misconception the parents might have about gifted children. They may think that gifted children are abnormal and as adults lead an unsuccessful life. Assure them that this is not true.

The following check list was formulated by the staff at the Education Service Bureau of the University of Pennsylvania to help teachers and parents recognize gifted children.*

I. PHYSICAL TRAITS

( )　1.　Tend to be stronger, healthier, taller, heavier than the average

( )　2.　Do not become fatigued as readily as the average

( )　3.　Dislike routine and repetitive tasks

( )　4.　Tend to mature earlier than others of the same age

( )　5.　Manual and motor abilities not so superior as are intellectual abilities

II. MENTAL TRAITS

( )　1.　Possess intellectual curiosity

( )　2.　Possess large and picturesque vocabulary which they use accurately — originality of expression

( )　3.　Have long span of attention

( )　4.　Show keen powers of analysis, synthesis and reasoning

( )　5.　Are able to work with abstractions

( )　6.　Learn rapidly — do well in academic work which they often master in about half the usual time

( )　7.　Have good memory — recall details

( )　8.　Show an outstanding degree of originality, resourcefulness, initiative and imagination

( )　9.　Display wide range of interests

( )　10.　Have the capacity for self-appraisal

( )　11.　Like to read — both intensively and extensively

( )　12.　Require less detailed and repeated instructions — often resist suggestions

( )　13.　Are capable of planning and organizing

( )　14.　Have great sensitivity to cultural stimuli

*"Guiding Your Gifted," a handbook for administrators and parents (Philadelphia: University of Pennsylvania).

( )　15.　Show an ability to see qualitatively as well as quantitatively

( )　16.　May appear bored or lazy unless challenged

( )　17.　Possess a high capacity for self-direction

III. SOCIAL-EMOTIONAL TRAITS

( )　1.　Tend to associate with those of same mental age

( )　2.　Are enthusiastic about activities — tend toward those which require thinking

( )　3.　Are generally good citizens

( )　4.　Have potential for leadership

( )　5.　May appear boastful due to positiveness of knowledge

( )　6.　Tend to enjoy individual activities

( )　7.　Possess acute sensitivity to normal problems of adolescence

( )　8.　Respond quickly to the feelings of others

( )　9.　Are concerned about school marks — feel parental pressure

( )　10.　Have cheerful disposition, tend to be optimistic

( )　11.　Are emotionally healthy

( )　12.　Show keen sense of personal responsibility

( )　13.　Are superior morally, high in honesty

( )　14.　Make an easy adjustment to new situations

( )　15.　Strive for group recognition
　　　　( )　a.　Rejected by peers
　　　　( )　b.　Evoke imaginary playmates

Science Fun for Slow Learners

Recess was just ending when Jerry came running across the playground with a jar covered with a piece of cardboard. He yelled, "Miss Bedreau, look what I have found buzzing around some bushes. What kind of bug is it?" Miss Bedreau looked at it closely and replied, "I am not sure, Jerry, but let's take it into class." In the classroom, the teacher carried the jar to the front of the room for all to see. Some children expressed concern that the bug might be lonely. Others thought it needed water to drink. Buzzy, the name the class eventually gave their bug, presented Miss Bedreau with what she needed to teach her slow learners about insects. She asked, "How many legs and body parts does Buzzy have? What kind of food does he need to eat? Do you think it would be a good idea to collect some other insects for study?" With interest aroused, the children agreed that they should collect other insects for study; several children offered to bring some the next day. The teacher cautioned them that they should only bring in insects and suggested that Jerry look in an encyclopedia to see if he could find how to tell an insect from other animals. Jerry found the information and with Miss Bedreau's help read the section to the class. An insect home was then prepared out of

an old, commercial, mayonnaise jar. It was labeled "Home of Buzzy and Other Insects."

A practice teacher watching Miss Bedreau said, "You know, the class was so enthusiastic about science that I was not even aware that it was a group of slow learners." The practice teacher did not realize that it was Miss Bedreau who made science exciting for her class. She knew first-hand

experience was extremely important in teaching slow learners. Reading difficulties often cause a child to fall behind in school and may be the main reason for him being placed in a slow group. Miss Bedreau's instruction centered around activities, experiments, observations, and reports. She used reading material only to supplement. She did not talk about science; she had children live science. As a result, her slow learners appeared far from slow in their interest and understanding of science. The following list gives some general suggestions and activities for teaching science to slow learners:

1. Rely as much as possible on all of the senses. Base as much of your science study on first-hand experiences in which a child can see, feel, hear, touch, smell, and taste the things being studied.

2. Texts and reading assignment should be used in order to help clarify some experiment or science activity.

3. The *science surprise box* is an activity which is popular with all students but especially with slow learners. Periodically the teacher displays a labeled box. On the front of the box is a statement about its contents. An example is:

    I am hard.
    I can push something without your seeing me push it.

I can pull something without your seeing me pull it.
I am iron and nickel.
What is my name?

The opening of the surprise box is a wonderful way to introduce an area of study to the class.

4. The *science discovery chart* is a chart or a bulletin board which has lines or pieces of string going to the objects on the board. A student prints what he thinks the object is and his name on a small card. He pins the card to the end of the string. After several children have had a chance to pin their cards on the board, the teacher then discusses their answers. A typical chart might show some simple machines: inclined plane, pulley, lever, wedge, screw, wheel and axle. A chart showing the different heavenly bodies in the solar system creates interest. The discovery chart also can be used to review or introduce an area of study.

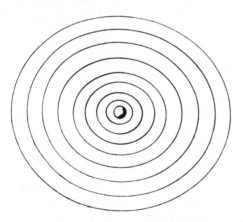

5. *Collection of the month* is a display of one pupil's collection such as: rocks, leaves, insects, shells, twigs, types of wood, or seeds. It is desirable to give every child an opportunity sometime during the year to show and explain his collection.

6. *A riddle card* has a science riddle written on it. Some teachers have been successful in having students write riddles which are placed in a box until the instructor is ready to use them. An example of a riddle card is:

Something in this room has stored sunshine in it.
We can see this sunlight again by changing how it is stored.
What will we have to do?

After several days if there is no answer to the riddle, the teacher may light a wood splint with a match. She would then ask if the children see any of the sun's light coming off the burned splint.

SCHOOL ENRICHMENT

The following list provides some general suggestions for enriching the science program in the whole school. Many of these activities aid in bringing attention to individual differences.

1. Establish science fairs, science nights, science displays, and science assemblies such as those sponsored by the National Aeronautics and Space Agency (NASA), Atomic Energy Commission, General Motors, and other private and industrial groups.

2. Give a science presentation to the PTA. Include the children demonstrating or explaining their projects. One sixth grade teacher had each pupil select one of the discovery lessons included in this book and set it up. The parents observed each project while the children explained the purpose of their demonstration. The superintendent was so favorably impressed that he later had several other sixth grades brought to

the school, and a repeat performance was given for their interest.

3. Establish a science newspaper for the school. The paper should have material from all levels of kindergarten through sixth or eighth grade and should include drawings and diagrams to help the non-verbal child. It could use some of the techniques similar to those found in American Education Publication school papers. "My Weekly Surprise," the kindergarten newspaper, is a good example.

4. Start a science club for those particularly interested in science. The club could meet at lunch time, before or after school. Parents are often willing to assist and head the activities of the club.

5. Take special trips to industries and laboratories. Blood banks, hospitals, greenhouses, agricultural experiment stations, and others make interesting trips.

6. Build a science camp for classes to use. Several school districts already have these. Areas in the mountains, bordering a lake, river, or pond lend themselves to this purpose. Many schools provide a two-week nature study program at these camps.

7. Provide special science classes during the summer.

8. Establish interest groups as a part of the regular period day. They may meet once a week and have a teacher, science consultant, or parent in charge. Children go from their classes to a special interest group. This technique has been particularly successful in Palo Alto. The entire school should be involved in the program; parents and other interested individuals in the community may help to direct the various interest sections in music, art, mathematics, and science. One famous scientist from a large western university participated in a program of this type. He worked with the science interest group and after meeting with them for several sessions said, "I have never had more fun teaching nor have I ever realized more fully how involved some science concepts are. I am convinced, however, that you can get the basic fundamental ideas of science across to any grade level if you just know how."

The University Elementary School at the University of Hawaii has tried interest groups in the third grade. The children chose art, music, or science. Books and other materials from these areas were displayed for several days in the classes before children made their decision. A science consultant took the science group and in the first meeting discussed science topics they could study. They decided on specific areas of study. The rest of the sessions were devoted to children doing experiments related to these areas of interest.

San Bruno Elementary School District, San Bruno, California, grouped into one class students particularly interested in science. Science interest was the sole criterion for selection although the class had a wide range of academic abilities. The teacher who was assigned to the class was very much interested in teaching science and was well prepared in science subject matter. He integrated reading, spelling, social studies, and mathematics with science. Mathematics was used in realistic and motivating ways in many of the science experiments. The teacher, parents and administrators of the district thought this arrangement was very successful.

9. Establish homogenous student groups. Academic and intellectual homogeneous grouping while usually done for the purpose of instruction in all areas does present advantages in science instruction. It helps to reduce the problems inherent in having wide variations of students in one class. It must be remembered, however, that a homogeneous class still requires a teacher to teach,

for individual personalities will continue to vary widely in interest. Grouping helps to reduce the magnitude of instructional problems but in no way does it lessen the demands placed upon the teacher. Remember, if all "A" students on the same grade level in a large school system were placed in one class, there still would exist a large range.

RECOGNITION

Everyone, including teachers and students, like to receive some recognition for his work. In some schools a great amount of recognition has traditionally been given for athletic endeavor. Seldom, however, does it approach equal recognition for academic excellence. There is no substitute for praise from teachers, parents, and other interested individuals. A scientist visiting a classroom to see the students' achievements in science can do much to encourage students to continue their scientific endeavors. We can learn much from the coaches in our school districts about how they motivate students. Coaches are usually masters in the techniques of giving and getting recognition for their athletes. Many of their methods can be

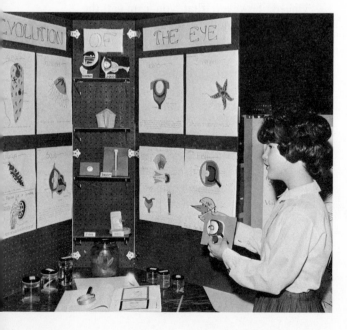

adopted for science achievement as well. Awards, whether they be stars on a chart, a pin, a certificate, ribbons, or an emblem on a sweater, have their influence. Elementary science fairs or science nights do as much for the science contributor as a football game does for the football player or a band concert for a band player. Displaying student science projects gives recognition and develops interest among children. Regardless of how the learning is reinforced, it is mandatory that the teacher be constantly aware that the student needs to receive reinforcement and positive recognition. The method by which the teacher does this can take many paths; all will contribute to better science learning and more varied achievement.

Summary

Most teachers state they teach for individual differences. This usually means giving special assignments to the better students. To organize an elementary class so that each pupil can progress on a science assignment at his own rate requires a dynamic teacher who is well prepared. Teachers, however, often do not regulate their teaching toward individual differences enough because it is easier to give all children the same material at the same rate.

There are several techniques teachers can use to insure better individual progress. Particular attention should be given to gifted students and the slow learners so that they achieve relative to their potential. Not only the classroom but the school as a whole can present enrichment activities for varied capabilities. Giving recognition for academic excellence insures higher achievement, better individual attention, and greater student growth.

Further Investigation and Study

1. Why do individual differences make teaching difficult?
2. What can you do to regulate your teaching to individual differences?
3. In what special ways would you insure maximum achievement of the gifted student?
4. What are some of the traits of the student excelling in science?
5. How can you motivate the slow learner in science?
6. How do you use a science surprise box, discovery chart, and riddle card?
7. How could you enrich the science program in the school?
8. What does recognition have to do with science achievement?

Encouragement of Creativity in Science

9

One day a teacher observed a small elementary classroom in a rural school in which the children were all involved in exciting tasks. The classroom was a workshop in which the students worked on a variety of activities simultaneously. A third grader enthralled with the mystery of a cocoon asked, "When will my moth hatch?" One girl was reading to try to find out what to feed her pollywogs. Two boys were busy watching the movement of their snails. A group of students were planting seeds in milk cartons and were arguing about how deep they should plant them. Another group watched a turtle eating his meal. The amateur weathermen recorded on the board temperature and barometric pressure changes they detected from their homemade instruments. There was diverse activity; and yet, there was order and purposeful work. Some children worked in groups, others by themselves on their individual projects. The observing teacher soon discovered that this was one of those periods set aside as a science interest period.

Some children were working on projects for the coming science night sponsored by the PTA. Some of the tasks being performed for this purpose were: the preparation of different environments such as a desert, an aquarium, and a bog terrarium; the building of a model to show how the planets move around the earth; the building of models of volcanoes and different types of faults; the construction of a replica of the Grand Canyon; the creation of murals on which were illustrated prehistoric animals and sea life; the preparation of various

131

collections of rocks, shells, insects, leaves, and twigs. Many children had also done experiments with plants and animals and had prepared them for display with cards explaining their results.

The children in this classroom were involved in many experiences which required some degree of creative ingenuity. Contrast this class with one in which the teacher stands in front of his fifth grade class and reads and talks about science. He says "Science is important, and we must learn it. Today I want to talk about a special field of science, blood. Now the body has blood. It is red and is pumped by the heart. The heart has valves which stop the blood from going backwards. Blood carries food and oxygen to all parts of our body. All parts of the body need oxygen. We get oxygen from the air and the blood absorbs it. The heart beats several times a minute." He stopped talking for a minute to ask two boys to pay attention. He then went on with his lecture for another fifteen minutes. Some of these children were attentive, but most of them squirmed in their seats. Others looked out of the window. One boy was obviously dreaming of happier times. It was evident that most of the children had forgotten the teacher. They were bored, the teacher was tiring himself wastefully, and the level of learning was low. Finally, they received a needed respite, recess. What chance was there for creativity to manifest itself in this uninspiring classroom? How much did the lecture-oriented teacher rob his children of a chance to discover their creative potential? The discovery and development of the creative genius of our youth is of prime importance in the educational process. It is precisely this ability that we must want to develop. Teachers, therefore, have a great responsibility to children and society to see that this ability is manifested to the maximum of the individual's potential. Osburn defines a creative person as

> . . . one who perceives and imagines hidden relations and has the impulse

to incorporate them in material form so that the others may perceive them also. Such people can and do frame in their constructive imagination poems, paintings, sonatas, and symphonies that have never before been perceived. It is they who can see "angels in a block of marble," "sermons in stones," and "theories in deep sea ooze."[1]

Dr. Paul Torrance[2] states:

> I have chosen to define creative thinking as the process of sensing gaps or disturbing missing elements; forming ideas or hypotheses concerning them; testing these hypotheses; and communicating the results, possibly modifying and retesting the hypotheses. I have been quite willing to subsume in this definition the major features of most other definitions which have been proposed.

The creative person may produce something original or make some innovation without truly creating something new in the academic world. The child, nevertheless, should have the experience of producing something new to himself. Science teachers should try to develop creative attitudes and processes and stress divergent rather than convergent thought. The essential difference between these two ways of thinking is that convergent thinking focuses on what is already known while divergent thinking focuses on discovering what is yet to be known.[3] The person able to break out of convergent or psychologically set ways of thinking may contribute the most to the advancement of science.

---

[1] J. W. Osburn, "Enriching the Curriculum for Gifted Children" (New York: The Macmillan Company, 1931), p. 37.

[2] Paul Torrance, *Guiding Creative Talent* (Englewood Cliffs, New Jersey: Prentice-Hall, Inc., 1962), p. 16.

[3] W. Getzels and P. Jackson, *Creativity and Intelligence* (New York: John Wiley & Sons, Inc., 1962), p. 14.

Research indicates science instruction in the schools has not rewarded the individual who is creative. Taylor,[4] in a study done on creative scientists, found little correlation between academic achievement and high creative production in industry. MacKennon[5] in studying outstanding creative individuals found the majority received C's and B's in school rather than A's. Numerous studies indicate that there is not a high correlation between I.Q. and creative potential. In other words, the student traditionally defined as gifted may not be creative and the creative individual is usually not gifted as determined by the I.Q. tests. Torrance[6] says:

> Traditional tests of intelligence are heavily loaded with tasks requiring cognition, memory, and convergent thinking . . . . In fact, if we were to identify children on the basis of intelligence tests, we would eliminate from consideration approximately seventy per cent of the most creative. This percentage seems to hold fairly well, no matter what measure of intelligence we use and no matter what educational level we study, from kindergarten through graduate school.

The National Merit Scholarship Corporation, which has given thousands of scholarships to high school graduates, became concerned about using solely intellectual criteria as a means of making their awards. In 1961 they gave 25 scholarships to students who had demonstrated creative ability but had not scored sufficiently high on tests to receive such an award. Intelligence tests and scholastic aptitude tests, because of their emphasis on convergent thinking, fail to discover the person with creative ability. Other tests are now being perfected to supplement the traditionally intellectual testing instruments in order to reveal children with creative ability.

Although intelligence and creativity are not the same, Ann Roe[7] found the minimum intelligence required for creative production in science is decidedly higher than the average I.Q. The fact that traditionally the individuals with the highest grades were not the creative ones indicates quite clearly that the schools have either not recognized this ability or have not rewarded it.

Can creativity be enhanced and nurtured in the elementary school? Torrance[8] reports that there have been outstanding examples of creative activity by individuals at an early age. In summarizing many research projects, he found variations of creative ability at different ages, but all age groups in the elementary school demonstrated some creative abilities. The development of creative attitudes and modes of thought probably is most critical in the elementary school. Children tend to be naturally creative, but creativity may be dampened before they leave school if the elementary teachers have not sought and kindled creative genius. Why have so few teachers really contributed to the development of creative abilities? Perhaps the easiest answer to this question is that the creative child may not be easy to teach. He usually does not want to follow the crowd, and his ways of thinking may be quite divergent from the norm. More often than not he refuses to accept a superficial statement about science or the environment. By requiring togetherness, the teacher may have stifled the child's creativity. Curriculum pressures may have prevented teachers from developing creative scientific abilities in their students. Teachers feel obligated to hurry through units of study in an effort to

---

[4]Calvin Taylor, "Some Implications of Research Findings on Creativity" (Unpublished paper, University of Utah, 1961).

[5]Donald MacKennon, "The Creative Individual," Broadcast #50250 V.E. Columbia Broadcasting System, University of California Explorer, Unpublished), January 28, 1962.

[6]Torrance, *op. cit.*, pp. 4-5.

[7]Ann Roe, "The Psychology of the Scientist," *Science,* 134 (August 18, 1961), pp. 56-59.

[8]Torrance, *op. cit.,* Chapter 5.

cover the material. These teachers present the material, but they fail to teach it. There is never any assurance that because a teacher covers the lessons, the students have learned them. An intelligent beginning teacher soon learns this fact: there is no more rewarding way to learn than through creative processes and activities. This is economical, too, for children prefer to learn creatively and, thus, more efficiently. Seemingly they do not cover as much science, but they do remember what they have taken part in creatively. Proof of this comes to any teacher who ponders her own experiences as an elementary pupil. The things truly learned almost always have some actively creative enterprise involved.

Creativity is not stereotyped in each field. Drevdahl and Cattell[9] found an overlap of factors important to creativity in comparing artists and writers with scientists. If a teacher is conscious of what research says about creativity, she will more likely discover the creative abilities of her students and modify her instruction in order to give children opportunities to demonstrate creative ability. In the process of creating stimulating teaching methods, the teacher herself will become more creative. Such qualities in a teacher are always in demand, for it takes a creative teacher to teach creative students.

How is a busy elementary teacher to recognize creative potential when she sees it? Creative individuals prefer difficult tasks and enjoy solving scientific problems. Being original and flexible thinkers, they respond rapidly to questions asked by the teacher and give more than the usual number of answers. They like to synthesize or see new implications. Their ability to make abstractions, analyze problems, and formulate new ideas, in the spirit of inquiry and discovery is pronounced. In science they may demonstrate persistent and sustained concentration

on trying to get a piece of apparatus to work or to solve some particular scientific question. Often they prefer to work on problems by themselves rather than in a group. Crea-

tive children are usually sensitive and individualistic; they often have a high sense of humor. They gain satisfaction from challenging activities and have high abstract and verbal intelligence with an immeasurable breadth of interest. The simplest way to identify the scientifically creative is to discover if they are extremely curious and if they like to become involved with problems related to science. Given freedom as well as direction, creative children often surprise the teacher with their capabilities and make the class a thrilling learning laboratory in which the teachers learns and grows with the children.

HOW TO PROVIDE FOR CREATIVE DEVELOPMENT

Creativity cannot be taught as a process; but by developing situations that demand imagination, originality, and problem solving, the children are more likely to be creative. The following list provides some

[9]J. E. Drevdahl and R. S. Cattell, "Personality and Creativity in Artists and Writers," *Journal of Clinical Psychology,* 14 (1958), pp. 107-111.

general suggestions for creative development. These arise from our present research in the field. If they are followed, a teacher should be on the road to more dynamic creative teaching.

THE CLASSROOM ENVIRONMENT:

1. Provide a classroom that allows and stimulates creative activity. Work on a long-range plan to evaluate your teaching in order to insure more creative endeavors by your students.

2. Build files, obtain resource books, and try to fill your room with science equipment and materials. This need not consist of highly technical, elaborate, or expensive supplies and apparatus. A large number of science experiments and problems can be done by using such things as milk cartons, seeds, spools, and general ten-cent store merchandise. See the Appendix for a list of materials readily available at little cost in most communities.

3. Allow time for students to work on demonstrations. Set limits to the freedom allowed to students, but do not dominate them. Science cannot be learned easily in a chaotic classroom;

neither will there be much creative activity in an authoritarian classroom. An example of this theory is illustrated by the following incident.

Bruce and Bob were excited. They had found an ant hill. They ran to their teacher's room and asked, "Miss Johnson, can we collect some ants and raise them in our room like Miss Hall's class does?" Miss Johnson replied, "No, we are studying simple machines this week. You were suppose to have studied ants last year." The spark of adventure kindled in Bruce and Bob was smothered by Miss Johnson's domination. What an opportunity she had missed to teach science. Miss Johnson could have easily permitted the boys to study ants and through her ability could have related some principles of levers to the studies of the ants' appendages. Instead she lost their interest by continuing with her planned activities. The boys had lost their desire to contribute to their science learning, and Miss Johnson had caused them to lose this spirit of inquiry and discovery.

CREATIVE TEACHERS:

1. Give positive reinforcement for creative work. Never laugh at a student's ideas or conclusions. Compliment children for sincere guesses even when the guesses may be bizarre. Do not criticize answers to questions. Try not to use the phrase, "That is wrong." Instead, respond positively by saying, "You are thinking and that is good, but you haven't quite discovered something else I can see." Try to eliminate negative statements from your criticism. Use instead, "That is good." "We are on the right track now." "That is a good idea." "Wonderful." "Great thinking." Nothing pays like praise. Above all, respond to the

child's answer; no reply is received as a negative response.

2. Welcome new ideas and demonstrate how pleased you are when a child comes up with a new idea. When this occurs, stop the class and say, "Did you hear what John said?" Explain his suggestion or idea and then say, "Isn't that a good idea? What great thinkers we have in this class."

3. Accept and encourage class students who deviate from the norm in the ways they think about science and do their science experiments.

4. Endeavor to differentiate between a child being impudent and one being inquisitive. Remember children usually are not impudent. They have problems communicating and often fail to say what they really mean. This does not mean that a teacher should be lax. If you think a child is being impudent, try to get him to explain his ideas. Otherwise, you may be fooled. Avoid head-on collisions before the class; use

private conferences.

5. Do not be afraid to do experiments you have not done. If you make a mistake or your demonstration does not work, turn the incident into a learning situation. Ask the class to see if they can discover what you did wrong. An example of an experiment that did not work the first time was done by a second grade teacher:

She took a fruit jar and filled it with water. She slid a three by five card over the top of the jar and inverted it. The water was suppose to stay in the jar because of the air pressure on the bottom of the card as illustrated. The teacher, however, had a flimsy card which bent and let air into the jar. The air forced the water out causing the experiment to fail, but the teacher did not look at it that way. She asked the class what she did wrong with this demonstration? Why didn't it work? One bright boy suggested using a round cap from a mason jar instead of a card. Other pupils suggested using a heavier cardboard. All of these suggestions were tried. The pupils had fun doing this demonstration, profited from the teacher's mistake, and learned a considerable amount of science.

Learn science with your children. They like to have the teacher learn with them, to be able to give the teacher advice, and to do experiments the teacher has not done. Give your children a chance to show you how they would solve problems. Have fun teaching science and don't take yourself or your instruction too seriously.

6. Require ingenuity. Ask your pupils how they would prove some specific problem scientifically. Give them problems and ask how they would find the answer. Tell them you want to show some scientific idea or principle. Ask how they would go about showing it. For example, ask them how they would

prove whether fertilizer is beneficial to plants. If they need some help, ask the following questions to help guide them. How many plants will we need? Should we put fertilizer on all plants? How much should we put on each plant? Do we need to think of anything else about our experiment before we try it?

7. Do not hurry pupils on their projects. Give them time to think how best to do a science project or solve a problem.

8. Give children opportunities to participate. Let them do experiments or demonstrations in front of the class, or have them tell the class about something they have seen or studied in

science. Ask questions but seldom tell them the answers. Let them discover the answer through the types of questions you ask, their background knowledge, and experimentation.

9. Give students choices. Ask: What should we study in science? What do you really want to know about the world? Can you think of an experiment you would like to do?

10. Make your class feel student questions are important. You should ask questions such as: How could we have

done our experiment better? What is wrong with our apparatus? How could we be more certain about our answers? Why do you think our results are so?

11. Try to instill the attitude that it is better to try and fail than not to try. Remember what was said in Chapter 1 about Ehrlich and Land's positive approach to failure. How many thousands of experiments have failed in the history of science? We can often learn more from our failures if we study the results carefully, A fourth grader has been trying to raise brine shrimp. He has raised several batches, but never has grown large ones. He has failed in a sense, but he has enjoyed his failures because he has more experiments to do. In the process, this student is learning to analyze problems and their results while having fun with science.

12. Be creative yourself in the methods you use to teach science. Vary your approaches and think of things children of different abilities may choose to do in studying science. Remember creativity is infectious. You inspire your children, and they in turn will inspire you. A teacher who is not creative can be a boring teacher because he himself is not inspired with teaching. Nothing is more boring than routine, but a creative teacher does more than a routine job. Furthermore, varied activities insure more attention to individual differences. Be experimental in your approach to teaching science and you are on your way to being creative.

13. Let the children take some initiative and responsibility for developing science lessons and for doing demonstrations and experiments. The more they do the more opportunity there is for them to grow.

14. Never overemphasize teamwork. Let students work as individuals on science tasks if they choose. Introduce more

individual study when the situation allows. Creative individuals often work best alone rather than in groups. An example is a gifted fifth grade student who was fascinated with butterflies. Her teacher discovered this and encouraged her to study them on her own. The girl spent a lot of time reading about them and making and arranging her collection. A professor from the local college heard of this student's interest and volunteered to assist her with some experiments with larvae experiments. In the spring she entered the elementary science fair and took a first place.

15. Encourage students to solve problems or construct and perfect some science equipment.

16. Stimulate, encourage, assist, recognize, and reward children for formulating hypotheses. Ask: Can anyone guess what will happen in this experiment if it is done in this way? What do you think is the best way we can find the answer to our question? An example of getting them to think creatively might be: How can we make a miniature greenhouse? What materials should we get? Who can design a better and less expensive greenhouse? How will we be able to determine whether one miniature greenhouse is better than another? What is your hypothesis about which greenhouse will be best? Pupils love to work on a project such as this.

17. Show your children creative work done by other students in other classes and grades.

18. The creative arts can be a valuable aid in teaching science. For example, have students write a play describing some scientific event or a science fiction story. Children enjoy writing science fiction stories. Have them draw a home, car, or city of tomorrow. Take these drawings and use them for the purpose of class discussion to illustrate science concepts and principles.

19. Above all, let children discover; do not tell them everything.

SELF-ENRICHMENT ACTIVITIES FOR TEACHERS OF SCIENCE

1. Keep up on science. Read *Science Newsletter* and *Science & Children*. The *Science Newsletter* consists of a few weekly pages describing the latest scientific developments. Any teacher can find out with relative ease what is going on in science. She will then be

prepared for those questions young-sters so often ask about modern scientific developments. The addresses and other pertinent information follow:

Science Newsletter, Science Service, Inc., 1719 N. Street, N.W., Washington 6, D. C. Cost $5.50 per year; weekly.

Science & Children, National Science Teachers Association, 1201 Sixteenth Street, N.W., Washington 6, D. C. Elementary membership $4.00; published eight times a year.

Nature and Science, The Natural History Press, Garden City, New York. Cost $3.00 per year; 18 issues a year.

Science World, 902 Sylvan Avenue, Englewood, New Jersey. Cost $1.50 per year; 16 issues a year.

2. Attempt to obtain a better background by reading science pocket books. Study and obtain some of the new scientific toys. They can do much to eliminate motivation problems when they are brought into class.

3. Return to college or the university to get additional training in psychology, science teaching, and science subject matter. Colleges are designing more and more good science subject matter courses. The National Science Foundation is now sponsoring many summer science institutes for elementary science teachers and supervisors. The teachers receive a stipend, tuition, and transportation costs to and from the college offering the institutes. The complete cost of the teacher's expenses are more than covered by these grants, and the work can be applied toward an advanced degree. Teachers without

strong backgrounds in science can obtain these grants. They need not be specialists.

4. Participate in science workshops and curriculum revision committees. Obtain suggestions from other teachers about how they develop creative scientific ability.

5. Collect tests and other curricular materials which demand creative enterprise.

Society requires an abundant supply of creative individuals. One need but look in the want-ad section of any newspaper to realize how true this statement is. The teacher — important both to the children today and to future generations — is one who insures that all potential is manifested to the maximum of his ability. He builds in those individuals — who have the capacity — the drive and desire for scientific creativeness.

Elementary teachers have a tremendous responsibility to fulfill these teaching objectives. In the final analysis, how they meet this responsibility will determine the progress of man in science.

Summary

We know from recent research that creative ability is widely distributed and that it can be nurtured or stifled. Creativeness does not necessarily correlate with intelligence, but creative scientists generally have an above average intelligence. Creativity manifests itself in many ways; and yet, the similarities between creative individuals seem to be rather high. Creativity is infectious, and teachers who are creative themselves obtain better achievement from students. The creative individuals are in the greatest demand in society. Schools traditionally have not rewarded creative children who have a tendency to deviate from the norm, who are divergent thinkers, and who are reluctant to accept superficial and dogmatic authority. Science teaching, because of the nature of science itself, is concerned with problem solving which can do much to foster the manifestation of creative abilities. Students must be actively involved in learning to make discoveries and to come to know science as a process as well as a body of knowledge. Science experiments which are designed to utilize the imagination, originality, and curiosity of children will most likely foster the development of creative thought and will build toward the attainment of better science teaching objectives.

Further Investigation and Study

BIBLIOGRAPHY:

Anderson, H. H. "Creativity and Its Cultivation," *Harper,* New York: 1959. Addresses presented at the Interdisciplinary Symposia on Relativity, Michigan State University, East Lansing, Michigan.

Barron, F. "The Psychology of Imagination," *Scientific American,* 199 (September, 1958), pp. 151-66.

Compton, A. H. "Case Histories of Creativity: Creativity in Science," *Nature of Creative Thinking.* New York: Industrial Relations Institute, Inc., 1953.

————. *Creativity of Gifted and Talented Children.* New York: Teachers College, Columbia University, 1959.

Drevdahl, J. E. and R. S. Cattell. "Personality and Creativity in Artists and Writers," *Journal of Clinical Psychology,* 14 (1958), 107-111.

Edgerton, H. A. "Two Tests for Early Identification of Science Ability," *Education and Psychological Measurement* (1959), 299-304.

Getzels, J. W. and P. W. Jackson. *Creativity and Intelligence, Explorations with Gifted Students.* London: John Wiley & Sons, Inc., 1962.

Ghesilin, B. *The Creative Process, A Symposium.* Berkeley, California: University of California Press, 1952.

Guilford, J. P. "Frontiers Thinking Teachers Should Know About," *Reading Teacher,* 13 (1960), 176-182.

_____. Interdisciplinary Symposia on Creativity," *Harper,* New York, 1959.

Kaugh, Jack and Robert DeHaan. "Helping Children with Special Needs," *Teachers Guidance Handbook,* Part II, Chicago Research Association, 1956.

Lowenfeld, Viktor. *Creative and Mental Growth.* New York: The Macmillan Company, 1957.

MacKennon, Donald, "The Creative Individual," Broadcast #5025V.E. 1790. Berkeley, California: University of California Explorer, January 28, 1962.

N.E.A. Conference Report, *The Identification and Education of the Academically Talented Student in the American Secondary School,* February, 1958.

Ornstein, A. F. "New Recruits for Science," *Parents Magazine,* 36, No. 2 (February, 1961), 42.

Osburn, W. J. and Ben J. Rohan. *Enriching the Curriculum for Gifted Children.* New York: The Macmillan Company, 1931.

Petersen, O. L. and J. Robinson. "Creativity: Some Aspects and Implications," *Science Education,* 43, No. 5 (December, 1959), 420-27.

Roe, Anne. *The Making of a Scientist.* New York: Dodd, Mead & Co., 1952.

_____. "The Psychology of the Scientist," *Science,* 134, No. 18 (August, 1961), 456-59.

Taylor, Calvin. "Some Implications of Research Findings on Creativity," Unpublished paper, University of Utah, 1961.

Torrance, Paul E. *Conference on Gifted Children.* Minneapolis: University of Minnesota Press, 1958.

_____. *Guiding Creative Talent.* Englewood Cliffs, New Jersey: Prentice-Hall, Inc., 1962.

_____. *Talent and Education, Present Status and Future Directions,* Papers presented at 1958 Institute on Gifted Children, Minneapolis: University of Minnesota Press, 1960.

Wilt, M. Elizabeth. *Creativity in the Elementary School.* New York: Appleton-Century-Crofts, 1959.

Witty, P., J. Conant and R. Strang. "Creativity on Gifted and Talented Children," Address given to American Association for Gifted Children. New York: Bureau of Publications, Teachers College, Columbia University, 1959.

QUESTIONS:

1. What is a creative person?

2. What evidence is there that the schools have inhibited the development of creative scientists?

3. When is the development of creative attitudes and modes of thought most critical?

4. Why do some teachers fail to teach creativity?

5. What are some of the traits of creative students?

6. What are some of the ways in which you would set the stage for creative activity in your classroom?

7. Why is it that a teacher who participates in in-service institutes or activities is more likely to teach for creative achievement?

8. Can you teach creativity? Explain your answer.

9. What kind of science experiences are likely to develop creative endeavor?

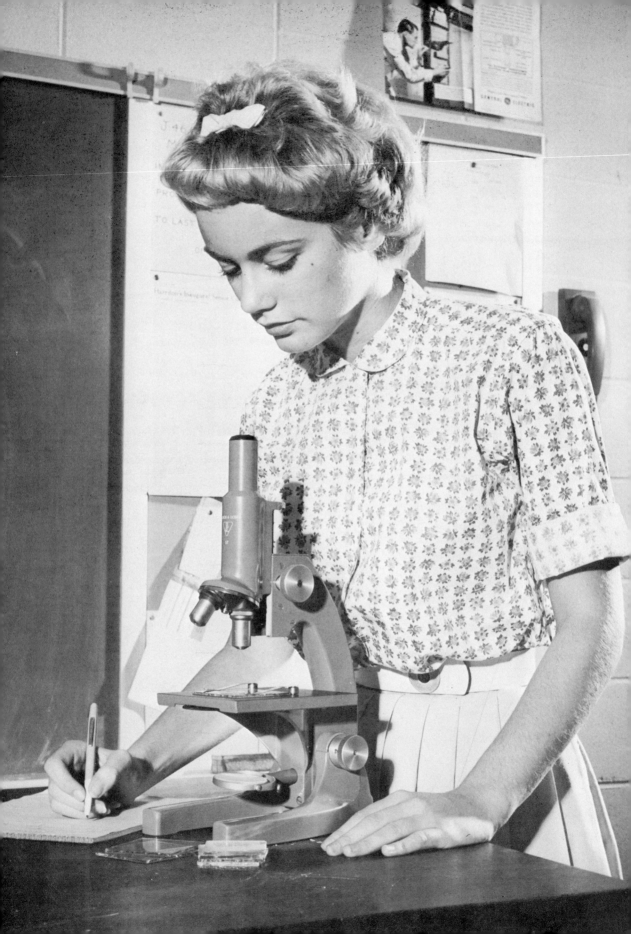

Evaluation As a Learning Experience

10

Once a teacher has a clear idea of what she will teach and how she will teach it, she is concerned with knowing to what extent children learn from her lessons. Chapters 1 through 6 of this book dealt with the purposes, goals, and activities for teaching science. This chapter will deal with specific procedures for evaluating the effectiveness of science teaching-learning.

Evaluation is a continuous process which is an integral part of teaching. It is not merely a test at the end of a science lesson or unit. Instead, evaluation goes on constantly during lessons and units and is clearly related to the teacher's goals and points of view on science teaching. The reader should remember the discovery lesson approach emphasized in Chapter 5. The constant questioning stressed there was not only a technique for guiding learning, but also was one of evaluating children's responses at each step of the lesson.

Besides being a continuous experience, evaluation is cumulative. Evaluation should be used to insure that all children are exposed to all areas of the science program throughout their elementary school years. To avoid omissions and to provide the teacher with information about the class, a cumulative science record should be kept for all children. A record of this type should be kept in the school office on each child so that his science exposure can be quickly and easily seen.

If evaluation is used merely to indicate areas of science to which children have been exposed or for classifying and categorizing students, a great value is lost. The same loss occurs if evaluation is interpreted only as arriving at numerical or alphabetical ratings for report cards. Children could easily equate evaluation with obstacles to be overcome in order to stay in the teacher's or parents' good graces. Much of the positive use of evaluation as a means of teaching and learn-

ing could be destroyed. Furthermore, the desire to learn more and build further science interests can be severely hampered by the evaluation approach which separates the good student from the slow learner. By coupling continuous evaluation with immediate application of what has been learned, the teacher can provide for:

1. the stimulation of students who learn rapidly to greater growth toward

CUMULATIVE SCIENCE RECORD							
Child's Name _____							
Date Entered School _____ Finished _____							
Topics	Grades						
	K	1	2	3	4	5	6
Magnetism and Electricity							
Earth in Space							
Living Things							
Sound and Light in Communication							
Weather							
Transportation							
Earth and Its Resources							
Others							

goals by the application of advanced work,

2.   the identification of specific weaknesses and difficulties in functional understandings (concepts, principles, generalizations), and the needed reteaching of varied activities skills or problem solving abilities, and

3.   the clarification, modification, or complete alteration of the goals as needed for the unit.

Our evaluation has another goal besides assisting the teacher in assessing and modifying her teaching procedures. This goal-self-evaluation is not solely for the student. As teachers and students actively engage in all levels of a study such as initial planning, organizing, and carrying out activities, they can be guided in developing ability to evaluate themselves. Knowing the general and specific goals can aid the pupil in checking himself all along the way. This makes the learner an active participant in the classroom activities. It also places some of the responsibility on him for learning and assessing what and how much he has learned. Self-guided evaluation stimulates healthy and realistic achievement goals.

A logical first step then in self-evaluations, especially for the teacher, is the setting of realistic goals. Chapters 1 through 4 presented these goals for science teaching in the elementary school:

1.   *functional understandings* such as concepts, principles, generalizations, and the facts needed.

2.   *problem solving skills* such as defining problems, proposing hypotheses and techniques necessary for the solution of problems, observational techniques, discussion, and interpretation skills.

3.   *scientific attitudes, interests, and ap-*

preciations such as open-mindedness and humility.

The easiest area to evaluate is functional understanding because a rich variety of tests are well known and widely used in the elementary schools. Some of these commonly used tests are fill-ins, true-false, multiple choice, short answer, or essay. The more difficult areas to evaluate in science teaching are attitudes, appreciations, and problem solving abilities. Difficulty occurs most often because of ambiguity and lack of specific clarification of what is being evaluated. For instance, instead of using the broad general area, "conducts careful observations," these specific observational skills should be listed: arranges experiments carefully and accurately, keeps good records of what he observes, checks what he sees, repeats experiments to double check. Because teachers have more difficulty with evaluation of scientific attitudes, appreciations, and interests, instruments and ways of evaluating these areas will be investigated first. It should be recognized, however, that any of the evaluative techniques in this chapter can be adapted and used for all three areas of the science program: functional understandings, skills, and scientific attitudes, appreciations, and interests. To avoid duplication of discussion of any technique in all three areas, the technique will be introduced in one area and mentioned briefly in others when it is applicable.

INSTRUMENTS FOR EVALUATING SCIENTIFIC ATTITUDES, APPRECIATIONS, AND INTERESTS

One of the most important ways of judging the effectiveness of science teaching is to evaluate the growth of individual children. This is especially true in the areas of scientific attitudes, appreciations, and interests. It becomes necessary in this area to assess a child's growth frequently in terms of his actions and behavior. The techniques that have been found to be useful for obtaining this information are teacher observations and anecdotal records, tape recordings, rating scales, checklists, interviews, children's work products, essay tests, and situation testing. Because behavior and actions are being evaluated, it is important to make observation and record keeping accurate and as free from subjectivity and prejudice as possible.

Teacher Observation and Record Keeping

Anecdotal records provide one style of form for recording children's overt behavior, attitudes, interests, and appreciations relative to goals of the elementary science program. The behavior to be assessed should be clearly understood by the teacher. This behavior should be specifically stated to avoid generalizations that are too broad or vague. Teachers have found that the following form has aided them in making their observations more accurate, systematic, and time saving as well as by providing a permanent record of behavior.

This anecdotal record indicates that the teacher observed and recorded the actions of Al W. on November 27. A brief description and quote is circled in the code for the category of scientific thinking and attitudes. The specific aspects of scientific thinking are delineated with clearly worded statements of what types of behavior and statements are indicative in children. In this case the teacher has five areas of consideration under the

topic of scientific thinking and attitudes:

1. uses such statements as, "I think" or "I am not sure" which avoids dogmatic statements,
2. offers a hypothesis or approach to solution,
3. changes his opinion when new evidence becomes known,
4. suggests ways to test hypothesis, and
5. is able to state relationships between facts discovered.

The code on the left side of the form systematizes and speeds up filing and recording. At a quick glance, the teacher knows that this record pertains to scientific thinking and attitudes in the specific area of No. 1. The same form with different categories can be duplicated and used for other areas of the science program. Later in this chapter, specific problem solving skills are presented. The teacher can use these for recording anecdotes of children's scientific or unscientific behavior. As these records accumulate, the teacher can begin to see the direction of growth in behavior and attitude. With a minimum of work each day, the teacher can move from guesswork to more accurate observation and record keeping. We are often legitimately criticized for lacking specificity in our evaluation of scientific attitudes, interests, and appreciations. If we really feel that these three areas are vital to science teaching, we must expend the extra effort necessary for adequate and objective observations and records. It is unsatisfactory to merely say that a child has improved in scientific thinking. We must have some records to substantiate our claims.

		Child's Name		J F M A My J Jy A S O N D	months
		Al W		1 2 3 4 5 6 7 8 9 10	days
				11 12 13 14 15 16 17 18 19 20	
		Categories Scientific Thinking		21 22 23 24 25 26 27 28 29 30	
I think or I am not sure		I.T.		31	
Offered a hypothesis		O.H.		Al tried several times to sink two	
Changed opinion		C.O		identical looking bars of soap in	
Tested hypothesis		T.H.		a dish of water. One always	
Stated relation behavior		S.R.		floated and one always sank. Al	
Facts		Others		said, "I don't think these two bars	
				of soap are the same."	

Tape Recordings

Another way of assessing attitudes and interests of each student is through the use of the tape recorder during science discussion periods.[1] Tapes can be made of the whole class, small groups of children, or selected individuals. Taken at two week intervals, accounts of discussions can then be analyzed at the teacher's leisure for specific examples of behavioral patterns. These sessions can be structured or free. In structured situations, teachers can present a problem and can have children suggest methods for solution. The free discussion session can use current events, hobbies, or any other topics of scientific interest to children. In many ways the tape recorded sessions have some important advantages over the written records of the teacher's observations. Greater objectivity is possible by using the tape recordings, and greater substantiation is possible through unlimited playback of the tapes. There is also great value in using these tapes directly with children as feed back and learning experiences in which they can be encouraged to use the recordings as self-evaluation. With the rapidly increasing use and availability of tape recorders in the elementary schools, greater utilization of them should be made in the evaluation of science teaching and learning.

[1]For a more detailed and informative description of this technique and its implications for science teaching see:
Lahron Schenke, "Information Sources Children Use," *Science Education*, 40 (April, 1959), 223-237.

Checklists and Rating Scales

A faster but perhaps less comprehensive way of assessing growth in scientific attitudes and appreciations can be secured through the use of checklists and rating scales. When a teacher wishes to define specific behavior, she can record incidents on a checklist. When the child makes a statement or acts in a way which fits into one of the categories, the teacher can enter the date into the proper category. As the teacher does this at regular intervals of two weeks, she can obtain a picture of the nature of the contributions and actions of the individuals. Such a checklist could be made for the category of scientific thinking and attitudes used on the preceding anecdotal record form.

Even a cursory examination of this sheet[2] can supply the teacher with evidence about her children. David Edrichs needs some help and encouragement; Sally Chin is coming along very well. Besides using this for her own evaluations and for modifying her own teaching procedures, Miss Blum can add this to the cumulative science record kept in the school office. A rating scale instrument for evaluating performance of a skill is presented on pages 150-51 of this chapter.

[2]The authors are indebted to the following author for her accounts of checklists and other evaluative devices for science teaching:
Brenda Landsdown, "How Good Was My Science Lesson?" *The Packet*, 16, No. 1 (Boston: D.C. Heath and Company, Spring, 1961), pp. 18-29.

CHECKLIST FOR SCIENTIFIC THINKING AND ATTITUDES Grade: 5 Teacher: I. Blum Year: Children's Names	Used "I think or I'm not sure"	Offered hypothesis	Changed opinion	Tested hypothesis	Saw relationship between facts	Admitted mistake and tried to correct it	Admitted he didn't know	Criticized and evaluated his own work	Gave credit to others when deserved	Consulted authority	Repeated work to validate results	Used more than one resource	Applied his science learnings to new situation	Detected difference between truth and fiction	Asked good science questions	Avoid jumping to conclusions
Boyer, Charles																
Chin, Sally																
Edrichs, David																
Gold, Merlyne																
Italle, Thomas																

Interviews

Personal interviews of individual or small groups of children enable the teacher to probe into their scientific attitudes and thinking. The face-to-face contact allows teachers to ask questions that develop as well as evaluate the methods by which children think about science. Interviews may last only a few minutes. Teachers may want to structure the interviews in advance by having the children consider a question before coming to the interview. Such questions as these might be used to stimulate children's thinking:

1. Why aren't there trees on the highest parts of mountains?
2. Why must cars be oiled and greased regularly?
3. Why did it rain yesterday?

The answers given are important primarily for the ways in which children attempt to answer and not for the amount of factual material verbalized. By asking how, why, when, and where, the teacher can find out much about the children. The dogmatic, "I know everything" personality will be quickly unearthed. Cautious, timid souls can be encouraged with still further questions like, "Who might help us find out about that?" Occasionally the teacher could employ materials for structuring the interview. For example, one could include a pencil sharpener to be opened and examined. Then the teacher

can ask, "What do you think the two wheels are for inside the pencil sharpener? What do they do?" In the section on evaluation of skills, practical situations are presented for assessing children's scientific thinking and attitudes with greater elaboration.

Children's Work Products

Children's work in all aspects of the elementary curriculum provide us with much evidence about their scientific thinking and attitudes. Children's writings, especially in the intermediate and upper grades, supply considerable information about their concepts of the world and their thinking processes. Often teachers can analyze children's ideas and thoughts better through their writings and oral dissertations than through other tests. Creative writing allows freedom for the child to explore scientifically and to speculate. Essays also give children a chance to pursue answers to the given question in a manner that is individualistic and creative. The student is not narrowly confined but allowed to roam as he sees fit within the framework of the question. Projects and reports provide the format for students to present examples of their thinking. This is discussed in this chapter under techniques for evaluation of functional skills.

Situation Evaluation

The teacher can set up situations in which the student is required to find the answer to a practical problem. The student should be unable to supply the answer from memory because ideally he would never have encountered the particular situation. Again this procedure is very valuable for assessing problem solving skills. An example of this technique is:[3]

---

[3]Additional information can be found in: Lester C. Mills and Peter M. Dean, *Problem Solving Methods in Science Teaching* (New York: Bureau of Publications, Teachers College, Columbia University, Science Manpower Project Monographs, 1960), pp. 76-79.

EVALUATION AS A LEARNING EXPERIENCE

At each of six tables around the room there was a piece of magnetite, commonly called lodestone, and a compass. Many patches of colored paint were on the surface of the lodestone. Students were instructed to find the location of the poles of the lodestone and to report their findings in relation to the color patches (North Pole, red paint; South Pole, yellow).

Following the assignment of the problem, the teacher observes and records the ways

Evaluating Children's Science Interests

All of the prior techniques are extremely valuable for obtaining and assessing children's science interests. If the program of science teaching is to be successful, the children should strengthen and broaden their science interests through the evaluation process. The teacher can determine progress in this way; she can also analyze the children's interest by their choice of books from the class, school, or local library. A questionnaire could be used to ask the children for books they have read recently as well as past favorites. Thus, in a very simple way, not overly demanding of the teacher's time, an overview of the science interests of children can be ascertained from their selection of reading materials. Generally, people select those subjects which they enjoy. By keeping a record of reading interest inventories over a period of time, a teacher can see if children increase their voluntary selection of science books as a result of her science program. Here is a sample of the type of reading inventories popularly used:

READING INTEREST INVENTORY				
Child's name: Sally Foster Grade: 6				
Name of book	Author	Dates read	Type of book	Opinions or comments

in which each child proceeds with solving problems as well as his attitude and interest for the situation.

Other types of records that children keep voluntarily on 3 x 5 index cards include a diary or daily record of books read.

Name
Book and author
Dates read
Comments
Opinions

EVALUATING PROBLEM SOLVING SKILLS

All the previously mentioned techniques and devices are also applicable for the evaluation of problem solving skills: teacher observation, anecdotal records, tape recordings, rating scales, checklists, interviews, children's work products, essay tests, and situations. In addition to the methods discussed for the evaluation of attitudes and interests, it is equally important to cover those concerned with evaluating the performance of the child in the problem situation.

Checklist and Rating Scale of Performance

In order to solve problems, children must develop skills in scientific thinking as well as in manipulative activities. If the teacher is concerned that his pupils develop skill in using some piece of equipment, it is important to be able to have some way of evaluating the pupils' growth in that particular

ability. The following is a description of a teacher's development of a rating scale for the purpose of guiding his observation of his pupil's skill in using a microscope.

I. Certain accepted procedures for the optimum use of the microscope are agreed upon:
    1. Handle the instrument with great care. Clean the lenses only with "lens tissue" or with a soft, clean cloth.
    2. Never focus the microscope downward toward the slide. Always move the objective downward while the eye is away from the eyepiece and then focus the microscope upward with the eye looking through the microscope.
    3. Arrange the mirror for optimum amount of light. Too much light is quite as unsatisfactory as too little light.
    4. Prepare materials for observation using the techniques most appropriate to the things being examined; comparatively large materials (minute crustacia, for example) require either depression slides or bridge arrangements so that they are not crushed; smaller items can simply be covered with a cover slip.

II. Having determined the desired behaviors, the teacher must prepare a checklist or a rating scale based upon these desired actions. Such a list might include:

Always   Sometimes   Never

Is careful in handling microscope.

Cleans lenses properly.

Focuses instrument properly.

Prepares slides correctly.

Arranges mirror for correct amount of light.[4]

This checklist for evaluating performance is similar to that one on page 151 and, therefore, does not require additional comment.

---

[4]Harold E. Tannenbaum and Nathan Stillman, *Science Education for Elementary School Teachers* (Boston: Allyn and Bacon, Inc., 1960), pp. 233-34.

CHECKLIST FOR PERFORMANCE WITH MATERIALS										
Grade: 6 Teacher: A. Goodman Year: Children's Names:	Used materials imaginatively and constructively	Made model, charts, etc.	Conducted experiment or demonstration	Tried new uses for materials	Original experiment tried	Discovery made	Perserverence shown in work	Clean-up responsibility well handled	Able to work with minimum of teacher direction and discipline	Worked within safety rules

The solving of science problems generally consists of complex procedures involving many steps, skills, and performances. Evaluation by checklists should endeavor to delineate these characteristics as specifically as possible. Children should be aware of the specific skills which are being evaluated. If possible, children should be encouraged to participate in setting up the items for the checklists.

Situation Evaluation

Whenever possible, problems should be set up that require the use of materials for their solutions. The ways in which the child moves toward solving the problem should be closely observed. In this case we are primarily interested in the child's problem solving techniques. The problem to be solved should be clearly and briefly described to the children and should preferably be one that they have not encountered previously. Other problems which the child has previously encountered may be selected in order to call upon their functional understandings of concepts and generalizations. Children are called upon to manipulate materials and to rearrange their functional understandings in such ways as to pose solutions for the specific problem. An example of a problem solving situation test is:

Children are presented with two apparently identical metal bars, one of which is magnetized, the other not. The students are informed of this and asked specifically to identify the magnet. The class has been exposed to how magnetic fields behave and how magnets attract nonmagnetized ferromagnetic materials.[5]

Teachers must be alert to determine the point at which frustration may set in for the students, what information the teacher should present for helping, and when to call the test to a halt. A follow-up session should also be used so that children and teacher can exchange approaches to the solution of the problem. It would be very advantageous to stress the different ways in which the problem could be approached. The teacher should use whatever record keeping she feels is necessary for proper utilization of the results of this evaluative technique.

Assigned Problem Solving Projects

Another type of assessment of problem solving skills can be done by assigning a problem for study which requires organizing, gathering, and reporting information. The child may have to consult resource books or people or conduct field work in order to acquire the needed data. Such a problem solving assignment could be assessed in the light of how the child gathers the information, organizes it into usable fashion, and interprets the findings.

[5]Excerpts from Mills and Dean, *op. cit.*, p. 77.

Paper and Pencil Performance Test

There are still other means for evaluating children's performances in addition to the direct observation method and the assigned problem solving projects. Such a technique is the paper and pencil performance test. Although not as meaningful in some aspects as measuring the direct performance of children, this test with careful arrangement of situations can present the child with an opportunity to show how he can apply the principles he has learned. The main advantage of this type of test is the rapidity with which the teacher can examine her whole class on any given performance or application test. If children were given the same test in which they handled the actual equipment and supplies, it would take days instead of minutes. Although something is lost in not having the child actually performing during the activity, much is gained in the more extensive coverage of testing.

It should be stressed that this is not a substitute for teacher observation of children's performance, but rather a supplementary instrument to be used in connection with direct observation. Both techniques deserve a place in the science education evaluation program. An example of a pencil and paper performance test is shown that can give the teacher rapid and valid evidence of his pupil's progress in their study of electricity and circuits:

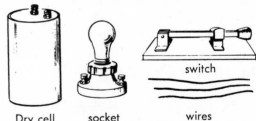

Dry cell   socket   wires

Here are pictures of the things we need to make a bulb light. Using all the things that are drawn, show how you would connect the wires so that the bulb will light.[6]

[6]Tannenbaum and Stillman, *op. cit.*, p. 248.

Since most children, especially those with a difficulty in language, respond better through their sensory organs, there is sometimes a loss when they are not working directly with science tools and equipment. The paper and pencil test, however, is a sort of transition between the purely manipulative and purely verbal tests. A child having difficulty with reading could have the question read to him. The answer then does not depend upon language response, but only assists the child to draw the connection needed to complete the circuit. There are many advantages of the pencil and paper performance test. Used in conjunction with direct observation and the other techniques of evaluation that follow, these tests will give the teacher much valuable information for use with his students in evaluating their growth. This is especially true in the areas of evaluating the functional understandings such as concepts, generalizations, and principles.

EVALUATION OF FUNCTIONAL SKILLS: CONCEPTS, GENERALIZATIONS, AND PRINCIPLES

As children progress through the elementary school grades, the need for greater use of written tests becomes increasingly important for these reasons:

1. In intermediate and upper grades rather than primary grades, pressures for more "objective evaluation" in science are greater as children are exposed to a greater emphasis upon "subject matter grades." In these grades this trend toward stress of subject matter is reflected on report cards.
2. As children's use of language increases, there can reasonably be greater emphasis upon meaningful written and verbal concept development.
3. As the child builds a background of science concepts, facts, understandings, and interrelationships, a greater need is presented for accurately assessing the child's knowledge.
4. With larger classes, as is generally the rule for the intermediate and upper grades, teachers require evaluation techniques that are fast, accurate, and easy to apply, score, and interpret.

One of the types of written testing devices is the short answer test. One major disadvantage is the superficiality and isolation of factual materials asked for rather than a breadth and depth of understanding. They do, however, offer the teacher:

1. opportunities to include wide ranges of items to be tested,
2. an ease of writing questions due to the shortness of each,
3. a minimum of time and effort required for scoring due to the shortness of the answers solicited, and
4. opportunities for involvement of the pupils in self-evaluation due to the ease of scoring and following up incorrect responses.

Basically, there are two kinds of short answer testing devices — recall and recognition examinations.

Recall Tests

As the term implies, recall questions ask the pupil to bring back to mind information that the student was exposed to in the past. Psychologists have indicated that people usually associate items to be recalled with other items and information and rarely, if ever, completely isolate them. The way in which individuals associate isolated items is still much of a mystery. Even tests of isolation, such as the inkblot designs used in the Rorschach test, evoke widely divergent responses due to the unique backgrounds and associations of individuals. Recall with children thus becomes a problem of framing questions in such ways as to stimulate the remembrance of the situations in which the intended information occurred. One of the ways that this is accomplished on recall tests is the formulation of a question so that only one word or a few words is needed to answer the query. This simple question and answer procedure might look like this:

1. What is the approximate percentage of oxygen in the air at sea level?
2. What are the machines called in a powerhouse that have turbine blades and produce electricity?
3. Name two organs of the human body.

Another way of accomplishing recall of information in a science content study is by supplying statements with blanks to be filled in. In this type of test children are asked to supply the missing word or words in the question. It is obvious that this type of question structures or leads the child to the desired answer to a greater degree than the straight question and answer test previously discussed. An example of this type might be devised in this way:

1. _____ is provided for chicks to serve as teeth to grind their food.
2. The part of the plane that develops the thrust that pulls the plane forward is the _____.
3. Two by-products of the process of photosynthesis are _____ and _____.

Recognition Tests

True and false tests are probably the most commonly used recognition tests in use today. For this reason, elaboration is un-

necessary, This sample presents the basic idea involved:

	True	False
1. Carbon dioxide is a by-product of photosynthesis.	____	____
2. The LaBrea Ranch in California is a famous fossil bed.	____	____
3. The crop of a bird is the bag filled with sand and gravel and mixed with digestive juices.	____	____

Even a cursory examination of the true or false tests reveals that guessing is encouraged which greatly reduces the validity and reliability of the tests. Because it is difficult to construct questions that are neither too obvious nor too ambiguous, this type of examination should be used very sparingly. Whenever possible, other types of recognition tests, such as the multiple choice test, should be given.

Multiple Choice Test

In this type of test, several alternatives are presented to the pupil from which he must select the one that makes the statement most correct. In this case, circle the correct word in each sentence.

1. Honeybees gather pollen on their a) wings b) tongues c) legs
2. Mosquitoes lay their eggs a) in food b) in running water c) on the blades of grass d) in still water
3. A scientist who studies rocks is called a) a geographer b) a geologist c) a geometer d) a geopolitist

Reasoning power can play a big part in the answering of this type of question and so-called educated guesses should be encouraged; actually these educated guesses usually are formulated from vague relationships that are seen or sensed. Very often the person cannot explain his reason for selection of correct choices in this type of question; he just knows. Because there are so many aspects of learning and teaching that are still mysteries to us, the teacher should not stand in the way of children learning. Intuition plays an important part in learning as well as in the scientific way of working. Besides the true and false and the multiple choice tests, there is a third type of recognition test, the matching test.

Matching Tests

By giving the pupil two columns of items and asking him to match the related items, the teacher can quickly and easily see if his student recognizes the relationships that exist between the items. There is less of a stress upon sheer memory or recall of fragmentary information because the materials are presented to the student for his correlation. Here are two columns of words that apply to the science study of our own bodies. Draw a line between the word on the right and the correct one on the left to show the proper relationship.

The word pelvis is correctly matched with the term trunk in the proper way.

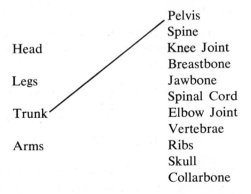

Head

Legs

Trunk

Arms

Pelvis
Spine
Knee Joint
Breastbone
Jawbone
Spinal Cord
Elbow Joint
Vertebrae
Ribs
Skull
Collarbone

Because matching tests are focused primarily toward measuring subject matter, it is not always indicative of the pupil's ability to perceive the deeper meaning or really un-

derstand the relationships between the items used on the tests. Stress upon mere verbalization and memory of isolated bits of information should be avoided. Teachers will find it necessary to employ all types of testing instruments in order to get a broad picture of the formulation of his children's science concepts.

Short Answer Tests

With all the drawbacks of the short answer tests, there is a wide use for these tests in science education for the elementary school. They offer the teacher an ease of construction and scoring not possible with other types of tests. The tests offer a greater degree of objectivity than other evaluating techniques, and the results of the tests can be helpful to the teacher for evaluating and reporting children's progress in science education to their parents. With the teacher's guidance, the simplicity of the tests can be useful for self-evaluative examinations for the children. Children can also be involved in writing examinations of this type as well as in scoring them. Teachers can be assured that the objective tests being discussed warrant the expenditure of time and effort required to construct them in the correct way. Correctly made, administered, and interpreted, the short answer test offers many advantages to the teacher; however, they should never be used as the sole testing device. They should only be used in conjunction with other types of oral and written tests as well as teacher observation.

Essay Tests

Essay tests aid in evaluating science understandings, especially in the intermediate and upper grade of the elementary school. Like all testing devices, essays present many serious disadvantages. At the same time they present many possibilities for gathering information. This brief summary reveals some of the more obvious advantages and disadvantages of the essay test:

1. Shows how well the student is able to organize and present ideas,

    but

    scoring is very subjective due to a lack of set answers.

2. Varying degrees of correctness since there is not just a right or wrong answer,

    but

    scoring requires excessive time.

3. Tests ability to analyze problems using pertinent information and to arrive at generalizations or conclusions,

    but

    scoring is influenced by spelling, handwriting, sentence structure, and other extraneous items.

4. Gets to deeper meanings and interrelationships rather than isolated bits of factual materials,

    but

    questions usually are either ambiguous or too obvious.

In an effort to offset the disadvantages, the teacher must carefully consider the construction of each essay question. The teacher should word the question in such a fashion that the pupil will be limited to a certain degree to the concepts being tested. For instance, it is better to use:

If you moved to Greenland, how would the days and nights differ from where you live now? How would the seasons differ?

THAN

Discuss the differences between the places in the world in relation to their days and nights throughout the seasons.

The second question is much too broad and does not give the pupil direction to know clearly enough what is expected.

The teacher will be able to successfully overcome or minimize the shortcomings of excessive subjectivity in scoring essay-type questions by preparing a scoring guide be-

forehand and by scoring each question separately. If a list of the important ideas that are expected is made, there is less chance for indecision while scoring.

Flexibility should be used, however, for a creative approach to the problems by the pupils; there are approaches and answers that the teacher may not have considered. The teacher should also give the student an explanation of his scoring so that the student can benefit from the test and use it for a further learning experience. Unless the student is fully aware of the teacher's analysis of his response to the essay question, little if anything is accomplished.

Standardized Science Tests

Standarized science tests try to measure the amount of scientific concepts, generalizations, and principles that a child has learned. They have several advantages that can be very useful for elementary science teachers.

1. Standardized sciences tests usually have a high reliability. In other words, they usually measure what is intended.

2. These tests usually contain norms and ranges of scores for each grade. Teachers have some comparison of his students with others who have taken the tests.

3. Some standardized tests identify specific areas of weaknesses and strengths of individual students.

4. The achievement levels and specific area strengths and weaknesses furnished can help the teacher select specific areas for his class's study for the year.

Standardized tests in science are becoming more widely known and used. The Mental Measurement Yearbooks[7] contain a com-

---

[7] Oscar Buros, ed., *The Mental Measurement Yearbook* (New Brunswick, New Jersey: Rutgers University Press, 1960).

plete listing and evaluation of all types of tests including science tests. Some of the tests more widely used in elementary schools today are:

EVALUATIVE DEVICE	GRADES	PUBLISHER	COMMENTS
American School Achievement Tests, 1957, Forms D, E, F, and G	4 — 6	Test Division of The Bobbs-Merrill Company, Inc., Indianapolis 6, Indiana	Forty multiple choice
California Tests in Social and Related Science, 1955, Forms AA and BB	4 — 8	California Test Bureau, Monterey, California	Three parts: health, safety, elementary science
Davis-Eells Test of General Intelligence or Problem Solving Skills	1 — 2 3 — 6	Harcourt, Brace & World, Inc., Tarrytown, New York	Realistic problems Children respond to verbal materials
Coordinated Scales of Attainment, 1953, Form A and B	4 — 8	Educational Test Bureau, Minneapolis, Minnesota	Sixty multiple choice
Iowa Every Pupil Test of Basic Skills	5 — 9	Houghton Mifflin Company, Boston, Massachusetts	Basic science understanding and skills
Metropolitan Achievement Tests, Forms A, B, C, D, and E	5 — 6	Harcourt, Brace & World, Inc., Tarrytown, New York	Fifty-five multiple choice plus application of principles to new situations
National Achievement Tests, Elementary Science, 1958, Forms A and B	4 — 6	Acorn Publishing Co., Inc., Rockville, Centre, New York	Eighty multiple choice plus practical applications
Sequential Tests of Educational Progress Science, 1957, Forms 4A and 4B	4 — 6	Educational Testing Service, Princeton, New Jersey	Critical skills and understandings
SRA Science Achievement Tests	2 — 12	Science Research Associates, Chicago, Illinois	Basic skills and understandings
Stanford Achievement Tests, Intermediate and Advanced Science Test, 1952, Forms J, M	5 — 9	Harcourt, Brace & World Inc., Tarrytown, New York	Sixty-eight multiple choice emphasizing fact retention rather than usage

Crossword Puzzles

Another technique for evaluating children's fund of functional skills is the science crossword puzzle. Generally children in the primary grades cannot handle the language required. Teachers in these grades can experiment with a few very simple crossword puzzles which incorporate words from primary reading lists. Intermediate and upper grade teachers will find children respond very positively to science crossword puzzles. In fact, children can be encouraged to originate their own puzzles at the conclusion of a science study. This puzzle was written by a student teacher working with fourth grade children:

DOWN	ACROSS
1. The planet on which we live.	4. Twinkle, twinkle little _____.
2. When the sun shines.	5. The earth is a _____.
3. When the sun rises in the _____.	6. The man in the _____.
4. The hot time of the year.	8. The time of the year when it snows.
7. When we see the stars.	10. The yellow ball that shines in the daytime.
9. When the sun is straight over your head.	11. The sun sets in the _____.

Summary

Evaluation is a continuous and cumulative experience. It is part of the learning activities of science teaching. Three areas of the science program should be continuously evaluated: functional understandings, problem solving skills, and scientific attitudes, interests, and appreciations. The following devices and techniques are for such evaluation: teacher observation and anecdotal records, rating scales, checklists, tape recordings, children's work products, situation problem solving, interest inventories, problem assignment projects, paper and pencil performance tests, short answer tests, essay tests, crossword puzzles, and other self tests. The eventual goal is self-evaluation by teacher and student.

Further Investigation and Study

1. Describe the role of evaluation in the elementary science program. You are urged to consult the following for additional information:

Fleming, Robert S., ed. *Curriculum for Today's Boys and Girls,* Columbus, Ohio: Charles E. Merrill Books, Inc., 1963, Chapter 15.

Lee, J. Murray and Doris Mae Lee. *The Child and His Curriculum* (3rd ed.), New York: Appleton-Century-Crofts, 1960, Chapter 15.

A.S.C.D. 1954 Yearbook, *Creating a Good Environment for Learning,* Washington, D.C., N.E.A., 1954.

2. Devise a cumulative science record form for your school using the school district, state, or other science guide.

3. Construct an evaluative device or technique for each of the three areas of the science education program: functional understanding (concepts, generalizations, and principles), problem solving skills, and scientific attitudes, interests, and appreciations. Specify the exact items to be evaluated. For additional help on test construction see:

Ahamann, J. Stanley and Marvin D. Glock. *Evaluating Pupil Growth,* Boston: Allyn and Bacon, Inc., 1958.

Burton, William H., Roland B. Kimball and Richard L. Wing. *Education for Effective Thinking,* New York: Appleton-Century-Crofts, 1960, Chapter 21.

Smith, Eugene R. and Ralph W. Tyler. *Appraising and Recording Student Progress,* New York: Harper & Row, Publishers, 1942.

Wood, Dorothy Adkins. *Test Construction,* Columbus, Ohio: Charles E. Merrill Books, Inc., 1961.

4. Select six children and observe their progress in scientific thinking skills for a period of two months. Set up a schedule for observation on a regular basis. Use the suggested anecdotal record form on page 146 for observing any of the three areas of science indicated in No. 3 above. Make a minimum of six recorded observations for each child and interpret hour findings. Be specific in the behavior to be observed.

5. Administer a science test to a group of children or an entire class. Select a science test other than an achievement test of scientific concepts of facts. Try to measure scientific attitudes, ways of thinking, problem solving skills, interests or appreciations. The following will supply you with catalogs for commercial tests:

Standardized Tests, California Test Bureau, Del Monte Research Park, Monterey, California.

Standardized Tests, Harcourt, Brace & World, Inc., Tarrytown, New York.

Educational Test Bureau, Minneapolis, Minnesota.

Educational Tests, Science Research Associates, Inc., 259 East Erie Street, Chicago, Illinois.

6.   Arrange a table or tables on which some very simple equipment is present. Structure a problem situation that students have not seen before and have students seek solutions. Keep a record of the responses children make in trying to solve the problem. For further help in structuring the situation see:

Jacobson, Willard J. and Harold E. Tannenbaum. *Modern Elementary School Science,* Science Manpower Project Monographs, New York: Bureau of Publications, Teachers College, Columbia University, 1961.

Mills, Lester C. and Peter M. Dean. *Problem Solving Methods in Science Teaching,* Science Manpower Project Monographs, New York: Bureau of Publications, Teachers College, Columbia University, 1960.

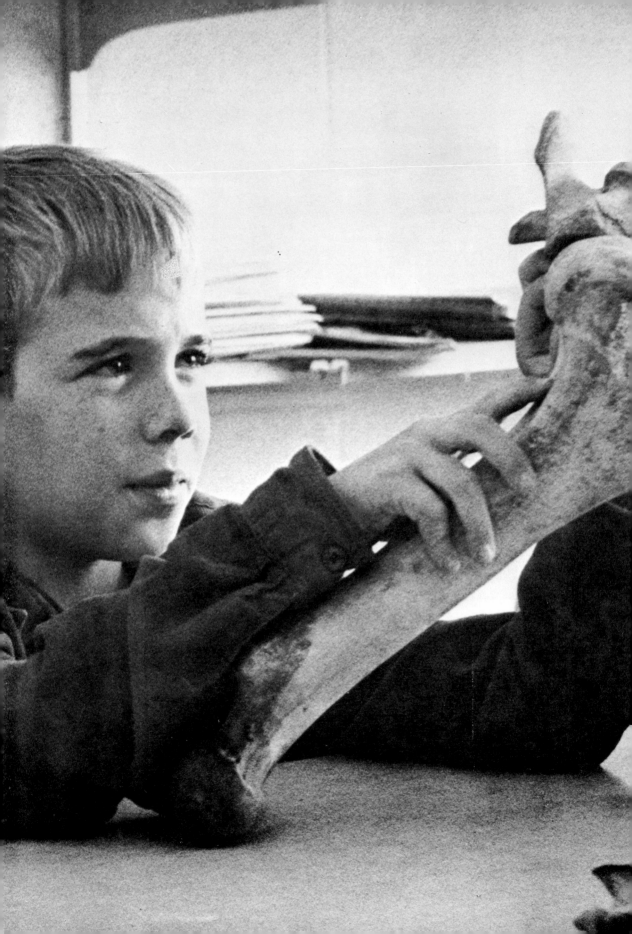

Discovery Lesson Plans and Other Activities for Teaching Science

Part 4

DISCOVERY LESSON PLANS

Section I   Biology

    A. The Structure and Function of the Body (Anatomy and Physiology)
    B. The Animal World (Zoology)
    C. The Structure and Function of Plants (Botany)
    D. Reproduction and Development of Plants
    E. Reproduction and Development of Animals
    F. Interrelationships Between Organisms and Their Environments (Ecology)
    G. Miscellaneous

Section II   The Physical World (Structure of Matter, Energy Relations, and Change of Matter)

    A. Air and Water Pressure
    B. Heat
    C. Sound
    D. Light
    E. Mechanics: Simple Machines and Forces
    F. Magnetism and Electricity

Section III Cosmology: Earth Science

    A. Astronomy
    B. Geology

Section IV   Student Experiments

    A. Geology
    B. Meterology — Weather
    C. Physical and Chemical Changes
    D. Miscellaneous

Section V   Pictorial Riddles of Science

The most significant gain to be expected from increasing the range and quality of teaching in the elementary school curricula is the effect on the cognitive faculties of the child and upon his image of the purposes and possibilities of education.— from Robert D. Hess, *Journal of Research in Science Teaching,* Vol. 1, Issue 1, 1963, page 23.

Elementary Science Activities

The following portion of this book contains tested elementary science experiences. Included are discovery lesson plans in biology, physical science, and earth science, plus several student experiments and pictorial riddles. Some of these experiences are demonstrations and experiments, written in a discovery lesson plan. It was shown in Chapter 3 that the discovery approach to science teaching in the elementary school has many advantages for teaching scientific ways of working as well as scientific concepts. There is greater involvement of the learner when the discovery approach is used. The learner also has a chance to participate in mental activities similar to the creative activities of scientists. Student and teacher interest in science is greater when the subject is approached through discovery lessons.

All of the following lessons have been tested by elementary teachers in four rural elementary schools and in the seventh and eighth grades of one junior high school. The teachers testing them had no special preparation in science. Science had not been a part of their curricula, except in the seventh and eighth grades, until the year these lessons were introduced. The teachers obtained better responses if the lessons were correlated with study in an elementary science textbook or a part of a science unit. All of the lessons have been evaluated by several elementary teachers and rewritten and modified to meet their suggestions. Although the lessons were originally written for teacher's use only, many instructors, especially in upper grades, found that the children could go through the lessons on their own with little help from the teacher. Some teachers had students present the demonstrations to the class. The response of the children to this procedure was generally good.

The topic areas of the lessons are those suggested by the recent national Feasibility Conference on elementary science education sponsored by the American Association for the Advancement of Science through a grant by the National Science Foundation. Outstanding scientists, teachers, supervisors, and science educators listed these topics as being the most important for the elementary school to teach.* The concepts for each lesson are taken from the list of principles of science thought by scientists to be important for any person having a general education. The complete list of these principles is available from the United States Office of Education.† No effort has been made, however, to cover all concepts and principles embodied in an elementary curriculum since such a project would require an entire book. The lessons are organized in departmental areas such as physical science, earth science, and biological science. This is done only for the ease of locating them by teachers whose school districts have not yet modified their curricula to embody the suggestions made by the Feasibility Conference. It is not suggested that they be taught departmentally nor necessarily in the order found in this book. These lessons are only sample lessons. In order to be of value in the elementary classroom, they would have to be supplemented and integrated with many other activities and similar lessons, preferably in units. For preliminary assistance, however, introductory suggestions have been made for using the lesson plans in each section. After a teacher has had experience in teaching several of these sample lessons, she will easily gain competence in designing others for her own curriculum.

At the top of each discovery lesson is listed the concepts and principles which the teacher is to develop. The instructor should not tell the class the purpose of the demonstration before beginning it. The objective is to have the students discover the concepts in the course of the lesson. Before the teacher goes into the classroom and presents a lesson, she should read it thoroughly and go through the steps of the lesson. Particular attention should be paid to the questions the instructor is supposed to ask. These are guide questions which are aids to the students in discovering the purpose of the demonstration and the science concepts involved. Although these lessons have been tested in actual class situations, no teacher can be certain a class will respond in a step-by-step manner through a lesson. A teacher obviously should modify the delivery of these lessons for her particular class. No two classroom situations are identical. One lesson plan, therefore, cannot meet the demands of all possible classroom situations.

---

*"Science Teaching in Elementary and Junior High School," *Science,* 133 (June 23, 1961), pp. 2019-2022.

†E. W. Martin, "Major Principles of the Biological Sciences of Importance for General Education," Selected Science Services, Circular No. 308-IV, Division of Secondary Schools, U.S. Office of Education, Government Printing Office, Washington, D. C.

H. E. Wise, "Major Principles of Physics, Chemistry, and Geology of Importance for General Education," Department of Health, Education, and Welfare, U.S. Government Printing Office, Washington, D. C.

The second part of each lesson, the student activity section, is for the purpose of evaluation to see how well the students understand the demonstration. Each lesson is marked according to grade placement. In some cases more than one grade range is given because the teachers in the lower grades found that they could teach certain concepts; whereas, teachers in higher grades could teach the entire lesson. For example, "4 — 6" means that teachers generally had success teaching the lesson at these levels; it does not mean that the lesson could not be used in higher grades. Explanations are often included in the body of the lesson for the use of the teacher. The "Teachers' Notes" are suggestions, made by teachers who have used the lessons, concerning the sequence of some of them or other information that should be taught with the lesson.

A teacher who has not used this approach may find it difficult at first. She may be tempted, like a child who has a secret, to give the answers away. Students who are accustomed to passive participation, which requires that they look as though they are listening to the teacher or that they memorize certain facts, will often be hesitant to participate in this type of learning. However, the fun that comes from the discovery orientation soon overcomes these problems, and students soon realize that science can be a live, dynamic subject requiring critical work. Some suggestions in using the discovery approach follow.

1. Be enthusiastic; start a demonstration or an experiment as though it were a riddle that is fun to solve. Ask such questions as, "Does anyone know what I am going to do with this equipment?" "Let's see who can be first to discover what is going to happen in this demonstration."

2. Always encourage your pupils. Use positive reinforcement. Don't criticize a student's poor efforts at thinking. If you think a student is off the track, don't say so. Say instead, "You have a point, and you seem to be really thinking," or "I am not quite sure what you mean, but I don't think it fits in with this problem; keep up that thinking." And when a child does come up with a good idea, compliment him. Tell him, "That is good......wonderful...... terrific — we really have some thinking going on in the classroom!" Continually encourage and give recognition to your students for making good hypotheses, suggestions, and conclusions. This is one of the most important principles to follow in teaching science. Remember that positive recognition and reinforcement contributes to better learning. This is a hard psychological principle to follow. It is so easy to become irritated with what appears to be a stupid answer to a question and say, "That's wrong." "Where did you get that silly idea?" If you operate your classroom in this manner, you will obtain little response. Why should your pupils take a chance and reap your sarcasm? They will play it safe and in so doing learn less science.

3. What appears to be a silly answer to you might be due to the inability of a child to communicate. A silly answer on the surface, when investigated further by questioning, may be full of insight.

4. Deliberately encourage students to make hypotheses (guesses).

5. Write down the students' hypotheses about the experiment or demonstration on the board.

6. Have the class consider each guess before an experiment is done. See if the children can eliminate some of them.

7. Always maintain an attitude that it is better to try to think and make mistakes than not to think.

8. Have fun yourself doing demonstrations or experiments.

9. If a demonstration doesn't come out the way it should, ask your class if any of them can help you figure out why. They may learn more from this experience than they would have if the demonstration had worked.

10. Above all, don't be afraid to do an elementary science demonstration if you don't know all about it. Your students don't expect you to know everything. They enjoy having their teacher learn with them, especially in science.

11. As much as possible, let students assemble the equipment for the demonstrations and do them before the class. You can help them and even teach them to get the class to discover what they are going to do.

12. Wherever possible, have the students work alone on experiments. They learn much more about equipment and how to do experiments this way. A section of the activities that follow is written for this purpose.

Section One   *BIOLOGY*

The Structure and Function of the Body

Anatomy and Physiology

1. What Is a Cell? [5–8]
2. What Do Our Bones Do? [4–6]
3. How Do Our Bones Look and Work? [5–8]
4. How Do Our Muscles Work? [7–8]
5. How Do We Breathe? [5–8]
6. How Does Blood Circulate? [6–8]
7. What Does the Heart Do? [7–8]
8. What Happens to the Food We Eat? [7–8]
9. Why Should We Chew Our Food? [7–8]
10. What Causes Our Bodies to Move? [6–8]
11. How Does Our Skin Protect Us? [2–6]
12. How Does the Body Maintain Its Temperature? [4–6]
13. What Is a Cavity? [2–6]

The Animal World

Zoology

1. How Many Different Types of Animals Do You Know? [4–6]
2. How Are Baby Animals Cared For by Their Parents? [1–6]
3. What Is the Difference Between a Frog and a Lizard? [1–3, 4–6]
4. How Do Spiders Live? [2–6]
5. How Do Ants Live? [1–6]
6. What Do We Know About the Birds Around Us? [K–3, 4–6]
7. How Do Birds Differ from Mammals? [6–8]
8. Do Animals Need Oxygen? [4–6]

169

The Structure and Function of Plants

Parts of a Plant

1. What Are the Parts of a Plant? [1–6]
2. What Is a Seed? [1–3]
3. What Is the Purpose of a Stem? [4–6]

Roots and Their Function

4. How Does Water Affect Roots? [4–6]
5. How Do Roots Move? [1–6]
6. How Does Water Get into a Plant? [4–6]
7. What Do Plants Need in Order to Grow? [1–6]
8. What Food Does a Plant Get from the Soil? [4–6]

Stems and Their Functions

9. Do Plants Know Which Way Is Up? [4–8]
10. How Can Plants Live from Year to Year? [3–6]
11. How Can We Tell the Age of a Tree? [2–6]

Structure and Function of Microorganisms — Bacteria and Fungi

12. How Do Bacteria Change Some Foods? [4–6]
13. How Can We Preserve Food? [2–6]
14. What Is a Fungus? [7–8]
15. How Does a Fungus Grow? [4–6]
16. How Does Yeast Change Some Foods? [7–8]

Structure and Function of Plant Leaves — Photosynthesis

17. Do Leaves Breathe? [2–6]
18. When Do Plants First Get Green? [K–6]
19. Do Plants Affect the Atmosphere? [4–6]
20. What Is Variation? [1–6]

Reproduction and Development of Plants

1. How Do Some Insects Develop from Egg to Adult? [1–6]
2. What Is the Purpose of a Flower? [4–8]
3. Why Do We Have Plant and Animal Breeding? [7–8]
4. Why Do We Have Crossbreeding? [7–8]

Reproduction and Development of Animals

1. How Do Some Insects Develop from Egg to Adult? [1–6]
2. How Does a Cocoon and a Polliwog Change? [1–3, 2–4]
3. Why Do We Look Like Our Parents? [4–6]
4. How Does Your Body Grow? [K–8, 7–8]

Ecology

Interrelationships Between Organisms and Their Environments

1. What Is a Pond? [1–6]
2. Is Life Affected By Its Surroundings? [4–8]
3. How Do Animals Affect Their Community? [3–6]
4. What Effect Does Temperature Have on the Activities of Animals? [1–6]
5. Is Life Affected By Temperature? [4–6]
6. How Do Earthworms Change the Soil? [2–6]

Miscellaneous

How May the Unwise Use of Various Substances Endanger Your Health and Safety? [5–8]

THE STRUCTURE AND FUNCTION OF THE BODY

ANATOMY AND PHYSIOLOGY

To develop a unit on structure and function it is desirable to start with some concepts about cells to point out their variations. Develop the idea that different types of cells produce varied structures and perform different tasks. Reinforce the concepts by having children read and show filmstrips which give examples of several kinds of cells. The local cancer society often has free materials available to teachers illustrating normal and abnormal cell types. These can be used as charts.

Several class sessions should be devoted to the lessons of bones and muscles. Have a football player dressed in his uniform come in and tell how the uniform protects each part of the body. A high school boy is usually excellent for this purpose. Cover the lessons on bones and muscles in the sequence found in this section supplementing them with reading assignments and other activities. Relate how the structure of a bone or muscle determines the function it serves.

Since breathing requires the use of the diaphragm muscles, those found between the ribs, respiration logically follows the study of muscles. Children should understand some principles of air pressure before this lesson is given. (See the section of the Discovery Lessons on Air Pressure.)

The lessons on blood and the heart should be used in a unit centered around the circulation of blood. Circulation systems can be studied from different animals illustrating variations in structure with consequent differences in function. For example, fish hearts have only two chambers; whereas, amphibians have three, and mammals have four chambers. Consideration of warm blooded and cold blooded animals can be very interesting to children and may lead to other related studies.

A separate unit should be organized around the relationship between the structure and function of the digestive system. Parts of this system, such as the mouth and stomach, are concerned with the physical breakdown of food. The mouth has teeth and jaws, and the stomach has strong muscles which contract and relax causing a churning of the food mechanically breaking it down. The stomach also secretes acids and enzymes which help to break down the food chemically. The first part of the intestine also has enzymes poured into it to continue digestion. The intestine is a long tube which serves as an absorber of food as it passes down the intestinal tract. Other organs such as the pancreas and the liver are associated with the digestive tract. These may be studied and specimens shown to the class as time allows.

The lesson "What Causes the Body to Move?" should be used with other lessons on nerves. The main purpose is to begin to build some concepts about the nervous system, to show its relationship to electricity, and to emphasize the dangers of electricity to the body. Emphasize that all but the simplest organisms have a nervous system and that all nerves function similarly.

"How Does Our Skin Protect Us?" is a lesson showing skin as a special body structure which has wide variations among animals. Have the class observe many different animal skins and suggest how each helps the animal to survive. Compare the skin of chickens, lizards, pigs, cows, horses, dogs, whales, fish, and man. Point out that there are nerves in the skin which sense pain, heat, cold, and pressure. Pinch a student to illustrate the sensation of pain, touch a student from behind to show how the body senses pressure. Blindfold a child and place his hand in cold or hot water or bring a warm object close to his hand. The important thing is to have children make the observations themselves and determine all they can about the nervous system.

The lesson "How Does the Body Maintain Its Temperature?" shows that the body maintains a narrow temperature range in which it operates effectively. The nervous system controls the body's thermostat mechanism within the temperature range desirable for life.

The lesson "What Is a Cavity?" fits well in a unit related to digestion and can be used to illustrate principles of structure and function. The teeth in the front of the mouth for example are used for tearing while those in the back are used for grinding food. Emphasis on nutrition for the purpose of building bones and teeth should be stressed.

WHAT IS A CELL?
[5 – 8]

Concepts

The smallest unit of life capable of existing independently is the cell.
The cell consists of many different parts.
Each part functions in a special way.
There are many types of cells.
All living things are made of cells.

Procedure

STEP 1. Cut an onion in half. Peel off an inside layer. On the outside of this layer you will find a transparent skin as thin as a tissue paper. Pull off a small piece of this skin and place it in a drop of water on a glass slide. Place on the slide one drop of iodine, methylene blue, or ink on top of the tissue. Flatten the tissue out and cover with a cover glass. See Diagrams 1 and 2.

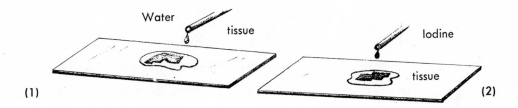

(1)   (2)

Ask: What do you think the iodine will do to the onion cells?

Place the slide on a projector or microprojector. Look at the onion cells through the low power lens.

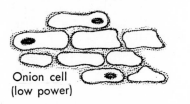

(3)   Onion cell
        (low power)

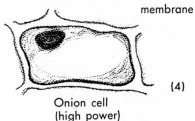

Cell
membrane

(4)

Onion cell
(high power)

Ask: What do you think you will see?
Do you see that the cells fit together like the bricks in a wall?

Each brick is a cell.

STEP 2. *Ask:* What do you think you will see if we look through high power?

Look at the stained cells through the high power lens. Each cell is surrounded by two thin lines. The inner line is called the cell membrane. A cell membrane surrounds all cells. The thick outer line is the cell wall.

Cell before staining  Cell after staining

Ask: Do you think all kinds of cells have cell walls?

Explanation: Only plant cells have cell walls. Cell walls are made of cellulose, a hard, nonliving material. The cell wall protects the cell and helps it maintain its shape.

STEP 3. *Ask:* What else do you see?

If you look carefully at a single cell, you will see within some cells a large dark spot called the nucleus. Not all cells will show them because of the thickness of the cell or the way the tissue was prepared.
The nucleus is probably the most important part of the cell.

Ask: What do you think is the purpose of the nucleus?

Explanation: The nucleus controls much of the activity that takes place within the cell. When a cell reproduces itself, or when a cell uses food or oxygen, the nucleus controls these activities.

Ask: What would happen if the nucleus were removed?

Explanation: If the nucleus were removed, the cell would die.

STEP 4. Gently scrape the inside of your cheek or lip with a toothpick. Then with a knife, scrape some of the white material on the toothpick into a drop of water on a glass slide. Spread the material out in the water and lay a cover glass over it. Examine the material with the compound microscope. You should be able to see some of the cells that line your mouth. The round spot in each cell is the nucleus.

STUDENT ACTIVITIES

1. What are cells?

2. What do cells look like?

3. What does the nucleus do?

4. How do animal cells differ from plant cells?

5. Draw below the tissue of an onion. Label the cells and the nucleus.

6. List some ways that different types of cells may vary.

7. Draw below the cells you saw that came from your mouth.

8. Write a few sentences about what you have learned about cells.

9. If a boy told you, "You are nothing but a heap of cells," what would he mean?

10. Answer the following true or false.
    _____ a. Every cell has a cell wall.
    _____ b. Every cell has a cell membrane.
    _____ c. Every cell sometime during its life has a nucleus.
    _____ d. One cell can divide and make two cells; that is the reason you can lose blood but still have blood.
    _____ e. The dark spot in the cell is called the nucleus.
    _____ f. A cell will live for a long period of time even if the nucleus is removed.
    _____ g. We stained out onion cells with iodine to make it possible to see the nuclei.

11. Why do the following diagrams of the same cells look different?

12. How have you found out what you know about cells?

13. How would you determine if hair is made of cells?

WHAT DO OUR BONES DO?
[4 – 6]

Concepts

√ Bones are the framework of the body.
  Bones are composed of calcium and phosphate salts.
√ Bones of an adult are different from the bones of a child.
  Bones are classified as round, flat, long, and short.
  Bones function according to their size and shape.
  Bones may have defects.
  Bones are made of organic and inorganic substances.
  Calcium is necessary for the development of bones.
√ X rays pass through tissue and can be used to tell where a bone is broken.

Procedure

STEP 1. Show a skeleton of a body.

> *Ask:* Does anyone know what this system of the body is called?
> How do you think the skeletal system helps the body?
> Where are places that bones form a protective covering for organs?

> *Explanation:* The head (cranium) protects the brain, ears, and eyes. The ribs protect the heart and lungs.

> *Ask:* Where are the places that bones are joined together so that you can move?
> Which bones help you to stand up?

Feel the top of your head.

> *Ask:* How many bones do you feel?

Feel the jawbone. Open and close your mouth.

> *Ask:* Does the bottom jawbone or the upper jawbone move?

Feel your backbone.

> *Ask:* Is it one bone?

> *Explanation:* The backbone is called the spine. The backbone is not one long bone, but a series of small bones. Each of these bones is called a vertebra. There are 32 vertebrae. Bones may support or protect parts of the body.

STEP 2. Have children bring in labels or containers showing the addition of vitamin D. Emphasize that not all diseases are caused by germs — the lack of vitamin D, the cause of rickets, is an example of a nutritional disease (caused by lack of good nutrition). You might raise a mouse on doughnuts to show the results of poor nutrition and lack of vitamins.

STEP 3. *Ask:* Does anyone know what a fracture is?
> Are there different types of fractures?

Hold up a chicken bone.

> *Ask:* How could I produce a fracture in this bone?

Break the bone.

> *Ask:* What kind of fracture is this?

Take another bone and crack it, but do not break it.

Ask: What kind of fracture is this?

Explanation: There are two kinds of bone breakage — the simple and the compound. Put the diagrams above on the board.

STEP 4. Show an X-ray picture of a good bone and one of a broken bone.

Ask: How many children have had broken bones?
What did the doctor do?

Demonstrate with a broken twig how a doctor puts a bone back in place.

Explanation: This is how some bones look when they are broken. This is how the doctor sets the bone. After the bone is set, it has to stay that way so that it will grow together.

Ask: What does the doctor do to keep the bone from moving?

Explanation: He puts the bone in a cast.

STEP 5. *Ask:* Does anyone know why older people may fracture their bones more easily than do children?

Place a bone in vinegar or weak hydrochloric acid and leave it, taking it out occasionally to see what happens. It may take two or more days for the acid to work sufficiently. After a couple days hold up the bone and try to break it. Hold up another bone not treated with acid and break it.

Ask: What did you notice about the way the bones differed?
Which of these two types of bones do you think are similar to those of older people?

Explanation: Children's bones haven't calcified as much as adult bones, so they are not as brittle.

Ask: What are bones made of?

Explanation: Bones contain organic material and calcium and phosphate salts. Show the class some milk and explain that the white material in the milk contains a lot of calcium and minerals necessary for bones to grow. Show the marrow or center of the bone to the class.

Ask: What is this part of the bone called?
What does this part of the bone do?

Explanation: The marrow is important for making blood and keeping the bone in good health.

Ask: What food should we eat in order to keep our bones growing and in good health?

Explanation: Point out the importance of milk and vitamin D, which is in enriched milk, to prevent rickets. If possible, show a picture of a child suffering from rickets.

STUDENT ACTIVITIES

True or False

_____ 1. Bones are composed of calcium.
_____ 2. Bones protect such vital organs as the brain, heart, and lungs.
_____ 3. Bones support the body.
_____ 4. It is not necessary to set a broken bone.
_____ 5. Rickets is a disease caused by not getting enough vitamin D.

Multiple Choice

1. The bones of the head are (a) long; (b) short; (c) flat.
2. The spine has (a) 34; (b) 36; (c) 32 vertebrae.
3. Rickets is caused by (a) a break; (b) lack of vitamin D; (c) dislocation.
4. An adequate diet is necessary for bone to (a) stretch; (b) grow strong; (c) break easily.
5. The longest bone in your body is the (a) finger bone; (b) ankle bone; (c) thigh bone; (d) arm bone; (e) backbone.

Completion

1. Muscles and bones help you to work and play by _(movement)_.
2. Bones grow in _(thickness)_ and in _(length)_.
3. X rays can be used to tell whether or not _(your bones are broken)_.
4. Eating certain foods will help your bones to grow _(strong)_ and _(healthy)_.
5. The three main functions of your bones are to
   a. Protect vital organs such as the brain, heart, and lungs.
   b. Support the body.
   c. Provide attachments for the muscles.

Discussion

1. Why is good food necessary for the bones?
2. What kind of food does a child need to maintain the growth and development of bones?
3. Discuss the following diagrams.

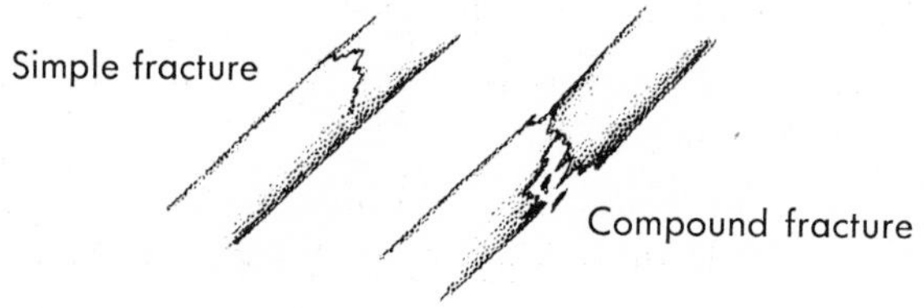

Simple fracture

Compound fracture

4. Explain why old people may have serious fractures.

HOW DO MY BONES LOOK AND WORK?
[5 – 8]

Concepts

Bones are hard, protect your body, and help you to move.
The bones in your chest protect your heart and lungs.
Bones work together to help you sit and stand.
Muscles are soft parts of your body.
Muscles make your bones move.
Your muscles and bones grow.
Many parts of your body work together.
Some of your bones protect the soft parts
    of your body.
Your ribs move as you breathe.
Muscles pull your ribs up.

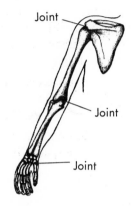

Procedure

STEP 1. Rub your head with your hand.

    Ask: Is your head hard?
          What makes it hard?

    Explanation: The bones make it hard. Your head bones protect your brain, ears, and eyes. Tell the students that they should never hit anyone in the head, because a bone might be broken that would injure one of these organs.

STEP 2. *Ask:* Can you feel the bones in your chest?
             What parts of your body are inside your chest?

    Explanation: Your chest bones protect parts of the body that are soft. The lungs and heart are very important organs protected by these bones.

    Feel your elbow as you move your arms.

    Ask: Where do your bones come from?

    Move your foot up and down. Move your arm up and down. Find the places where bones come together.

    Ask: What do we call the point where bones come together?

    Explanation: The word *joint* will probably be used when they feel the places where the bones come together.

Ask: Do all bones move?

Explanation: Put your arms up, move your legs back and forth, feel the muscles when you do these things. Most bones can be moved by muscles but many bones such as those found in the head do not move.

STEP 3. Have the children place their hands on their chests.

Ask: What is this part of your body?

Have them take a deep breath.

Ask: What happened to your chest when you breathed?

If possible, let the children see a human skeleton. If possible, bring in a skeleton or bones from animals in the butcher shop. Show the class examples of joints and of the different types of bones. Show them marrow and explain that this makes blood and may help to repair blood.

Ask: What happens to your bones as you grow?
     How can you help your marrow and bone cells to keep your bones growing and healthy?

Emphasize the importance of eating good food, especially milk, vegetables, and fruit.

STUDENT ACTIVITIES

Discussion

1. Can you feel something move as you breathe? What?

2. What pulls your ribs up?

3. Why is your head hard?

4. What do your chest bones do?

5. What makes a skeleton?

6. How do your bones feel?

True or False

_____ 1. You can feel some of your bones.
_____ 2. Bones are soft.
_____ 3. The bones in your chest protect your heart and lungs.
_____ 4. Bones pull your ribs up.
_____ 5. Bones do not grow.
_____ 6. Muscles do grow.
_____ 7. Bones protect your body and help you move.
_____ 8. Your whole body works together.
_____ 9. Bones are living material.

Completion

Complete the following statements. Choose your answer from the words at the right.

1. _____ move your feet.   hard
2. Your bones come together at the _____.   protect
3. _____ make a skeleton.   joint
4. Your heart and lungs are in your _____.   bones
5. Bones _____ your body.   muscles
6. Your head is _____.   chest

HOW DO OUR MUSCLES WORK?
[7 – 8]

Concepts

Muscle cells make it possible to move parts of our body.

There are two different types of muscles: voluntary and involuntary.

Muscles are arranged in pairs and work on opposite sides of the bone.

There are three types of levers that are employed by the muscles to help move various parts of the body.

Procedure

STEP 1. *Ask:* Has anyone in this room ever seen a muscle?

Hold up an uncooked chicken leg and wing (a frog leg may be used).

Ask: Does anyone know how the chicken is able to move its legs or wings?
What kind of tissue do you mainly see around the bones, of the wing and leg?

Explanation: Most of the tissue you see and most of the meat we eat is muscle. The chicken has several hundred different muscles to move various parts of its body. Muscle tissue covers the body in sheets and bands that lie between the skin and skeleton.

Ask: Does anyone know the names of his body muscles?

Explanation: Some common voluntary muscles are biceps (located in the front of the upper arm), triceps (the large muscle at the back of the upper arm), deltoid (large, triangular muscle of the shoulder which raises the arm away from the side).

STEP 2. Pull the skin off the chicken leg. Point out several of the different bundles of muscles.

Ask: Can anyone show me one of his muscles?

Explanation: The most common reaction to this is for someone to double up his fist and bring it up close to his shoulder. Have the class take a good grasp of the triceps (underside of the upper arm; see diagram) and hold it while they raise their lower arms.

Ask: What happens to the triceps when you raise your arm?

Have the class lower their arms.

Ask: What happened to the arm the second time?
Why did the upper part of the arm get thicker when the arm was raised?

Explanation: To raise your arm, the muscle has to contract. As it contracts, it becomes shorter and thicker, forming a "bump." Have all the class flex their arms to show their bicep. Teach them the names of these upper arm muscles. The bicep (bysep) is composed of two muscles connected to the bone by a tendon. The tricep (trycep) is three muscle parts connected to the bone by one tendon. The triceps lie on the opposite side·of the arm. The chief characteristic of all muscles is that they can contract. This is because of the special function of the cells which form muscles. When one muscle contracts, the opposite one on the other side of a bone is relaxed.

STEP 3. *Ask:* If a muscle can only contract, how can we return our arms to their original position?

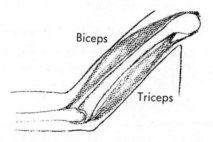

(1)

Explanation: Muscles work in pairs. Our biceps contract to raise our arms. To lower our arms our triceps must contract and the biceps must relax. All bones are moved this way. *Example:* When you show someone how strong you are, you "make a muscle" by contracting your biceps, and your forearm is pulled up toward your shoulder. If you want to lower your arm, you relax your biceps and contract your triceps. As you bend your arm back and forth at the elbow, each of these muscles relaxes and contracts over and over. Draw Diagram 1 on the board to show how skeletal muscles work.

STEP 4. Show the lower part of the chicken bone to the class.

Ask: Can anyone point to a tendon on the chicken leg?

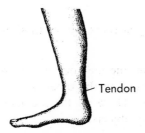

(2)

Pull the tendon up and down in an effort to show how it could move the lower part of the leg. See Diagram 2.

STEP 5. *Ask:* Does anyone know how a muscle is fastened to the bone?

Explanation: Some muscles are connected directly to the bone, whereas others are connected to a tough, nonstretchable cord, or tendon. (Write "tendon" on the board.)

Ask: Does anyone know where he can feel a strong tendon in his own body?

Explanation: If you reach down and grasp the back of your foot just above the heel, you can feel the strong tendon called the Achilles tendon that connects the muscle of your leg to your heel bone. (Write "Achilles" on the board.) Raise yourself on the ball of your foot. You can feel the calf muscles tighten and bulge as they contract and pull upward on your heel.

Ask: Do you suppose that a muscle can lift as much weight as it does just by contracting?

Explanation: If it were not for joints, the muscles would not be able to move any part of the body. The way that the muscle is fastened to the bone also makes a difference.

STEP 6. *Ask:* What is the right way to lift an object so that you don't strain your muscles?

Demonstrate by picking up two objects as shown in Diagram No. 3.

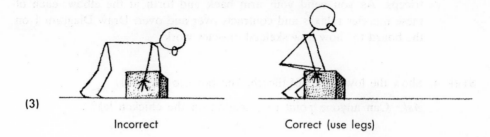

(3)

Incorrect   Correct (use legs)

Ask: Why do you think one method of lifting objects is better than the other?

Explanation: In one method you use more of your skeleton and many more muscles than in the other, so there is less likelihood of straining any one muscle. Have all the members of the class practice the right way to lift heavy objects.

STEP 7. *Ask:* Does anyone know how you can lift more weight?

Explanation: A lever is often used.

Ask: Can you give me an example of a lever?

Explanation: A lever is a device consisting of a bar turning about a fixed point, the fulcrum, using power or force applied at a second point to lift or sustain a weight at a third point. Our joints act as the fulcrum, our muscles as the force, and the weight is that part that we are raising. Some examples are a seesaw, rowing oars, and fishing poles.

Ask: Can you show me any lever in the human body?

Explanation: Lowering the elbow, rising on the toes, and flexing a muscle are all examples of levers in action.

STUDENT ACTIVITIES

Discussion

1. What is a tendon?
2. What is a lever?
3. What are the names for the muscles in the upper arm?
4. What does the word *contract* mean?
5. When you double up your fist and bring it up close to your shoulder, why does this "make a muscle?"
6. Briefly tell how a muscle works.
7. Explain the best way to lift heavy objects.
8. Draw and label the biceps and triceps on the following sketch.

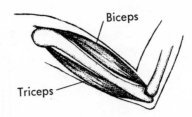

True or False

_____ 1. Every skeletal muscle moves a bone.

_____ 2. The circulatory system furnishes the muscle with CO_2.

_____ 3. The faster our muscles work, the slower the digestive system has to work.

_____ 4. A tendon is a tough, nonstretchable cord which fastens the nerve to the muscle.

_____ 5. We use one muscle to lower and to raise the foot.

_____ 6. The deltoid is a muscle which helps to rotate the thigh.

_____ 7. "Tri-" means three, and "bi-" means two.

_____ 8. Muscle tissue covers the body in sheets and bands that lie between the skin and skeleton.

_____ 9. When we eat roast beef, we are eating beef muscle.

HOW DO WE BREATHE?
[5 – 8]

Concepts

When we exercise, our breathing increases.

Breathing increases because we produce more carbon dioxide; carbon dioxide causes the diaphragm to work more rapidly.

When the diaphragm moves up in the rib cage, it forces air out of the lungs. When it moves down, air is pulled into the lungs.

When we exhale, we exhale gases and water vapor.

Procedure   I.   Breathing

STEP 1. Take a glass tube as shown in Diagram 1 and place a one-holed cork or rubber stopper in one end through which a glass tube is inserted. To the tube attach a balloon as shown. Cover the other end of the glass tube with a piece of pliable rubber or a part of a balloon.

Ask: What do you think will happen to the balloon inside the glass tube if I pull down on the rubber cover at the bottom of the tube?

What do you think will happen if I push up on the rubber cover?

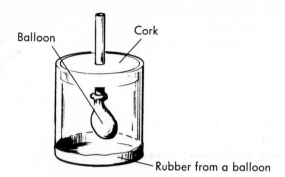

STEP 2. After the students have discussed this demonstration, demonstrate the process.

> *Ask:* Why does the balloon change shape?
>   Where in your body do you have something that works like this demonstration?

Write on the board the word "diaphragm" and explain to the class that we have a wall that separates our chest cavity from our abdominal cavity. Tell them that the wall is called the diaphragm and that it moves up and down, causing the lungs to inflate or deflate. Show the class a diagram, model, or chart of the lung cavity.

Procedure   II.   What Do We Exhale?

STEP 1. *Ask:* When we breathe out, what leaves our mouth?
>   How could you prove that moisture leaves our mouth?

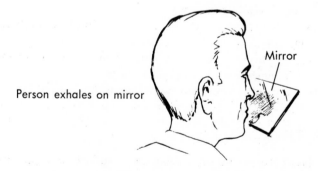

Obtain some mirrors and give them to the students. Have them hold the mirrors near their noses. Each time they exhale, a little moisture will appear on the mirror.

> *Ask:* Where does the moisture come from?
>   Why does it collect on the mirror?
>   What kind of gas do you think we also exhale?

Explanation: Tell the class that the air is a little over 79 per cent nitrogen and a little over 19 per cent oxygen. What happens to the nitrogen? We do not use the nitrogen from the air. We inhale and exhale the same amount.

Ask: What gas in air do we need to breathe?
What gas do we exhale more of than we inhale?

STEP 2. Obtain some limewater or take some calcium hydroxide and mix it with water. Let it settle. Have a student blow through a straw or a glass tube into the limewater.

Carbon dioxide
and limewater
gets milky

Limewater

Ask: What happens to the limewater as exhaled air is blown into it?

Explanation: When carbon dioxide gas is added to limewater, it changes to a milky color.

Ask: What two things have we learned about what we exhale?

Procedure III. Rate of Respiration

STEP 1. *Ask:* Do we breathe at the same rate all the time?
What would we have to do in order to make our breathing increase?

Have some student close his mouth and hold a mirror near his nose. Have some other student watch the mirror and record on his individual activity sheet how many times the student breathes .a minute. The breathing rate should be determined over at least a three minute period.

Ask: Why do you think we should determine the rate over three minutes rather than just one minute?

Explanation: If you count it over three minutes, you are more apt to average out error owing to counting, poor observation, and a small variation in the person's breathing.

STEP 2. Have several students jump up and down ten times or more. Determine the rate of breathing in the same way you did for a person at rest.

Ask: Is breathing increased? If so, why?

STEP 3. Have a student note the number of times the heart beats while a person is at rest compared to after he has exercised.

> *Ask:* How does the heart vary in its pumping action at rest compared to a person exercising?
> What does the heart pump through the lungs?
> If the heart pumps faster, will it pump more blood per minute?

> *Explanation:* More blood will pass through the lungs per minute to pick up oxygen and give off carbon dioxide. The lungs must breathe more rapidly in order for the blood to receive the necessary oxygen.

> *Ask:* Why must the blood pass through your lungs when you exercise?

> *Explanation:* When you exercise, you need more oxygen for the "body" tissues to convert fuel into energy. You breathe faster and your heart pumps blood faster. It passes through the lungs and picks up more oxygen.

STUDENT ACTIVITIES

1. Record the number of times a person breathes.

	At Rest	After Exercise
One minute	_____	_____
Two minutes	_____	_____
Three minutes	_____	_____

2. What is the average number of times a person breathes per minute at rest?

3. What is the average number of times a person breathes per minute after exercise?

4. What makes a person breathe faster?

5. Why did we count the number of times a person breathes over several minutes rather than just for one minute?

6. Draw a diagram below of the chest. Label the diaphragm, lungs, chest (pulmonary) cavity, and any other parts you think should be labeled.

7. What gas do we need from the air?

8. What do we exhale?

9. How did we prove that we exhaled water?

10. How did we prove that we exhaled carbon dioxide?

11. What gas do we breathe in from the air that our body does not use?

12. Check the questions below which seem logical and which could be used to test further any hypotheses you have made in this experiment.

_____ a. Exercise causes the heart to beat faster.

_____ b. Less oxygen in the blood causes the heart to beat faster.

_____ c. An increase in carbon dioxide in the blood causes the heart to beat faster.

_____ d. Exercise causes a person to breathe faster.

_____ e. More oxygen in the blood causes faster breathing.

_____ f. A person needing oxygen naturally breathes faster.

13. Which of the above statements seem to be best for explaining the change in breathing? _____

14. Diagram how the size of your chest varies when you breathe.

HOW DOES BLOOD CIRCULATE?
[6 – 8]

Concepts

The heart beats and pumps blood throughout the body.
Other animals have hearts.
Blood moves rapidly through the blood vessels.
Blood vessels are not all the same size.
Blood circulates.
All animals have individual variations.
Some animals are warm-blooded; some are cold-blooded.

Procedure

STEP 1. Obtain several live earthworms. Place them on a paper towel so that every two or three students will have a worm to watch. Have them look carefully at the worm and see if they can find a blood vessel. There will be one that is easily seen on the back of the worm. Have them watch this vessel closely to determine how it changes in color.

Ask: Have you found the blood vessel on the worm?
Does the vessel seem to have the same color all the time?
Why doesn't it have the same color all the time?
What is going through the blood vessel to give it that color?
Do you think the earthworm has a heart?
See if you can count how many times the heart beats a minute.

Record on the board how many times the heart beats as stated by several students. Make an average of these in order to get the average beat. Explain the meaning of "average."

STEP 2. _Ask:_ Why do we average these numbers in order to get the number of times the heart beats for a worm?

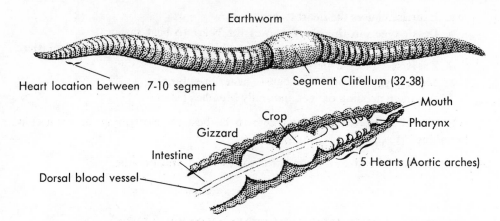

Earthworm

Heart location between 7-10 segment

Segment Clitellum (32-38)

Mouth

Crop

Pharynx

Gizzard

Intestine

5 Hearts (Aortic arches)

Dorsal blood vessel

Explanation: Because each worm is a little different from the next worm, and the persons who watched the heart might have made a mistake. We then average out the mistakes. Scientists use this same procedure when collecting data.

STEP 3. *Ask:* What is a warm-blooded animal?

Explanation: One whose body temperature remains nearly the same, regardless of the temperature of the environment.

Ask: Is man a warm-blooded animal?
    Do you think the worm is a warm-blooded animal?
    How could we tell if a worm is a warm-blooded animal?

Place some worms in cold ice water, or a refrigerator for a few minutes. Now count the number of times the heart seems to beat.

Ask: Does the heart of the worm seem to beat faster or slower after you take him out of cold water?

Explanation: A worm is a cold-blooded animal, which means that its body temperature is the same as the temperature of the environment. The colder the conditions, the slower the body's functions. The heart, therefore, beats more slowly.

STEP 4. Have some students look in a biology book and make a chart of the circulatory system of the worm for the class to study.

STUDENT ACTIVITIES

1. What is a warm-blooded animal?

2. Does blood seem to move in the worm's blood vessels most of the time?

3. Do you think the worm has a heart? Is this an assumption you made about the worm or a fact?

4. Snakes and turtles are cold-blooded animals. Do you think they would be more active on a cold day or a warm day?

5. Why is it more desirable to be a warm-blooded animal?

6. Why can't you see blood vessels all over the worm's body?

7. Why did you use several worms in determining how many times their hearts beat?

8. Why is this method more scientific?

9. Why did you place the worms in cold water?

WHAT DOES THE HEART DO?
[7 – 8]

Concepts

The heart pumps the blood through the body.
The heart beats many beats a minute.
When you exercise, the heart beats faster.
The heart has four chambers.

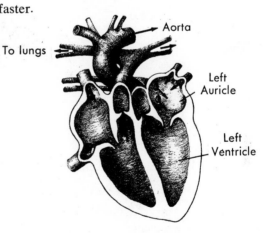

Procedure

STEP 1. *Ask:* Does anyone know where his heart is?

Have some students listen to the hearts of other students by placing their ears over the chest of other students.

Ask: What do you hear?
Why do you think the heart sounds something like a drum?
What makes the drum noise?
How many of you know what a heart looks like?

Obtain a calf or sheep heart from the butcher market and show it to the class. This can be stored in a jar of alcohol and used from year to year for observation. If you can't show them real hearts, show them some pictures of hearts or a chart.

STEP 2. Hold up a blown-up balloon partly filled with water.

> *Ask:* How is this balloon similar to the heart?
>> What would the water in the balloon represent that would be found in a heart?
>> What do you think will happen if I release the end of the balloon and push on the side of the balloon a little?

Demonstrate the push of liquid out of the balloon.

> *Ask:* How do you think the heart moves blood out of its chambers?

Explanation: The heart is similar to the balloon in that it has liquid in it called blood, but the heart actually pumps blood to all parts of the body. Point out that it actually is two pumps, one on the left and one on the right side. The sound they hear is the heart pumping.

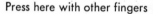
Press here with other fingers

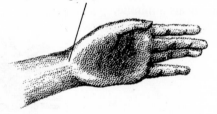

(2)

Taking the pulse

STEP 3. Have the students feel their pulses as shown in Diagram 2.

> *Ask:* What do you feel?
>> What do you think causes the little beats that you feel?

Explanation: The pulse is caused by the surge of blood that passes through the blood vessels each time the heart beats. Explain further that good food, proper rest, and exercise are needed to keep the heart in good condition. Have students listen to other students' hearts. Then have those whose hearts had been listened to jump up and down. Listen again to the beats and record the results on the board.

> *Ask:* What happens to the rate of the heart after exercise?

Explanation: When you exercise, your muscles need more oxygen and food. Your heart pumps faster so that more blood can be sent to the muscles carrying these vital materials; at the same time, blood takes away waste materials from the muscle.

BIOLOGY

STUDENT ACTIVITIES

1. Make a diagram of the heart, showing its four chambers.

2. What causes the noise you hear when you listen to the heart?

3. What does the heart do for you?

4. What makes your pulse work?

5. What does the heart pump?

6. What happens to the heart when you exercise?

7. Why is the heart so important?

8. If the heart beats all the time, why is it possible for a person to bleed to death?

9. What forces the blood out of the heart?

WHAT HAPPENS TO THE FOOD WE EAT?
[7 – 8]

Concepts

Large food particles must be broken down into smaller molecules before they can be absorbed.
The breaking down of food by chemical means is called digestion.
Food must be dissolved before it can be used by the body.
Starch is a food.
Starch must be changed to dissolved sugar in order for it to pass through the lining of the small intestine.

Procedure

Obtain: Cornstarch, sugar, iodine, spoon, two glasses, cracker, two balloons.

STEP 1. Hold up a cracker.

Ask: How is the cracker going to help the body when I eat it?
What is going to happen to the cracker?
Is the cracker ready to be used by the cells?
How is the body going to prepare this cracker for use?
Will the body use every bit of the cracker?
What is going to happen to that which is not used?
Where is the body going to digest this cracker?
What substances does your body contain to break down the cracker into usable substances?

Explanation: The body produces chemicals which break down the cracker. Let us do some experiments outside the body to see how some things are digested in our bodies.

STEP 2. Put a teaspoon of cornstarch (or a cracker ground into powder) in a glass of water. Put a teaspoon of sugar in another glass of water. Stir each with a spoon.

Ask: Why is the starch water cloudy?
Why is the sugar water clear?
Has the starch dissolved?
Has the sugar dissolved?

Let the glasses stand for one day.

Ask: What happens to the starch?
How does this help to explain why starch has to be changed so the body can use it?

Explanation: The starch will not dissolve.

STEP 3. Stir the starch and water again until the starch is mixed with the water. Take a teaspoon of starch water mixture and put a drop of iodine into it.

Ask: What color does the mixture turn?

Explanation: Starch plus iodine will turn blue or blue-black. This is a test for starch. The blue-black color shows that there is starch in the mixture.

STEP 4. Take a funnel lined with a piece of paper towel and set it in an empty glass. Stir the starch into the glass of water again. Slowly pour some of the starch water into the filter paper. After the water has run through, look at the inside of the paper.

Ask: Is there any starch left inside the funnel?
Did any go through with the water?

Test the water by adding a drop of iodine.

Ask: What color does the mixture turn?
Is there starch present?

Try the sugar water to see if the sugar will go through a paper funnel with the water.

Ask: How can you tell if there is sugar in the water before and after you pour it into the funnel?

Explanation: Taste the sugar water.

Ask: Which do you think could go through the wall of your intestine better— the starch or sugar?

Explanation: Sugar is a much smaller molecule than starch. Starch is broken down by digestive enzymes into a simple sugar which passes easily through the wall of the intestine into the blood vessels. The blood then carries the sugar to all parts of the body.

STEP 5. Make about a one per cent starch solution by taking one gram of flour and adding it to about 100 cc of water. Stir the solution well. Obtain three test tubes. Collect about 20 cc of saliva from your mouth. Put 10 cc of saliva in one test tube and 10 cc in another. Label one of the saliva test tubes the control. To the other tube add 10 cc of the starch solution and one or two drops of iodine to give the typical dark blue starch test. Add the same amount of iodine to the saliva control tube and to another tube containing only starch solution. Label the tubes as shown in Diagram 1.

(1)

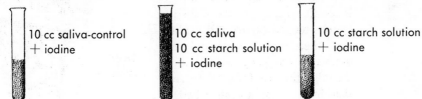

10 cc saliva-control + iodine

10 cc saliva
10 cc starch solution + iodine

10 cc starch solution + iodine

Ask: Why did the one tube turn blue and not the other?

Why do you think we added saliva?

What do you think will happen to these tubes as we let them stand?

Let the tubes stand for a period until the blue color in the starch-plus-saliva tube disappears.

Ask: What tube changed color? Why?

Explanation: In your mouth you produce an enzyme or chemical which breaks the starch down into sugar.

Ask: Why do you think you should chew your food well?

Explanation: The more you chew your food, the more enzyme is produced to break down the starch. In addition, the mechanical action of chewing itself helps to break food up into smaller pieces so that the enzymes in the stomach and intestine can work on it easily.

STEP 6. Take two clear plastic bags (jars may be used instead). Pour equal amounts of water into each bag. Place two cubes of sugar into each bag. Tie the ends of the bags. Place one bag aside. Let it stand still. Swish the water in the other one by churning it up and down and around.

(2)

Non-vibrated   Sugar   Vibrated

Ask: What do you see happening in the two bags?

Why does the sugar dissolve in one bag?

Explanation: The sugar cubes in the bag being swished around dissolved faster because of the churning movement of the water around them. The water dissolving the sugar in this manner is similar to the way our stomachs churn and digest food. When the food we eat goes into our stomach, it is churned and mixed with the chemical juices that come into the stomach from glands.

Ask: Why should we chew our food well before we swallow it?

Explanation: The finer the food, the less churning necessary to dissolve the food, and the more easily the chemicals produced in the stomach can work on it. Place Diagram 3 of the digestive system on the board and explain that there are several different organs of the body which aid in the digestion of food. Point out that food is mainly absorbed in the small intestine.

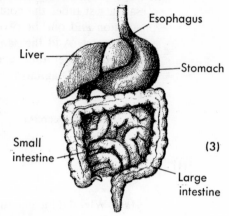

(3)

STUDENT ACTIVITIES

True or False

_____ 1. Food should be chewed into small particles before it is swallowed.
_____ 2. It is important that the stomach juices mix well with the food in the stomach.
_____ 3. The stomach is constantly churning.
_____ 4. The stomach must be strong.
_____ 5. Digestion of food is aided by the movement of the stomach.
_____ 6. Chemicals aid in the digestion of food.

Short Answer

1. What is starch changed to by your stomach?
2. What is a good test for starch? How does it work?
3. In the demonstration with the three test tubes, starch and saliva, what tubes were the control tubes?
4. Why did the color of the test tube containing starch, iodine, and saliva change?
5. Why should you chew your food well?
6. What must happen to big molecules before they can get into your blood stream?
7. What does the stomach do to food?
8. What did the sugar cubes in the water demonstrate?
9. Why does the stomach move and churn the food that is swallowed?

WHY SHOULD WE CHEW OUR FOOD?
[7 – 8]

Concepts

Before most food can be used by the body, it must be digested.

Large pieces of food must be broken into small pieces in order for digestion to be effective.

We have special organs in our body which produce chemicals to break food molecules into smaller molecules.

The body needs food so that it can grow and repair itself.

Procedure   I.   Saliva Helps Us to Swallow

STEP 1. *Ask:* Why should you chew your food well?

Chewing breaks food into smaller pieces

Large molecules of starch + saliva ⟶ smaller molecules of sugar

Besides breaking the food into small pieces in your mouth by chewing, what else happens in your mouth?

Why do we have saliva?·

Break some dry bread with your hands, and show the many pieces of it to the class.

Ask: If you had no saliva in your mouth, how do you think your ability to swallow would be influenced?

STEP 2. Mix some water with bread and form it into a small ball. Do not press the ball too hard, but show that it is loosely consolidated into the ball.

Ask: Can you see one reason for having saliva?

What purpose does it have?

Do you think it would be difficult to swallow dry bread?

Explanation: Saliva helps to consolidate food so that it can be swallowed easily. Since saliva is slippery, it decreases friction and aids food to pass down the digestive tube, the esophagus, to the stomach fairly easily. Dry bread would be difficult to swallow because it would stick to the walls of the esophagus.

Procedure II. Saliva Digests Starch

STEP 1. Obtain the following: starch (flour or corn starch will do), dilute iodine, three test tubes, eye dropper, and a piece of cloth. Put a teaspoonful of starch in a glass of cold water and stir the mixture thoroughly. Take a funnel and collect into a beaker saliva from your mouth. Number the tubes. Add to test tube no. 1, water, saliva, and iodine; to test tube no. 2 add starch solution and iodine; to test tube no. 3 add starch solution and saliva. Stir the solution and allow to stand.

STEP 2. After several minutes add a few drops of iodine to test tube no. 3 containing saliva and starch.

Ask: What happened to the following?
   Tube 1: saliva plus iodine
   Tube 2: starch plus iodine
   Tube 3: starch plus saliva plus iodine

Have the class record the results on the student activity page.

STEP 3. *Ask:* Why do you think the tube with the starch, saliva, and iodine changed color?
   Do you think the saliva must have changed the starch in some way?
   What is a test for the presence of starch?

Explanation: The test for the presence of starch is to add iodine. The starch will change in color to blue-black. In the third tube the saliva has a chemical (an enzyme) that breaks starch down into smaller sugar molecules. Since the starch is changed to sugar, there is no way to get a starch test. This experiment proves that the starch must have been changed chemically by the action of the saliva. The more food is chewed, the more saliva is produced, and the more likely the starches are to be changed into sugar in the mouth.

STUDENT ACTIVITIES

Short Answers

1. Record your results for the following:

Tube 1

Tube 2

Tube 3

2. What purpose does saliva have?

3. What is the starch test?

4. Why should you chew your food well?

5. Why would it be hard to swallow if we had no saliva?

6. Draw a diagram of the head and outline where the glands that produce the saliva might be located.

True or False

_____ 1. Saliva is produced in the mouth.

_____ 2. Starch placed in water will turn black.

_____ 3. Saliva changes starch into sugar.

_____ 4. Iodine added to sugar will make the sugar turn black.

_____ 5. Iodine added to starch will make it turn blue-black.

_____ 6. If something turns blue-black when iodine is added to it, it is possible that it has starch in it.

_____ 7. The more you chew your food, the easier it is for the stomach to digest it.

WHAT CAUSES OUR BODIES TO MOVE?
[6 – 8]

Concepts

Nerves are sensitive to touch, chemicals, and electricity.

Man is not sensitive to very low voltages.

Since our nerves are sensitive to electrical shock, we must be very careful not to get shocked.

Don't handle electrical equipment with wet hands.

In order for current to flow, there must be a complete circuit. In this experiment the worm must be touched by both wires to complete the circuit.

Dry paper is a nonconductor of electricity.

Procedure

STEP 1. Obtain some earthworms so that there is one for every two students. Give each student a blunt metal object. Tweezers will work very well.

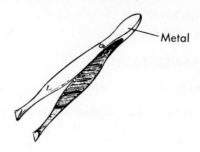

Metal

Ask: How did the worm know that you touched him?

What picked up the signal in the skin telling the worm that he had been touched?

How was this signal carried to the brain?

You might show a chart showing nerves of some animal or man and state that worms have nerves similar to those shown on the chart.

STEP 2. Give each student a little vinegar (an acid). Have them soak the tip of a piece of paper in the vinegar.

Lemon

Ask: What do you think the worm will do when you touch him with the paper soaked with the vinegar (an acid)?

Have the student touch the worm with the paper.

Ask: Was the worm stimulated by the acid?

How do you know he was stimulated by the acid?

What picked up this chemical stimulus and transported it to the brain?

STEP 3. Take a dry cell and hook up a copper wire to each electrode as shown in the diagram.

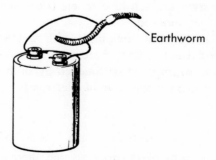

Earthworm

Ask: Are humans sensitive to electricity?
    Do you think worms would also be sensitive to electrical shock?

Touch both wires of the dry cell battery yourself.

Ask: Why don't I get a shock from this battery?
    Should a person ever touch a battery or any electrical piece of
        appartus as I did unless he knows how it really works?
    Do you think that the worm will react if I touch it with these two
        wires?

STEP 4. Touch the worm first with one wire and note the reaction (by this
    reaction you can tell the magnitude of his reaction due solely to tactile
    stimulation). Then, touch the worm with both wires and see how he
    reacts to electrical stimulation.

Ask: Why did I touch the worm first with only one wire and then with
    two wires?

Repeat the experiment but wrap the worm in waxed paper. (The electrical current will not pass through the paper.)

Ask: Why doesn't the worm react now?
    What can we conclude about animals being sensitive to electricity?
    Why do you think too much electricity might kill you?
    Why shouldn't you ever pick up any electrical appliance or un-
        screw a light bulb when your hands are wet?

STEP 5. If possible, dissect a frog, taking out all of its organs and exposing its
    backbone. (*Note:* All the above experiments may also be performed
    on toads or frogs.) The silvery strings you see entering and leaving
    the spine are the nerves.

STUDENT ACTIVITIES

Questions for Discussion

1. What stimuli are animals sensitive to?

2. How is a signal carried from the skin of an animal to its brain?

3. Why is electricity so dangerous?

4. Why shouldn't you touch any piece of electrical equipment if you don't know
   much about it?

5. Why shouldn't you touch anything electrical when your hands are wet?

6. Why is it a bad idea to have a radio near a bathtub or even in a bathroom?

7. What are the cords that carry electrical impulses to your brain?

8. Why did we have to touch the worm with both wires before it reacted to the
   electricity?

9. How are nerves stimulated?

HOW DOES OUR SKIN PROTECT US?
[2 – 6]

Concepts

The skin protects us from germs.
A cut or wound in the skin lets in germs.
Germs may cause infection.
Antiseptics kill germs.
Heat can kill germs.

Procedure

STEP 1. Select three perfect apples (a, b, c) and one partly rotten apple (d).
Obtain two needles.

Ask: How can I sterilize these needles?
What does it mean to sterilize things?

Sterilize two needles by heating them with a match. Puncture apple (a)
with a sterile needle in three places. Apply iodine or another antiseptic
over only two of these punctures. Push the second needle into soil and
then into apple (b). Place (a), (b), and (c) in a warm place for
several days.

(a) Three punctures with sterile
needle; and iodine applied on
two punctures

(b) Puncture with needle
stuck in soil

(c) Control

Ask: Why didn't I puncture apple (c)?

Explanation: This is the control. Define "control."

Ask: What do you think will happen to the apples if we let them
stand out in the heat for several days?
How will they look?
Will they look alike?

STEP 2. Have the students observe the apples daily. After several days have passed:

> *Ask:* What spot on the apple is most rotten?   Why?
> What is the difference in the apples?
> What part of your body does the skin of the apple represent?
> What did the puncture do to the apple?
> What would get into the apple after it was punctured that did not get in before?
> Do germs spread?

STEP 3. *Ask:* How is your skin like the apple skin?
> Why did we apply iodine, an antiseptic, over two of the punctures in apple (a)?   Define "antiseptic."
> Did the germs grow as well in these punctures as the one where we did not use the antiseptic?
> What does the antiseptic do?
> Could you see the germs?
> If you can't see them, how can they do so much harm?

Explanation: Harmful bacteria and fungi will reproduce very rapidly, producing in the body millions of their own kind in the matter of a few hours. These organisms often produce harmful substances which injure the healthy body tissues.

Ask: What does soil have in it?

Explanation: Soil contains millions of microorganisms. Some of them are harmful.

STEP 4. *Ask:* In addition to applying an antiseptic to a wound or a cut, what else should we do?

Explanation: The area should be cleansed, an antiseptic should be used, and the wound should be covered with a bandage or Band Aid.

Ask: Why should you cover the wound with a sterile bandage?
> Why shouldn't you use an old sheet or a used bandage on a wound?

STUDENT ACTIVITIES

Questions for Discussion

1. Explain what this demonstration showed.

2. Why should you use an antiseptic?

3. Why shouldn't you eat dirt, since it has a lot of very good minerals in it?

4. Why should you apply a bandage to a wound?

5. How are the skin of the apple and your skin similar?

True or False

_____ 1. Our skin is a protective wall against infection.

_____ 2. Germs may reproduce very rapidly.

_____ 3. Harmful germs make poisons that kill the good parts of our body.

_____ 4. Harmful germs can also infect food.

_____ 5. One way to sterilize a needle is to heat it in the flame of a match.

_____ 6. You should never pick your skin to get a splinter out with a needle unless it has been flamed.

_____ 7. Soil contains many germs.

_____ 8. Bandages keep out dirt.

_____ 9. To say that something is sterilized means that it has no germs on it or that the germs have been killed by heat or an antiseptic.

HOW DOES THE BODY MAINTAIN ITS TEMPERATURE?
[4 – 6]

Concepts

The normal human body temperature is about 98.6 deg. Fahrenheit, but this varies slightly with everybody.

The body temperature under normal conditions seldom goes higher than 99 deg. during the day, unless something is wrong.

When you are sick, the temperature goes above this figure.

When the body gets too warm, it perspires in order to lower the temperature.

In order for water to change into water vapor, it must absorb heat.

By doing this, it takes away heat from some source and cools it.

Procedure

STEP 1. Have each student touch one hand with his other hand.

> *Ask:* Does your hand feel warm or cold?
> Why do you think it feels warm?

> *Explanation:* Your body burns foods and gives off heat.

STEP 2. Put several thermometers into the mouths of different students. After a few minutes have the students read the thermometers and write their findings on the board.

Ask: From these data what do you think might be the normal body temperature?

Caution: Many students do not know how to take the temperature. Explain this to them before inserting the thermometers in their mouths. Disinfect the thermometers by placing them in alcohol. Explain the importance of doing so.

STEP 3. Fill a paper cup with water. Be sure that the cup is not wax-covered. Place it over a burner, as shown in the diagram.

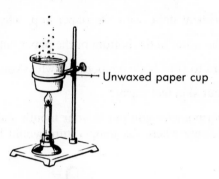

Unwaxed paper cup

Ask: Why doesn't the paper cup burn?
Why doesn't the temperature of the paper get hot enough to burn?
What is happening to the water in the cup?
Do you think the water is absorbing heat from the flame?
When water changes from a liquid into a vapor, does it absorb much heat?
From this experiment, does it look as if the evaporation of water requires a lot of heat?
What do you think will happen to the paper cup when all of the water has been evaporated?
Why do you think it will burn?

STEP 4. Tell the students to feel under their arms.

Ask: Are your armpits damp?
Why are they damp?
When you get hot, why do you think you perspire more?
When that perspiration leaves your body in the form of vapor, does it take away from your body any heat?
How do you think the perspiration gets out of your body?

Have the students look at a drawing, chart, or model of the skin. Show them the pores of the skin.

Ask: What do you think will happen to these pores if you don't keep your skin clean?

STUDENT ACTIVITIES

1. What is the normal body temperature of a human?

2. How does your skin keep warm in the winter?

3. When water absorbs a lot of heat, it will change from water into _____.

4. Why do you perspire more on a hot day?

5. What are the small openings in your skin through which the perspiration passes called?

6. In the experiment done with the paper cup, why didn't it burn?

7. What does the water in the bottom of the paper cup absorb?

8. What happens to your body temperature when you are sick?

9. Why does your skin feel warm?

10. Draw the thermometer you put in your mouth and mark the normal body temperature. Indicate where the temperature would be if the person were sick.

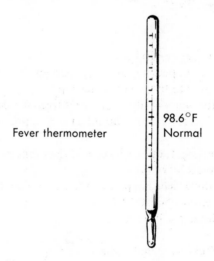

Fever thermometer   98.6°F
                                 Normal

WHAT IS A CAVITY?
[2–6]

Concepts

Humans have two sets of teeth.
Molars are our grinding teeth, and our other teeth are for tearing.
The outer part of the tooth is called the enamel, and the inner part of the tooth is called the pulp.

BIOLOGY

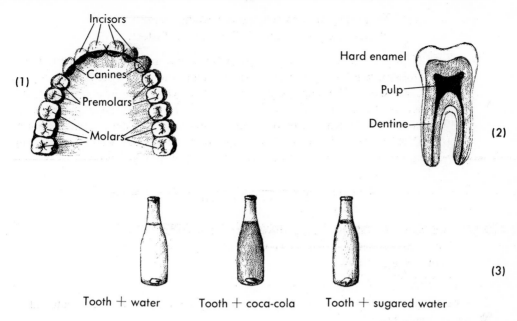

(1)

(2)

(3)

Tooth + water   Tooth + coca-cola   Tooth + sugared water

Procedure

STEP 1. *Ask:* Does anyone know what a cavity is?

Obtain some teeth from your local dentist and preferably a model or set of false teeth. Hold these up in front of the class.

Ask: What do your front teeth do?
What do your back teeth do?

Have a student chew an apple.

Ask: What teeth did he use at first?
What teeth did he use second?
What teeth do you think tear and which grind food?

Explanation: The incisors and canines tear food; the molars grind it. See Diagram 1.

STEP 2. Hold up some examples of cavities. Make a diagram of a tooth on the board and label it (see Diagram 2).

Ask: Can anyone show how a cavity might be formed in this tooth?

Have a student diagram a cavity in the tooth.

Ask: Does anyone know how we can prevent cavities from developing?

Take three teeth, preferably from the mouth of the same animal such as a cow or horse. Place one tooth in a pop bottle containing only water. Add another to a bottle containing Coca Cola, and a third to a bottle with sugared water. See Diagram 3.

Ask: What do you think will happen to the teeth?
Which one do you think will decay the fastest?

Explanation: The tooth will probably decay most rapidly in the Coca
Cola because of the high sugar content and acid found naturally in
Coca Cola. The sugar supports bacteria which produce acid that dissolves the enamel of the tooth. After several days have the students
observe the teeth and record their results on the student activity section.
Discuss the desirability of washing your mouth with water or brushing
your teeth after having eaten or drunk any kind of sweet.

STUDENT ACTIVITIES

1. Record below what happened to the three teeth tested.
   a. Tooth in water.
   b. Tooth in sugared water.
   c. Tooth in Coca Cola.

2. Why do you think it is a good idea to wash your mouth out with water after
   having eaten sweets?

3. Why should you brush your teeth after every meal?

4. Make a diagram of a normal tooth and label it.

5. What causes the feeling of pain in a tooth?

6. Why should you go to a dentist if your teeth are painful?

7. Make a diagram of a tooth with a cavity in it.

8. A cow has a lot of molars. Can you think of any reason for this?

THE ANIMAL WORLD

ZOOLOGY

This section is mainly devoted to a study of animals. The lessons may be incorporated into several different units. The first three lessons involve familiarizing
children with animals, their care and structural and functional variations. The
lesson "How Many Different Types of Animals Do You Know?" can be especially
good in showing structural differences. Encourage children to make comparisons of
animals and note how certain structures particularly adapt animals to perform
such tasks as swimming, flying, walking, and digging.

The fourth and fifth lessons "How Do Spiders Live?" and "How Do Ants Live?" introduce students to a study of animals in their environment. They can see how animals vary in their behavior in daily living. Have the children study how ants behave compared to other animals such as frogs. Have them discover and study the social arrangement of ants compared to the non-social organization of frogs or spiders. The pupils should look for similar behaviors in other animals.

The lesson "What Do We Know about the Birds Around Us?" encourages children to observe birds and notice how they vary. This lesson shows that birds build different types of nests, vary in size and color. The teacher can point out that different features of the body enable birds to perform varied tasks. For example, a bird with a long slender beak can use it to probe in sand to find clams or insects; whereas, a bird with a short thick beak might use it to break open seeds. Many other features can be studied to see how the structure particularly helps the bird to survive. The lesson "How Do Birds Differ from Mammals?" is written so that students must make accurate observations of different life forms. From these observations the students are forced to analyze the characteristics which make a mammal differ from birds.

HOW MANY DIFFERENT TYPES OF ANIMALS DO YOU KNOW?
[4 – 6]

Concepts

Each animal lives in a place (environment) which is good for it.
The way the animal is built depends on where it lives.
Animals that live on dry land breathe by lungs.
Animals that usually live in water breathe by gills.
Land animals usually move by legs and may run, hop, or crawl.
Many land animals have claws and sharp teeth.
Some animals live in water, some on land, some in the air, and some both in water and on land.
Animals that fly have strong wings and light bones.

Procedure

STEP 1. Have your students bring to class different types of animals or pictures of animals. Obtain from the local butcher or meat market a fish containing gills. Dissect off the gill covering so that the students can see the gill. (A diagram of a gill might be drawn on the board if a fish is not available.)

Ask: Does anyone know what this is called?
What does the gill do for the fish?

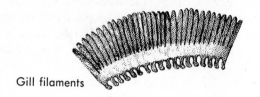

Gill filaments

STEP 2. Have the students observe a fish in an aquarium.

Explanation: As the fish swim, water passes over their gills and the fish gets from the water tiny particles of air. The air is absorbed by the blood vessels in the gills.

Ask: Could we breathe under water?
     Why can't we breathe under water?
     What would we need in order to breathe in water?
     What do we have that permits us to breathe in the air?

Explanation: If possible, obtain a piece of lung from the slaughterhouse, bottle it in alcohol for permanent display, and show it to the class. Explain that land animals must have lungs in order to live.

STEP 3. Show some pictures of various animals having claws and sharp teeth.

Ask: What parts of these animals' bodies are built for getting or capturing food?

Show the class some pictures of stuffed birds.

Ask: What advantage do these animals have over other animals?
     Why do you think these animals can fly?

Have a student try to jump up with someone holding the seat of his pants. Tell him to try again with no one holding him.

Ask: Why couldn't he jump very high the first time?
     Do you see why an animal that doesn't have very light bones
        would have a hard time flying?

Show the class some chicken bones. Break one so that the students can see how it is constructed, and have them compare this with a steak bone. Request that students bring in other pictures of birds and explain how they are built for flying and getting their food.

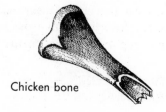

Chicken bone

Beef bone

STEP 4. Have the class keep lists of animals that live in the air, in the sea, in lakes, on dry land, underground, and part of their time on land and part in water.

Ask: Do you think that animals that live in the ocean can also usually live in lakes?

Explanation: Generally marine animals can not live in fresh water. A salmon is an exception. After some time discuss the lists with the class.

STUDENT ACTIVITIES

Questions for Discussion

1. What kind of bodies do animals have that live on land, in the water, in the air, and on land and in water?

2. How do animals differ in kinds of teeth they have?

3. What does a lung look like?

4. What does a lung do?

5. What does a gill look like?

6. What does a gill do?

7. How do animals breathe in water?

8. Why can't you breathe in water?

9. Why can't a cow fly?

True or False

_____ 1. Animals must have food and air (oxygen) in order to live.

_____ 2. How an animal lives depends on where it lives. They usually have to live in one type of place.

_____ 3. Many animals live on dry land and breathe air through their lungs.

_____ 4. Most land animals move by legs and may walk, run, hop, or crawl.

_____ 5. Many land animals have claws, which they use in climbing, fighting, and eating.

_____ 6. Meat-eating animals have claws and sharp teeth for tearing meat.

_____ 7. A lot of animals live in water, and most of them can take air out of the water.

_____ 8. Fish have gills which take air out of the water.

_____ 9. Most animals can swim well.

_____ 10. Many animals can fly in the air; they have strong wings and light bodies.

_____ 11. A few animals live underground and dig tunnels in the soil.

HOW ARE BABY ANIMALS CARED FOR BY THEIR PARENTS?
[1 – 6]

Concepts

Many baby animals are cared for and fed by their parents.
Baby animals grow up to look like their parents.

Procedure

STEP 1. Obtain animals such as guinea pigs or hamsters and a cage so that the children can watch the animals take care of the young. A hen with a few young chicks may also be used, but these should be kept outside of the classroom because of the noise they make.

Ask: How does the mother take care of her babies?

Explanation: The mother takes care of her babies by washing them, feeding them, and keeping them warm.

STEP 2. Tell the children that they can feed baby pets too. Young animals must sometimes be given food until they are capable of getting it for themselves. Chickens are a good example of this.

Ask: Do you think the babies will grow up to look like their parents?

Discuss with the children how their mothers care for infants at home.

Ask: Do all animals have to be cared for by their mothers?

Explanation: No. Reptiles such as turtles, snakes, and lizards hatch from eggs and are not generally cared for by their mothers.

STUDENT ACTIVITIES

True or False

_____ 1. Babies grow up to look like their parents.

_____ 2. Some animal parents take care of their babies.

_____ 3. Children cannot feed baby animals.

_____ 4. Some animals must be given food until they are able to get it for them-selves.

Questions for Discussion

1. Give three ways a mother takes care of her babies.

2. If you had a baby brother or sister at home, how would your mother take care of it?

3. How do you take care of your pets?

WHAT IS THE DIFFERENCE BETWEEN A FROG AND A LIZARD?
[1 – 3, 4 – 6]

Concepts

A frog is called an amphibian.

Amphibians are animals which may spend part of their life in water and part on land.

Amphibians have a tadpolelike stage which lives in water and has toes without claws and skin that is slippery.

A lizard belongs to the group of animals called reptiles.

Reptiles have skin covered with scales; there is no tadpole stage; toes, if present, have claws; they usually produce eggs with shells.

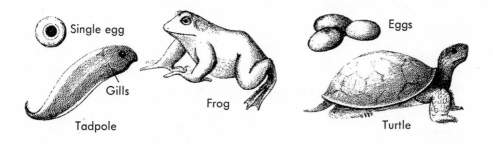

Procedure

STEP 1. Bring a lizard and a frog to class and show them to the students.

[1–3]   *Ask:* What differences do you see between a lizard and a frog?

You may have the students write down the differences they see.

Ask: Where does the frog like to live?
Where does the lizard like to live?
What do the polliwogs turn into?
Have you ever seen a polliwog that produced a lizard?
What do the skins of the two animals look like?
How do the toes of the lizard differ from those of the frog?

STEP 2. Show the class live snakes, turtles, and lizards. Pictures or preserved specimens may be used if animals are not available.

Explanation: Explain that all reptiles have scales and usually hatch from eggs. Show examples or pictures of other amphibians such as toads or salamanders.

Have the students collect some polliwogs and raise them in the aquarium with plants.

Explanation: Amphibians are animals that may live parts of their lives in water and part on land. They all have tadpolelike stages when they live in water, and their toes never have claws on them.

STUDENT ACTIVITIES

1. Draw some examples of reptiles.

2. Make some drawings of amphibians.

3. Name three types of amphibians.

4. Name three types of reptiles.

5. How can you tell the difference between a reptile and an amphibian?

6. What does a tadpole turn into?

7. Where do snakes come from?

8. How would you know that a turtle is a reptile?

HOW DO SPIDERS LIVE?
[2 – 6]

Concepts

A spider has four pairs of legs and a body divided into two segments.
All spiders capture and feed on other animals.

Part of a spider's body is called the spinneret, the abdominal silk-producing
   gland.

Some spiders build small silk cocoons to keep their eggs safe and dry.

Many young spiders dangle from threads which are carried by the wind.

Spiders are found in nearly all land areas.

Spiders are useful to man because they eat insects.

The bite of most spiders is not harmful to human beings.

Procedure

STEP 1. Have the class collect several common garden spiders in jars and put
        them in a terrarium or large jar with a lid punctured with small holes.
        The jar should have some twigs and soil in it. They should observe the
        spiders for several days to watch them spin webs, lay eggs, and make
        egg sacs.

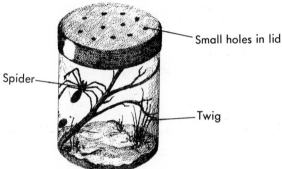

Caution: The children should be warned to be careful not to let the
spiders bite them.

Ask: What type of food do you think we should put in the jars so that
       the spider will have enough to eat?

Catch small live insects and place them in the jar with the spiders. Live
flies are good for this. After the class has observed the spiders for
several days:

Ask: What can you tell me about the way a spider lives?

If the spider spins a web:

Ask: What did the spider make?
       Does anyone know what part of the body the spider uses to spin
          the web?
       Did you see any small sacs that the spiders made?
       Do you have any idea what is inside of these sacs?

Take one of these and open it so that the students can see the small
eggs inside.

Ask: What do you think these small objects are?

Explanation: Spiders reproduce by small eggs.

STEP 2. *Ask:* How is the spider's body constructed?
How many legs does it have?
How many parts are there to the spider's body?
What does the spider eat?
How does he get his food?

Explanation: Spiders have two main body parts, the head and the abdomen. Spiders feed on other animals, such as insects, and for this reason help to keep the insect population controlled.

Ask: Do all spiders spin webs?

Explanation: Not all spiders make webs; some hunt insects on the ground. Those that make webs have on the end of their abdomen a spinneret. Point out how even spiders may have many variations. The class might wish to continue its study of the spiders and wait for the young to develop from the eggs.

STUDENT ACTIVITIES

True or False

_____ 1. The body of a spider is divided into two main parts.

_____ 2. Spiders are found in all land areas.

_____ 3. Spiders possess spinnerets, which they use to protect their young.

_____ 4. Spiders feed on plants.

_____ 5. Spiders kill insects and thereby help man keep insects down.

_____ 6. Spiders have eight legs.

_____ 7. Spiders' legs have joints.

Short Answer

1. Why are spiders useful to man?

2. Does the spider belong to the insect family? How do you know?

3. How does a spider catch his prey?

4. What type of web does a garden spider spin?

5. How do spiders that do not make webs get their prey?

6. What kind of food did your spiders eat?

7. Why do you think spiders will not eat dead bugs you put in the jar?

8. Explain where the spiders put their eggs and what happens to the eggs.

HOW DO ANTS LIVE?
[1 – 6]

Concepts

Ants are social insects.
All insects have three parts to their bodies and six legs.
Ants are helpful because they help keep the forests and fields clean.
There is a division of labor in an ant colony.

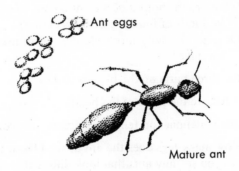

Ant eggs

Mature ant

Procedure

STEP 1. Fill a large glass jar two-thirds full of soil (a commercial jar for
mayonnaise will do). Place a moist sponge in the jar. This sponge is to
be moistened once a week. Set the jar in a pan of water. Place a piece
of black paper around the jar. (The paper may be removed when observing the ant colony.) Put bread, cake, sugar, seeds, or meats in the
jar. Colonies of ants can be purchased from a biological supply house
(see appendix for addresses). Cost is usually not excessive. Put a
colony of harvesting ants, including a queen, the workers, and larvae in
the jar. Allow the ants to work in their new home for a day before the
children observe them.

Ask: Why do we place the black piece of paper around the jar?

Explanation: To give the ants a dark place to work.

Ask: Why do we set the jar in a pan of water?

Explanation: This prevents the ants from escaping.
Allow the students to observe the ants at work.

Ask: What kinds of work do the ants seem to be doing?
How is the work that the ants do similar to what we do in our
communities?

Explanation: The ants gather food, build nests, clean the nests, care for the young, and defend the nests. The ant community is something like a small city.

Ask: What do we call an ant community?
　　　Are there different types of ants in an ant colony?
　　　What are they?

Explanation: Each colony has a queen, workers, eggs, young, and winged forms.

Ask: Do different types of ants do different work in the colony?

Explanation: The queen lays the eggs. A colony needs a queen in order to survive.

Ask: What are the homes of the ant colony like?
　　　What kinds of food are the ants eating?
　　　Observe the ants more closely. How many body parts does the ant have?

Draw the three parts on the blackboard.

Ask: What are the parts of the head?

Draw the antennae or feelers. Explain the compound eyes.

Ask: How many legs does the ant have? (Draw them.)
　　　Do you see any ants that look different?

Explanation: The queen and the males have wings. The queen is also larger than the other ants.

STEP 2. *Ask:* What do the eggs look like?
　　　　　What do we call these eggs?
　　　　　How are ant colonies useful to us?

Explanation: They carry soil to the surface. They open the ground to air and moisture. They dispose of the decaying bodies of insects.

Write any new words on the blackboard.

STUDENT ACTIVITIES

1. Complete the following sentences by circling the right word.
    a. Ants live in (colonies, cities).
    b. A (king, queen) ant is needed before the ants can work.
    c. Ants live in (castles, tunnels).
    d. Ants have (three, four, six) legs.

2. Name three kinds of food that the ants eat.

3. What are the eggs laid by the queen called after they start to develop?

4. Draw a picture of an ant's body.

5. What kinds of work do the worker ants do?

6. All the ants have some kind of work to do. Draw a line from the type of ant to the type of work the ant does.

    Worker   Lays eggs

    Queen   Gathers food

    Young ant   Protects the nest

7. Are ants useful to us? Why?

8. All insects are not social; ants are social. What does this mean?

9. A spider has eight legs. Is it an insect? Why?

10. What is a grasshopper?

WHAT DO WE KNOW ABOUT THE BIRDS AROUND US?
[K – 3, 4 – 6]

Concepts

Birds vary in color and size.
Birds sing different songs.
Birds make different kinds of nests.
Birds eat many different kinds of food.
The male may have different plumage than the female.
Some birds migrate.
Some birds change color with the season.
Birds care for their young.
Some birds chase other birds.

Procedure [1–3]

If time permits, you might take the class on a short field trip, helping them to see the different kinds of birds, hear them, look at the nests, and watch the birds eat. If time as well as transportation factors prevent you from doing this, small pamphlets with pictures of the birds and folders explaining them can be obtained from the Audibon Society for a nominal fee. It would be wise to choose pictures of birds that are a common sight in the area in which you live. This makes the children become more interested in the lesson. Old birds' nests and different feathers might also be brought into the classroom.

Field Trip [4–6]

The field trip teaches observation as well as the lesson on birds. You might see some of the following:

English Sparrow. (1) What kind of bird is that? (2) What does it eat? (3) Does he live here all year around?

Cardinal. (1) What kind of bird is that? (2) What does he sound like when he sings? (3) What does "Mrs. Cardinal" look like? (4) With what are they building their nest? (5) What does the nest look like? (6) Where are they building the nest?

Redheaded Woodpecker. (1)Where is the woodpecker building his nest? (2) How does he build the nest? (3) What kind of food does the woodpecker eat?

Hummingbird. (1)Is the father hummingbird a different color from the mother? (2) Where do they get their food? (3) Are they as big as the cardinal or sparrow? (4) Why can't we find their nests?

Starling. (1) Why aren't there any other birds living near the starling? (2) What color is the starling? (3) Is he the same color as the woodpecker? As the cardinal?

Robin. (1) What kind of bird is that? (2) Do they stay here all year around? (3) How do they care for their young? (4) Where do they build their nest?

Scarlet Tanager. (1) Are "Mr." and "Mrs." Tanager the same color? (2) What happens to Mr. Tanager in the fall? Why?

Questions like the preceding examples and many others can be asked about the birds as you see them, and about the different nests that you see. Old nests might be collected and brought into class and discussed. Caution the students about not destroying a nest with eggs in it. You might also point out that birds' beaks and feet vary depending on what they eat or where they live (e.g., hooked beaks are birds of prey; webbed feet belong to birds that live around water).

Classroom

The same type of questions may be asked about the various pictures of birds as you show the pictures to the children. Afterwards, you might have the children color pictures of birds or do puzzles about the birds. Students enjoy making bird feeders in the winter and setting them outside the classroom window in order to observe the birds more closely. Have someone show the pictures or describe a bird to the class and see how many birds the children can name. You might also make flash cards with a bird on one side and the name of it plus other information on the other side.

STUDENT ACTIVITIES

True or False

_____ 1. All birds live in the same place all year long.

_____ 2. Some birds change color with the season.

_____ 3. All birds are the same color.

_____ 4. There are many different sizes of birds.

_____ 5. All birds eat only fruit.

_____ 6. Most birds are good parent birds.

_____ 7. There are many different kinds of birds.

_____ 8. All birds build their nests with only mud.

_____ 9. Birds sing many different songs.

_____ 10. All birds build their nests on tree limbs.

Short Answer

1. Name three kinds of birds in which the male and female are a different color.

2. What are seven things that birds eat?

3. Do birds change color with the season? Why?

4. Name ten birds that we have talked about in class or that you have seen around your home.

5. Name at least one bird that doesn't like other birds.

6. Name five places that birds build their nests.

7. What are some of the materials birds use to build their nests?

8. Why do birds vary in color and size?

9. Name three birds that stay here in the winter.

10. Name four birds that leave here when winter comes.

11. Name one bird that changes color with the season.

HOW DO BIRDS DIFFER FROM MAMMALS?
[6 – 8]

Concepts

Birds are the only animals that have feathers.
Both mammals and birds are warm-blooded.
Birds have two legs and two wings.
The female mammal has glands for nourishing its young with milk.
Mammals are more or less covered with hair.
Birds do not vary in structure as much as mammals.
The bones of birds are somewhat hollow and light in weight. Mammal bones
    are not so hollow and are proportionately heavier in weight.
Birds tend to eat approximately the amount of their weight in food every day.
Mammals do not eat so much.
Birds use a great deal of energy in flying and therefore need a great amount of
    food.
Female birds lay eggs.
Almost all female mammals give birth to live babies.
A very few mammals, such as the platypus, lay eggs.

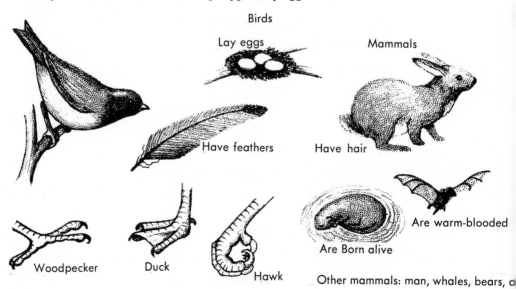

Procedure

STEP 1. Using a live or stuffed bird and mammal as demonstration models,
        have the children point out the differences between the two animals.
        Discuss these differences. Have a chicken bone and a beef bone for

students to examine. Cut the chicken bone in two. Let students see how light in weight it is compared to the beef bone. Get a cross section of the bone of a bird, such as a sparrow or a robin. Let the students see how lightweight the bone is.

STEP 2. If possible, obtain the wing bone of a bird or chicken or turkey. Show how man has two legs, two arms, and two hands. Show how the bird has two legs and two wings, the three parts of the wing being somewhat similar to the upper arm, lower arm, and hand of man. Encourage children to bring their pets to school; have a "pet day," or have a pet show. Many children raise rabbits, kittens, dogs, hamsters, goldfish, birds, guppies. The observance of each other's pets is a great motivation toward learning something about animals.

STEP 3. Have students list the differences between birds and mammals on the board. They may include:

Birds: feathers, beak — no teeth, wings, ears covered by feathers, eyes on side of head so as to see forward and backward, warm-blooded, breathe air, and lay eggs.

Mammals: warm-blooded, glands to feed milk to young, have hair covering body, with the exception of one Order — all mammals are well developed, give birth to live babies.

STEP 4. Summarize by asking the class some of the following questions:

Ask: Why do birds have feathers?

Explanation: They aid in flying and protect them from the weather.

Ask: Is a whale a mammal?
How do you know it is?

Explanation: A whale breathes air, has some hair, and suckles its young.

Ask: Do you think humans are mammals?
Are humans warm-blooded?
Do they suckle their young, breathe air through their lungs, and have hair on their bodies?
Do birds lay eggs?
Do rabbits really lay eggs, even though we sometimes say the Easter Bunny has left pretty, colored eggs?

STUDENT ACTIVITIES

Short Answer

1. Give some characteristics of a bird.

2. Give some of the characteristics of mammals that we discussed in class.

3. How does the covering of a bird's body differ from that of other animals?

True or False

_____ 1. A bird is an animal with feathers.

_____ 2. A bird's body is covered with fur.

_____ 3. Mammals are animals whose young are fed on milk.

_____ 4. All mammals are warm-blooded.

_____ 5. Mammals have feathers.

_____ 6. The young of most mammals are hatched.

_____ 7. The bones of birds are hollow.

Multiple Choice

Underline the word or words which makes the meaning of the sentence correct. Write the letter that preceeds your choice in the blank.

_____ 1. A bird's body is covered with (a) scales; (b) hair; (c) feathers.

_____ 2. A bird needs feathers (a) to make it heavier; (b) to protect its body; (c) to aid it in finding food.

_____ 3. Mammals are covered with (a) scales; (b) feathers; (c) fur or hair.

_____ 4. Which of the following is a mammal? (a) dog; (b) frog; (c) bird.

Completion

Write in each blank the word or group of words needed to make the sentence true.

1. A _____ is an animal with feathers.

2. A _____ is an animal whose young are fed on milk.

3. All birds have _____ legs and _____ wings.

4. Mammals are covered with _____.

5. The young of most _____ are born alive.

DO ANIMALS NEED OXYGEN?
[4–6]

Concepts

Animals need oxygen in order to live.
Oxygen dissolves in water. Some animals need the dissolved oxygen in water.
A gas will dissolve more in a cool liquid than in a hot liquid.
Oil is lighter than water; therefore, it floats on water.
Fish breathe through gills.

Procedure

STEP 1. Obtain some mosquito larvae from a stagnant pond or tin cans that have been filled with water and placed near a pond or lake. Adult mosquitoes often deposit their eggs in these. Attempt to get the wrigglers, as shown in Diagram 1. Place these wrigglers into two different jars. Cover the jars.

(1)

Wriggler

Ask: How do these wrigglers appear to breathe in the water?

Have the class note the small tube, shown in Diagram 1 above, through which the mosquito larvae breathe.

Ask: How would you go about killing wrigglers in a pond?
   Do you think that the mosquitoes would die if you cut off their air supply?
   What would you put on water to clog the tubes of the mosquitoes?
   Do most animals need oxygen in order to live?

STEP 2. Place some oil in one jar. Cover both jars with Saran Wrap or waxed paper and watch the wrigglers for several days. Be certain to leave enough air in the jars. The wrigglers in the jar with no oil will eventually metamorphose into mosquitoes.

Ask: What do you notice about the wrigglers?
   Where did the mosquitoes come from in the jar without the oil?

STEP 3. Boil a pint of water for several minutes. Pour the hot water in a jar and cap it. Cool the water. After the water is cooled, place a small goldfish into the jar and cap the bottle. Be sure that the water in the jar reaches the top of the lid. Place another fish in a jar in which the water has not been heated.

(2)

Ask: What do you think will happen to the fish in the jar in which the water has been heated?
   Why does the fish in the water that has been heated seem to vary in its movements compared to the other fish?
   Why did I first heat the water and then cool it?

Explanation: When you heat the water, the oxygen escapes.

Ask: Do animals in the sea need oxygen?
How do the animals in the sea get the oxygen they need?
Do most animals need oxygen?

Caution: If the fish turns on its side, take it out of the water quickly, shake it in the air by the tail for a few seconds, and place it into a jar of regular unheated water.

STUDENT ACTIVITIES

1. What gas do animals need in order to live?

2. Why did the wrigglers die when you placed oil on the water?

3. Wrigglers change or develop into what kind of animals?

4. When you heat a liquid, what happens to the gases dissolved in it?

5. Why does the oil go on top of the water in the experiment with the mosquitoes?

6. What happened to the fish placed in the jar of water which was heated and cooled?

7. Why did the fish in the jar of heated water differ in its reactions from the other fish?

8. When the fish was taken out of the jar, why was it necessary to shake it in air for a few minutes?

9. How do animals get the oxygen they need if they live in water?

10. Draw a wriggler and show how it gets air.

THE STRUCTURE AND FUNCTION OF PLANTS

PARTS OF A PLANT

The first three lessons "What Are the Parts of a Plant?" "What Is a Seed?" and "What is the Purpose of a Stem?"can be used together in one unit to develop ideas about the structure of plants. The development of a seed can also be used to show growth processes and the ordered way a seed produces a plant. Each part of a seed has a particular function; for example, the embryo produces a new plant, the cotyledons or endosperm supply food to the body of the developing plant until it can obtain raw materials from the soil and air and make its own food. The mature plant has several structures, each specialized for a particular function; flowers for reproduction, stems for conduction and support, leaves for production of food, and roots for anchorage of the plant and absorption of water and minerals. Flowers which have brightly colored petals, give off odors or contain nectar to attract insects and are insect pollinated. Flowers which lack these features such as those of the grains are wind pollinated.

WHAT ARE THE PARTS OF A PLANT?
[1 – 6]

Concepts

Plants have leaves, roots, stems, and flowers.
Not all plants have all the above four parts.
Leaves may make food.
The stems carry minerals and water from the roots to the leaves and flowers.
Flowers make seeds which can produce more of the same type of plant.
Some roots store food.

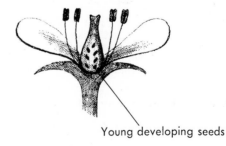

—Flower

—Leaves

— Stem

—Roots

Young developing seeds

Procedure

STEP 1. Hold up a plant with leaves, roots, and stem.

Ask: Who can name all the parts of a plant?

Point to the roots.

Ask: What are these called?

What purpose do they have for the plant?

Explanation: The roots generally serve two main purposes — they absorb water and minerals and pass these raw materials on to the stem, and they anchor the plant so that it does not blow away.

STEP 2. Hold up a carrot, radish, turnip, parsnip, or sugar beet.

Ask: Do all roots look alike?

What do you think these roots do besides absorb water and anchor the plant?

Have you ever eaten any of these plants?

Why do you think you eat them?

What do they have in them that you need?

Explanation: Some roots store food. The carrot is a plant that takes two years to bloom. It stores food in the root so that the plant can survive during the winter. When spring comes the next year, it pushes up a new stem which will have flowers, bloom, and produce seed. We eat the carrot root because it has valuable stored food containing many vitamins.

STEP 3. Hold up some stems from several different plants.

Ask: What does a stem do for a plant?

Do all stems look the same?

Where would the leaves or flowers grow if there were no stem?

How does water get from the roots to the leaves and flowers?

What carries it up there?

Hold up a plant which has had all of its leaves stripped off it.

Ask: What do you think would happen to this plant if I planted it and kept picking off all the leaves?

Explanation: The plant would die, because the leaves make the food that a plant needs in order to live.

STEP 4. Hold up several flowers.

Ask: What do the flowers do for the plant?

Pull the petals and sepals off the flower and locate the little seeds found in the ovary of the plant. See diagram.

Ask: What do you think these little things are that I found in the flower?

Explanation: They are undeveloped seeds. When mature, they would become seeds capable of reproducing the plant. Summarize the demonstration by asking the class to name the parts of a plant and tell what each part does.

BIOLOGY

STUDENT ACTIVITIES

Questions for Discussion

1. Label the diagram.

2. What purpose does the root serve for the plant?

3. What good are flowers to the plant?

4. What good are stems to the plant?

5. Where is food made in a plant?

6. Where might food be stored in a plant?

7. Write the names of some plants that store food.

True or False

_____   1. A plant has roots and a stem.

_____   2. A plant can live without water.

_____   3. The roots get food from the soil.

_____   4. Roots hold a plant in the ground.

_____   5. A plant can live without air.

_____   6. Stems carry water from the roots to the leaves.

_____   7. All leaves look alike.

_____   8. Flowers make seeds.

_____   9. All stems look alike.

_____ 10. Green plants need sunshine.

_____ 11. Plants need soil in order to grow.

_____ 12. Soil is important only because it holds the plant upright.

WHAT IS A SEED?
[1 – 3]

Concepts

Seeds store food.
A seed has a young undeveloped baby plant in it called an embryo.
Seeds usually sprout faster when it is warm.
The embryo gets food it needs to grow from the storage area of the seed.

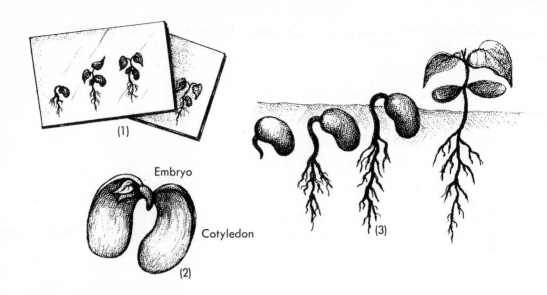

Embryo

Cotyledon

(1)

(2)

(3)

Demonstration

STEP 1. Take some seeds (bean and corn). Place them on some well-soaked paper towels, some stiff cardboard, or a piece of wood. Wrap with Saran Wrap or waxed paper, as shown in the diagram. Make two or more of these demonstrations. Place one of them near a heater and the other in a cool place.

Ask: Which seeds do you think will start to grow first?

STEP 2. At the same time you do the above experiment, take some seeds and place them on some wet paper towels in a dish. Cover the dish with Saran Wrap or waxed paper. After several days, when the seeds have swollen considerably, have the students crack them open and locate the embryos (the undeveloped baby plants). See the seed diagram. (Teachers may have to help children open the seeds.)

Ask: Why is the embryo so small compared to the entire size of the seed?

Where does the embryo get its food while it is growing?

Why do you think the seed has to have so much stored food in it?

Explanation: The major part of a seed contains reserved food for the embryo. This is needed by the embryo until it grows large enough to make its own food.

STEP 3. *Ask:* What do you think will happen to these seeds if we don't plant them in the ground?

Do you think they will die?   Why?

STUDENT ACTIVITIES

1. Draw a cut-open seed just about to sprout. Label the embryo and the parts of the seed that will become the root and the stem. (In grades 1-2 place the diagram on the blackboard and have the children point to the parts rather than making individual diagrams.)

2. Draw the steps that a seed goes through in developing into a plant.

3. How are the seeds grown in a jar near a heater different in their growth from those in the other jar?

4. Can you conclude from this experiment that temperature affects the rate at which seeds sprout?

5. How was it possible for the seeds we planted on the wet paper to grow into little plants?

6. Where did they get the food they needed in order to grow?

7. Why do seeds die if they are not planted in the ground after they have sprouted?

WHAT IS THE PURPOSE OF A STEM?
[4 – 6]

Concepts

Water must move from the roots to the leaves if a plant is to make food and live.

One of the main purposes of the stem of a plant is to carry water from the roots to the leaves.

There are little tubes inside the stem that carry water to the leaves.

The water moves up the stem by capillary action and by osmosis.*

Procedure

STEP 1. Obtain a stalk of celery with leaves on it, red ink or red food coloring, water, and a drinking glass. (A carnation or some other flower stem may also be used.) Put some water in the drinking glass and color it with the ink or food coloring. Cut a small slice off the bottom of the stalk of celery and set the stalk into the glass of colored water. Place it

---

Teachers Note: You may want to do some additional lessons to show capillarity or osmosis. These words are defined for your convenience below:

Capillary action is a force which causes water to rise, usually in tubes and vessels.

Osmosis is the process of water and dissolved materials moving from a region of greater concentration of these substances to a region of lesser concentration.

in a sunny window and leave it for several hours. If you use a carnation, it might be more interesting to set it up as shown in Diagram 2.

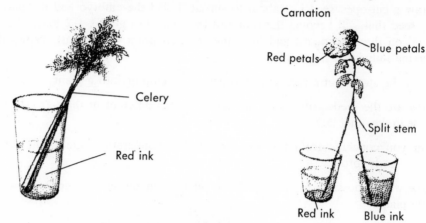

STEP 2. Cut open the stalk of the celery.

Ask: What do you see?

Explanation: The colored water will have passed up the tubes in the stalk, giving them a red color which can be traced through the stem. It will also be possible to see how the tubes branch out into the leaves.

Ask: What is the purpose of the tubes?

Explanation: One of the main functions of the stem is to carry water from the roots to the leaves so the leaves can use it to make food. The water travels from the roots to the leaves through the little tubes.

STEP 3. *Ask:* Do you think the temperature might have any effect on how rapidly the solution moves up the stem?

Explanation: The water will move up the stem faster if the temperature is warm. You might repeat the experiment, using several pieces of celery and placing some in a refrigerator and comparing their rate of flow with those at room temperature.

STEP 4. Obtain a blotter and glass of water. Put an edge of the blotter in the water.

Ask: What do you think will happen?

Explanation: The blotter will soak up the water and will soon be wet above the water level.

Ask: Can you see any connection between this demonstration and the movement of water up the tubes in the stem of a plant?

Explanation: In both cases the water moves upward to some extent by capillary action.

True or False

_____ 1. There are little tubes in the stem of a plant which carry water from the roots to the leaves.

_____ 2. Water must get from the roots to the leaves if a plant is to make food.

_____ 3. Stems hold up the leaves of a plant so they can receive sunlight.

Questions for Discussion

1. What is one of the main purposes of the stem that was brought out in this lesson?

2. What is the name of the process by which water moves up the stem of a plant to its leaves?

3. Place a mark on the celery stem at level to which the ink rose.

4. What do you think would have happened if we put the stems in warm water with ink instead of cold water?

STRUCTURE AND FUNCTION
OF PLANTS (Cont.)

ROOTS AND THEIR FUNCTION

The following lessons "How Does Water Affect Roots?" "How Do Roots Move?" "How Does Water Get into a Plant?" "What Do Plants Need in Order to Grow?" and "What Food Does a Plant Get from the Soil?" all have to do with the needs of the plant. It is desirable to start with the function of the roots in obtaining water for the plant. Show also that an excess of water may be harmful. Gradually build by successively using the lessons in the order found in this section. Emphasize that plants are living and have certain needs as do all organisms. Have the children discover what these needs are. Point out that minerals are important in producing strong healthy plants. This is also true for healthy human bodies. Point out how the structure of the small roots and root hairs, because of their large surface area, are particularly adapted to absorb water from the soil.

HOW DOES WATER AFFECT ROOTS?
[4 – 6]

Concepts

Roots seek water.
Roots grow downward.
Water is needed for seeds to grow.
Water can pass through very small holes in pots.

Procedure

STEP 1. Take an aquarium or a wooden box and place soil in it. Place two porous flower pots at either end of the container in the soil so that the tops of the pots are about a half inch above the soil. Stopper the drainage. Add water to one pot. Plant bean seeds about an inch and a half below the surface of the soil throughout the container. Cover and press the soil over the seeds with your hands.

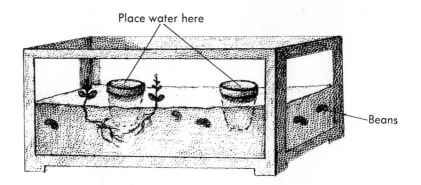

Ask: What do you think will happen to the seeds?

STEP 2. Have the class observe the growth of the seeds for several days.

Ask: Why did the seeds grow at one end of the container but not at the other end?

After the plants are about 12 inches high, take the flower pots out of the soil, being careful not to disturb the soil around the pots. Have the students look at the holes the pots left.

Ask: What do you notice that's different about the two holes?

Explanation: Around the hole of the pot which contained water you will find small roots.

Ask: Why do the roots grow in one pot hole and not in the other?

Explanation: The water passes through the pores of the pot into the soil around it. The dampness of the soil causes the seeds to sprout, and the roots are then attracted to the source of the water and grow toward the pot.

STEP 3. Have a student dig up the soil around the pots.

> *Ask:* How does the presence of roots change with the distance from the pots?
>
> Are there more roots closer to the wet pot?
>
> Is this evidence that roots are attracted to water?

STUDENT ACTIVITIES

1. Write what happened to the seeds in this experiment.

2. Why did they grow in one end of the container and not the other?

3. Where did the water come from that the seeds needed to grow?

4. From this demonstration, how do you know that roots grow toward water?

HOW DO ROOTS MOVE?
[1 – 6]

Concepts

Roots move around objects in the soil, such as rocks.
Seeds need water in order to sprout and grow.
Roots grow downwards.

Procedure

STEP 1. Obtain some bean seeds. Soak them in water for a day and then place on the bottom of a pan containing a wet paper towel. Cover the top of the pan with Saran Wrap. When the seeds have sprouted, place them on blotting paper, or on several layers of paper towels, between two pieces of glass. The two pieces of glass should have some applicator sticks or tongue depressors between them in order to give the seeds some room to grow. See Diagram 1. Place some obstacles in the way of the seeds, as indicated in the diagram.

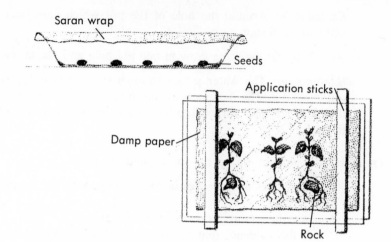

Ask: Why do you think I put the seeds in water for a few hours?

Why did I place them on the wet paper towel?

Why don't bean seeds that your mother has in her cupboard at home sprout?

Explanation: Seeds need water in order to sprout. Too much water, however, will kill them since they also must be able to get air.

STEP 2. *Ask:* What do you think will happen to the roots when they hit the obstacles in their way?

How do you think seeds can sprout and grow in rocky soil?

Have the class observe the seeds for several days.

Explanation: During the course of this experiment the roots will grow down and turn away from the obstacles in their paths. Sometimes the seeds become infected with a fungus growth. The fungi spores are either on the seeds themselves or are present in the air. If the seeds become contaminated, explain to the class that the fungus likes the same conditions necessary for the growth of the seeds. The fungus will infect the seed and kill it.

STUDENT ACTIVITIES

1. Have the class record on the board how the seeds sprout.

2. Have them make some drawings of the seeds and how they move around obstacles.

3. Summarize by asking orally the following.
   a. Which way do roots grow?
   b. What do seeds need in order to sprout?
   c. Why couldn't seeds grow on the top of rocks?

HOW DOES WATER GET INTO A PLANT?
[4 – 6]

Concepts

Roots absorb water through small root hairs.
When you transplant or pull a plant, you damage the root hairs.

Procedure

STEP 1. Obtain a package of radish seed. Place in the bottom of a pan or dish
a paper towel which has been folded several times. Soak this towel so
that it drips with water. Place on top of the towel several radish seeds.
Cover the dish or pan with Saran Wrap. See Diagram 1.

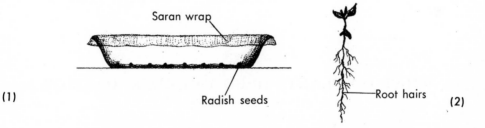

Saran wrap

(1)

Radish seeds

Root hairs

(2)

Ask: What do you think will happen to our radish seeds?
Why do you think I placed them on a wet paper towel?

Explanation: This was done to insure enough moisture for the seeds to
sprout. However, too much moisture could cause them to drown. This
is the reason that you don't place them in a bowl of water. Seeds need
oxygen in order to sprout, and they cannot get it easily if they are constantly flooded.

STEP 2. Have the class observe the seeds for several days.

Ask: What do you notice about the roots?
Do you notice any roots that are smaller, compared to other
roots?
Does anyone know what we call the smaller roots?
Does anyone know where the roots actually absorb water and
mineral from the soil?

Explanation: The smaller roots are called root hairs. It is through
these very small tender roots that the water and minerals are absorbed.
See Diagram 2.

Ask: Why do you think it isn't good for you to pull garden plants unless they are weeds?

Why do you think it is fairly difficult to transplant plants?

Explanation: Transplanting often does injury to the root hairs so that the plant may wilt and die.

STUDENT ACTIVITIES

1. Have the students make drawings of the radish root and label the root hairs.

2. They may also want to write small paragraphs about how their radish seeds sprouted and developed root hairs.

3. Review the demonstration by asking them to describe what they have found out about plants from watching the radish seed develop.

WHAT DO PLANTS NEED IN ORDER TO GROW?
[1 – 6]

Concepts

Plants need food in order to grow.
Plants need some water in order to grow.
Plants need light in order to grow.
Too much water may kill some plants.

Procedure

STEP 1. Soak several seeds (pea, bean, or lima) in water overnight. Collect six small milk cartons. Puncture a few holes in the bottom of four of the cartons so that excess water can drain out of the soil. Fill the cartons with topsoil and plant two or three seeds in each of the six cartons. Water all of the cartons so that the soil is damp but not soaking. Usually, watering every two or three days is ample. When the plants are a few inches high, separate the two cartons that do not have holes in the bottom. Keep these filled with water so that the soil is always soaking. Stop watering two other cartons. Place the last two cartons in a dark place where they get no light, but water them regularly. Have the students observe how their plants are growing each day.

BIOLOGY

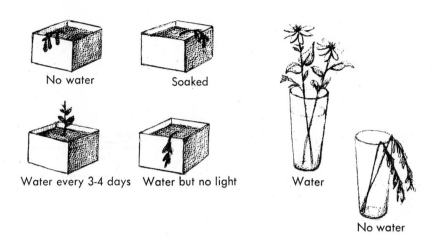

Ask: Why did the plants in the dark die?

What do you think plants usually need in order to live?

Why do you think the plants in the cartons which were soaked died?

Explanation: Generally plants need light in order to live (fungi and bacteria are exceptions). Most plants need well-drained soil in order to grow well. The plants in the soaking cartons died because the soil was always flooded. Roots need oxygen, and when they are covered with water they usually do not get an ample supply. Potted plants generally need good drainage in order to grow and live well.

STEP 2. Ask: Having watched this demonstration, what can we say about plants? (Point out to the class that there are water plants such as those you see in aquaria that can live very well in water.)

Pick some flowers and place some in water and others in a dry vase. Let them stand for several hours.

Ask: Why don't these two groups of flowers look the same?

Why did one group wilt?

What do flowers need in order to be healthy?

STUDENT ACTIVITIES

1. Have the class make drawings of what happened to their plants and label them. Write the labels on the board for the class: No Light, Too Much Water, Light and Water.

2. Have them make conclusions about the needs of plants.

WHAT FOOD DOES A PLANT GET FROM THE SOIL?
[4−6]

Concepts

Minerals are important for proper nutrition in both plants and animals.
If a plant or animal doesn't have the proper minerals, it will not grow as well.
Plants, like animals, can become sick if they do not eat properly.

Procedure

STEP 1. Plant six small cartons with beans, peas, or lettuce seed. Let them grow until they are several inches high. Cuttings of a coleus plant may substitute for seeds. Feed two plants with plant food as suggested on the package. Plant food can be obtained from the local dime store. Feed two other plants with three times as much plant food as suggested. Water the remaining plants, but do not give them fertilizer.

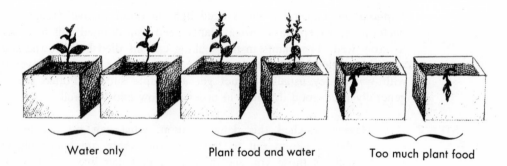

Water only   Plant food and water   Too much plant food

STEP 2. *Ask:* What plants do you think will grow the best? Why?

Explanation: The two plants which are fed plant food as suggested will probably grow the best. This food contains minerals which are vital to good growth of the plant. However, an excessive concentration of the mineral can be detrimental to the plant, just as the right amount of fertilizer on a crop is desirable, but too much mineral may cause a salty soil which will kill the plant. If you do not get harmful effects on the group of plants being fed an excessive amount of plant food, increase the dosage and the plants will soon appear sickly.

STUDENT ACTIVITIES

1. What effects do minerals have on plants?

2. True or False
_____ a. Minerals can influence plants in a bad manner.
_____ b. The same minerals are necessary for all plants.
_____ c. Minerals are important in plant growth.
_____ d. Some plants need only one mineral to live in their healthiest conditions.
_____ e. Plants grown with no minerals present will die.
_____ f. The control plants had no minerals present.
_____ g. Minerals are nutritional.
_____ h. Minerals are the only nutritive materials necessary for plants.

3. Can you outline an experiment whereby you would test to see if plants would grow well in the presence of sulfur?

4. You might want to look up in a book to determine what other minerals plants need in order to grow well and test them on various plants. If you have such an idea, ask your teacher if you may do this experiment or perform it at home and bring your results to class.

THE STRUCTURE AND FUNCTION OF PLANTS (Cont.)

STEMS AND THEIR FUNCTIONS

The lessons "Do Plants Know Which Way is Up?" "How Can Plants Live from Year to Year?" and "How Can You Tell the Age of a Tree?" have to do with the structure and function of stems. All these lessons can be included .in one unit on certain grade levels. The lessons show that there are wide variations found among stems. Children should be encouraged to collect various stems for observation. The way stems respond to light and gravity is embodied in the first lesson. Children discover that plants, like all forms of life, respond to stimuli.

DO PLANTS KNOW WHICH WAY IS UP?
[4 – 8]

Concepts

Light and gravity play a role in determining how a plant will grow.
Roots respond to gravity.
Stems are affected by light.

Procedure

STEP 1. Make several cuttings of geraniums and coleus or other plants that will root easily in water. Place several of the stems so that they are right side up and invert several others.

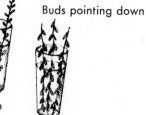

Buds pointing down

Buds pointing up

Ask: What do you think will happen to the plants placed in the water? Why do you think some of the plants are placed upside down in the water?

Explanation: Roots must be placed downward in order to grow.

STEP 2. Take any potted plant; a geranium or coleus will do. Place the plant on its side near the window.

Ask: What do you think will happen to the stem of the plant placed near the window?

Observe it for several days before making a conclusion.

STEP 3. Take several bean seeds and place them on a well-soaked paper towel in a dish or pan. Cover the pan with Saran Wrap or waxed paper, so that the water does not evaporate. When the seeds have sprouted and have roots an inch to two inches long, place them on another well-soaked paper towel between two pieces of glass. Tape the two pieces of glass together so that the water will not evaporate from the paper towel.

Tape

Seeds on soaked paper covered by glass

Caution: Be careful not to press too hard on the seedlings or you will crush them. Place the seedling so that the roots are up and the rest of the plant is down.

Ask: What do you think will happen to the roots? To the stem?

Explanation: This portion of the experiment may be repeated in the dark to show that light is not needed for the roots to change direction and grow downward.

Ask: Is light needed for the roots to grow downward?

Explanation: No. Gravity apparently causes the roots to change direction; however, light does have some influence on the stem.

Ask: Is light needed for the stem to grow upward?

STEP 4. Tell the class that the response of stems to light is called phototropism (photo — "light," and tropism — "to change or turn"). The response of roots to gravity is called geotropism (geo — "earth," tropism — "to turn").

STUDENT ACTIVITIES

Questions For Discussion

1. When you place plants in pots near windows, why do they grow toward the window?

2. If you had a potted plant near the window and wanted it to grow straight rather than lean toward the window, what would you do?

3. What does phototropism mean?

4. Explain what happened to the plant cuttings that were placed upside down.

5. Explain what happened to the seeds that were placed between the two pieces of glass.

6. Why do you think the plant cuttings which were turned upside down didn't root?

7. What is geotropism? Give an example.

8. Why is it important when you make cuttings that you place them in the water right side up?

9. Why is it important to be certain that you have seeds planted correctly?

10. If you wanted to sprout a sweet potato and you placed it partially submerged in water, but it produced no sprouts, what do you think you might have done wrong?

11. What will happen if roots are not placed in water right side up? Why?

Matching

Part A	Part B
1. Gravity	_____ turns because of light
2. Phototropism	_____ roots respond to this stimulus
3. Light	_____ turns towards earth
4. Geotropism	_____ stems respond to this stimulus

True or False

_____ 1. Light is necessary for roots to change direction.

_____ 2. Plant cuttings will grow when placed upside down in water.

_____ 3. When seeds are placed between two pieces of glass, the stems turn and grow up.

HOW CAN PLANTS LIVE FROM YEAR TO YEAR?
[3 – 6]

Concepts

Plants make food and store it.

In leafy trees the leaves and buds are formed this year for next year.

Food is stored in the fruit, roots, and stems of plants.

We eat leaves, roots, and stems of plants.

Plants have different kinds of structures.

Procedure

STEP 1. Place on the desk, some radishes, carrots, beets, potatoes, celery, spinach, cabbage, lettuce, and some fruit.

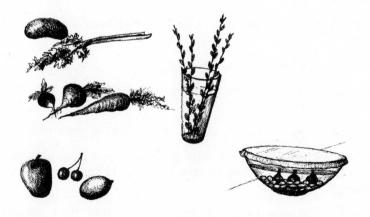

Ask: What are these?

Do they all have food in them?

How do you know they all have stored food in them?

Which of the things on the desk are roots? Stems and leaves?

Write on the board:

Examples

Stems: Celery   Sugar cane

Potato (remember roots come off a stem and the potato
has roots below it. Therefore it is a stem.)

Roots: Beets   Carrots

Turnips   Radishes

Leaves: Spinach   Lettuce

Cabbage   Greens

Fruit: Apples   Cherries

Plums   Oranges

STEP 2. Take some carrots, beets, or turnips and place them in soil in a pot or milk carton.

Ask: What do you think will happen when we plant these in soil and take care of them?

Do you think these roots will make leaves?

Do you think they have stored enough food to build or make new leaves?

Take some forsythia, willow, or other twigs from trees in the winter and place them in water in the classroom.

Ask: What do you think will happen to these twigs when spring comes?

Do you think they will bud?

Where do you think the new leaves will come from?

Show the students the buds.

STEP 3. Take some bulbs and place them in water as shown in the diagram. Cover the dish and bulbs with a plastic bag in order to prevent excessive evaporation.

Ask: What do you think will happen to the bulbs?

Do you think they will form leaves and flowers?

How do you think the plant is able to make leaves and flowers if it can't get any of the mineral it needs from being in the soil?

Explanation: The plant this year makes food and stores it in the roots or stems for next year. The buds that come out this year on the trees were actually formed last year.

Ask: What do you think will happen to a plant bulb if you cut off the leaves after it has bloomed?

Why must it have leaves?

What do the leaves make and send to the bulb so that it can sprout again next year?

Why do you think the bulbs will die if they are raised only in water?

From what we have seen with twigs, roots, and stems of plants, how do you think plants store food?

STUDENT ACTIVITIES

1. Where do plants store the food they make?

2. Draw the buds of the twigs you had in class before they started to bud.

3. Draw them after they started to bud.

4. Give some examples of plants that store their food in: leaves, stems, roots, fruits.

5. Draw what happens to a bulb when it starts to sprout.

6. Why shouldn't you cut the leaves off a lily plant after it has bloomed?

7. What do the leaves of a lily plant do for the plant?

8. What happened to your carrot roots after you planted them?

9. Why does a carrot have to have leaves?

10. When twigs leaf out, where do the leaves come from?

HOW CAN YOU TELL THE AGE OF A TREE?
[2 – 6]

Concepts

The age of a tree may be determined by counting the number of growth rings.

A tree grows from the outer edge of the wood to the inner bark.

The year that there is a lot of rain the tree will have a thicker growth ring.

Procedure

STEP 1. Obtain several cross sections of trees and tree limbs of different sizes. High school shop teachers will usually cut the cross sections for you if you don't have a saw available. Give every two students a section. Have the class examine the cross section.

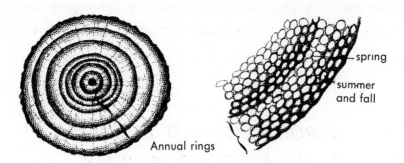

Annual rings

Ask: What do you notice about each section?
How are the sections alike?
What do you notice about the rings?
Why are some rings thick and others thin?
How old do you think your section is?

Explanation: Each year just below the bark, a new ring is added on to
the thickness of the tree. If the ring is thick, this indicates that the cells
which make up the ring had ample water, grew larger, and produced
more cells during the year. The thicker the ring, the more rain there
was during the growing season.

STEP 2. *Ask:* Why did you count the rings?
Do you think that there is a ring for each year?
What area of the rings is summer growth?
What area of the rings is spring growth?

Explanation: The inner part of each ring was produced in spring.

Ask: Do trees grow during winter?
Does each tree grow from the center or on the outside?
Can you think of an experiment we can do to show where the
growth is in trees?

STEP 3. Invite a forest ranger or other resource person to speak to the class on
how they use information gained from core sampling and other growth
ring studies.

STUDENT ACTIVITIES

1. How can you tell the age of a tree?

2. Why are some rings thick and others thin?

3. Where does growth take place in a tree?

4. Draw a diagram of your cross section and label the areas of spring and summer
growth.

5. How can you tell the climate of an area from the growth rings of one of its trees?

6. How can you tell the age of a living tree without cutting it down?

STRUCTURE AND FUNCTION
OF MICROORGANISMS

BACTERIA AND FUNGI

Most of the following lessons on bacteria and fungi can be included in one unit in the order given in this section. Develop the concepts that microorganisms are extremely small, divide and reproduce rapidly, and produce chemicals capable of changing foods or organic materials.

Microorganisms have certain needs as do all living things. By depriving them of conditions necessary for rapid cell division, man can prevent their destructive action on foods and, therefore, preserve foods longer. All microorganisms are not harmful. Emphasize the necessity of cleanliness to prevent harmful bacteria and fungal infections. Some are very beneficial such as those used in the cheese industry, certain antibiotics, and in decay. The bacteria which cause decay help to keep our beaches and forests clean by returning organic material to the soil.

HOW DOES BACTERIA CHANGE SOME FOOD?*
[4–6]

Concepts

Milk is a compound.
Milk may be soured by the action of bacteria.
Apple juice can be turned to vinegar by the action of bacteria.
Bacteria multiply slowly in a cold environment.

Procedure

STEP 1. Pour small amounts of milk and apple juice into two separate small glass containers. Place these near a window in a warm place.

Teacher's note: Do after "How Can We Preserve Food?"

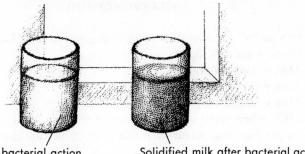

Milk before bacterial action   Solidified milk after bacterial action

Ask: What do you think will happen to our milk and apple juice if they are left in the room?

After a day or two have the students look at the milk and juice.

Ask: What has happened to the milk and juice?
What do you think the milk will taste like?
Why is it sour?

Have a student dip his finger in the milk and lick his finger. Have him report to the class the taste.

STEP 2. Test the milk with some blue litmus paper by placing it in the milk to see if it is acid or base. Define "acid" and "base."

Explanation: If blue litmus paper changes to red, the milk or juice is acidic. Bacteria change the milk sugars to acid.

Ask: Why do you think the milk soured?
What caused the milk to be changed?
How do you think we could have prevented the milk from souring so fast?

Explanation: Bacteria cause the sugars in milk and apple juice to be changed into acids (lactic acid in milk and acetic acid in apple juice). In the process, carbon dioxide is produced and leaves the solution in the form of small bubbles such as are seen when a pop bottle is opened. Refrigeration slows down the rate at which bacteria multiply.

STEP 3. *Ask:* Can you see the bacteria in the milk or juice?
How do you know they are there if you can't see them?
From this demonstration do we have direct or indirect evidence that there are bacteria?

Explanation: You have indirect evidence, because you did not actually see the bacteria.

Ask: Why do you think we cannot see bacteria?

Explanation: You can't see them without a microscope because they are so small.

STUDENT ACTIVITIES

1. Mark with an "x" the two statements that give the most important meanings the demonstration has developed.
   _____ a. Milk is a compound.
   _____ b. Milk will not sour.
   _____ c. Milk contains fat particles which float.
   _____ d. Milk, when acted upon with certain bacteria from the air, will sour.
   _____ e. Apple juice has sugar in it which bacteria can change to an acid called vinegar.

2. What happened to the milk after it remained in the room for a couple of days?

3. Would the fact that bubbles were constantly moving to the surface of the juice and milk indicate that there might be some chemical change occurring?

4. What would you do to prevent the milk from souring so quickly?

5. Mark the following statements "true" or "false."
   _____ a. Bacteria are always present in air.
   _____ b. Bacteria cause meat to spoil.
   _____ c. Bacteria do not multiply as rapidly in the refrigerator.
   _____ d. Cottage cheese is made from milk which has been soured by bacteria.
   _____ e. Vinegar is made from apple juice which has been changed by bacteria.
   _____ f. Bacteria can cause food to become rotten.

6. Why do you think your mother uses soap and water on your dishes and rinses them in very hot water?

HOW CAN WE PRESERVE FOOD?
[2 – 6]

Concepts

Spoiling of food is caused by bacteria and molds.
Food can be preserved by canning, salting, drying, refrigeration, and chemical means.

canning   salting   drying   refrigeration   chemicals

Ways to preserve food

Bacteria cannot live well in an acid solution.
Bacteria do not reproduce rapidly in a cold environment.
Bacteria will not multiply without moisture.
Sterilization and immediate sealing will prevent spoilage.

Procedure

STEP 1. *Ask:* What causes food to spoil?

What ways do you know to prevent food from spoiling?

Can you suggest any experiment to do in order to determine how best to preserve food?

Obtain a package of frozen peas. Partially fill six small jars with the defrosted peas. Allow the jars to remain unsealed for an hour so that bacteria from the air can contaminate all of the jars.

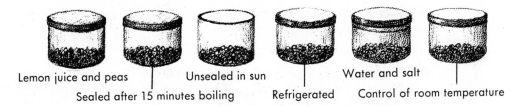

Lemon juice and peas | Unsealed in sun | Water and salt
Sealed after 15 minutes boiling | Refrigerated | Control of room temperature

Ask: Why do we leave the jars exposed in the room?

STEP 2. Number the jars 1 through 6. To jar No. 1, add some lemon juice, an acid. Seal the jar and allow it to remain at room temperature. Place jar No. 2 and its lid, not attached to the jar, in boiling water and allow to boil for 15–30 minutes. Then seal the jar and allow to remain at room temperature. Place jar No. 3 unsealed in sunlight or a warm place. Seal and place jar No. 4 in the refrigerator. Fill jar No. 5 with water which has dissolved in it a teaspoon of salt. Leave jar No. 6 covered at room temperature; this is the control.

STEP 3. Have the students check the jars each day and record their findings on the activity sheet. After two or three days:

Jar No. 1

Ask: Why was the acid added to the first jar?

Did the acid help to preserve the food?

Do you think bacteria and fungi can grow well in acid?

Jar No. 2

Ask: Why did we boil this jar and lid?

What does heat do to the bacteria and fungi?

Did we sterilize the jar and peas?

Why did we seal the jar soon after boiling it?

Explanation: The jar was sealed immediately to prevent bacteria in the air from contaminating the peas. Boiling kills germs.

Jar No. 3

Ask: Why was the jar placed in sunlight?

What has happened to the peas placed in this jar?

Have much mold or bacteria grown on these peas?

Why haven't the mold or bacteria grown well?

Explanation: Bacteria need water in order to reproduce well. These seeds dried out fairly quickly, so not many of the bacteria or molds had a chance to get started. This is the reason that dried fruit, peas, and beans can be stored for long periods.

Jar No. 4

Ask: What has happened to the seeds placed in the refrigerator?

Why haven't the mold or bacteria grown well in the refrigerator?

Explanation: Bacteria reproduce best generally when there is a fairly warm temperature.

Jar No. 5

Ask: What has happened to the seeds in this jar?

Does it look as if they are still fairly well preserved?

Can bacteria grow well in saturated salt water?

Explanation: Many bacteria cannot grow well in salt water, because the bacteria lose moisture from the cell to the salt water. They are starved for moisture although they are in salt water.

Jar No. 6

Ask: What has happened to the last jar?

What conditions have contributed to the growth of bacteria and mold in this jar?

Explanation: The bacteria have air, water, food (the peas), and plenty of moisture. The room is fairly warm. All of these conditions are necessary in order for bacteria to grow well. In food preservation usually one of the above-mentioned requirements is eliminated so that bacteria cannot reproduce rapidly.

STUDENT ACTIVITIES

1. Record below what you saw happen in each of the jars.

	First Day	*Second Day*
Jar No. 1		
Jar No. 2		
Jar No. 3		
Jar No. 4		
Jar No. 5		
Jar No. 6		

2. Which of the jars seemed to have the least growth of bacteria or fungi?

3. True or False
   _____ a. Sealing a jar will prevent the growth of bacteria.
   _____ b. Acid will not prevent the growth of bacteria.
   _____ c. Bacteria grow best in salt water.
   _____ d. Bacteria must have moisture in order to grow.
   _____ e. Dried fruit will not keep.
   _____ f. Boiling has no effect on bacteria.
   _____ g. One way to preserve fruit is to dry it.
   _____ h. All food is capable of becoming rotten owing to bacteria.
   _____ i. The sixth jar proved that the best way to preserve food is to leave it
             unopened at room temperature.

4. Name several ways to preserve food.

5. What kind of conditions do bacteria need in order to grow well?

6. To stop bacteria from entering a jar, the jar must be _____.

7. Circle the best of the following answers:
   a. Cooling will (increase, decrease) the growth of bacteria and fungi.
   b. Preservatives have (little, no) effect on foods.
   c. (More, Less) moisture will increase the possibility of spoilage.
   d. Preservation plays a (large, small) part in keeping food.

WHAT IS A FUNGUS?
[7–8]

Concepts

Fungi are important to nature because they are scavengers.
Some fungi are harmful.
Some types are quite useful to man.
Fungi have no chlorophyll.

Procedure

STEP 1. Show a mushroom growing in a piece of soil in its original state.
Students should observe that the mushroom is sandy-colored, is smooth
umbrella-topped, and has thin spokes or gill-like perforations on the
under side. Show a mushroom that has been removed from the soil
but still has attached a mass of cells, called a mycelium. There are
white rootlike strands which penetrate the soil.

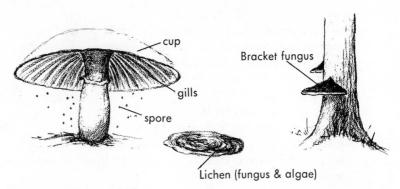

Ask: What is a fungus?
  What is a mold?

Explanation: A fungus is a plant. The fungus can produce a mold
or growth. Fungi is the plural of fungus. Fungi have no true roots,
but have a mycelium structure instead. The mycelium eats food, and at
certain points may produce upwards a case containing spores. Spores
are later dispersed in the air to start a new fungus plant.

Ask: About how many different kinds of fungi are there on our earth?
  Make a guess.

Reference books state there are about 80,000 to 100,000 species.

STEP 2. *Ask:* Why do we have fungi?
  Why not burn fungi or pull them up, as we do with weeds?

Explanation: Some fungi live on the *remains* of other plants and
animals. Others are harmful to other living plants and animals. Fungi
convert the remains of plants and animals into rich soil. Green plants
depend upon the products fungi return to the soil. Without these
products, green plants would have a difficult time surviving.

STEP 3. *Ask:* If fungi are plants, what appears to be different about them from
  ordinary plants?

Explanation: Most students will observe that the fungi are not green,
nor do they have the customary leaf structure or root structure of
most plants. Because fungi are not green, they cannot manufacture
their own food. They contain no chlorophyll, the chemical that most
plants need in order to make food in the process of photosynthesis.

Ask: A fern also grows from spores, but unlike a fungus makes its own
  food. How can you tell that a fern makes its own food?

Explanation: Because it is green in color, and therefore must have the
vital chemical, chlorophyll.

STEP 4. *Ask:* Do you think fungi are harmful or useful to man?

In what ways might they be harmful?

Aside from enriching the soil, in what ways might they be useful?

Show pieces of bread with mold, fruit with mold, grain with mold.

Ask: Does anyone in class have athlete's foot or have you seen a case of athlete's foot?

Are these examples of harmful molds?

Grow some molds in the classroom. Fungi will also attack wood, cloth, leather, glass, and other materials. Show some samples of penicillium, streptomycin, and aureomycin as examples of useful products made from molds.

Ask: Can one eat toadstools without fear of dying?

Can one eat mushrooms?

Explanation: Point out that it is very difficult to tell the difference between the edible mushroom and the poisonous toadstool. Therefore students should never eat wild mushrooms.

STEP 5. *Ask:* What are some other kinds of fungi?

What are they like?

What are they used for?

Show a sample of mold on a piece of rotten wood. This is an example of a saprophyte, the most common type of fungus. Another type of fungus is the parasites. They grow on live material. The saprophyte lives on dead material.

Ask: How does a parasite get its food?

Explanation: By living on or in another plant or animal. Some parasites live only on certain hosts — in other words, they are "specialized."

STEP 6. Show a rock with lichens growing on it. Get some algae from a pond or aquarium. Explain how lichens and algae could grow together on the rock.

Ask: Do you think algae and fungi could form a partnership?

Certain fungi do form partnerships. Lichens are plants consisting of an alga and a fungus growing together. The alga makes food for the fungus, and the fungus makes a mat or "bed" on which the alga lives. Show a piece of Roquefort or blue cheese. Explain how the mold produces enzymes that affect the cheese and produce a particular flavor.

STUDENT ACTIVITIES

The items which follow will help you to find out whether you have learned the main ideas about fungi. Read the directions carefully and then complete each part of the exercise.

Multiple Choice

_____ 1. Fungi contain no (a) energy; (b) spores; (c) scavengers; (d) chlorophyll.

_____ 2. The most common type of fungus is the (a) enzyme; (b) parasite; (c) saprophyte; (d) aureomycin.

_____ 3. Which one of the following can a person eat without fear of being poisoned? (a) certain kinds of wild mushrooms; (b) umbrella-shaped toadstools; (c) spotted toadstools; (d) chrysogenum; (e) mushrooms.

_____ 4. Athlete's foot is a type of (a) scar tissue; (b) scabies; (c) fungus; (d) lichens.

Questions For Discussion

1. Explain the difference between a mold and a fungus.

2. Make a diagram of a mycelium.

3. What does the mycelium do for the fungus plant?

4. How can you usually tell whether a plant makes its own food or not?

5. Explain why fungi are not green in color.

6. Give three beneficial uses for fungi.

7. When can you enjoy eating a mold?

8. How is food canned so that it will not become moldy?

True or False

_____ 1. Fungi are not plants.

_____ 2. All fungi are useful, but molds are not.

_____ 3. Penicillium and streptomycin are examples of drugs made from molds.

_____ 4. One can tell by the color if a fungus is useful or not.

_____ 5. Mycelium is one of the new wonder drugs.

_____ 6. Some species of fungi are parasites.

_____ 7. When you eat "blue" cheese, you are eating some mold in the cheese.

_____ 8. A fern grows from spores, yet it makes its own food.

_____ 9. A fern is a fungus.

HOW DOES A FUNGUS GROW?
[4 – 6]

Concepts

Fungi are plants.
Fungi are sometimes parasites.
Fungi reproduce by spores.
Mildew is one type of fungus.
Mold is another type of fungus.
Fungi need warmth, moisture, and usually darkness in order to grow well.

Procedure I. Orange Peel

STEP 1. Peel an orange and wet the peeling. Place the peeling in a plastic bag
in the dark.

Orange mold

Ask: What do you think is going to happen to the peeling?
Do you think it will become moldy?

After several days take the bag out of the dark.

Ask: What is that green material on the peeling?
Does anyone know what kind of mold this is?

Explanation: This will probably be one of the green penicillium molds
which grows well on orange peelings.

Procedure II. Bread Mold

STEP 1. Obtain four pieces of bread. Wet one piece and place in a sealed
plastic bag in the dark. Wet another and place in a sealed plastic bag
where it will receive a considerable amount of light. Wet another and
place in a dish where it will dry out. Place a fourth piece on a dry
plate. Have the students record on their activity pages each day what
happens over a four day period.

Bread mold — Sporangium with spores — Stolon rhizoid

Ask: What happened to each of the pieces of bread?

Why did the dampened bread change?

What is on the bread?

Do you think it is growing?

How could we prove that the mold is growing?

Explanation: Leave the bread in the bag for another day and see if the mold becomes larger. If it does become larger, it is logical to conclude that it is growing. The idea of measuring accurately the size of the colonies might also be introduced.

Ask: Why didn't the bread placed in the sunlight become very moldy?

Do you think mold grows better in the dark or in the light?

Why didn't the mold grow well on the dry plate?

Can you draw any conclusions about mold and its needs for water?

Procedure III. Mildew

STEP 1. Give each student a small plastic bag (the plastic bags you get from the cleaner or laundry will do). Cut into small pieces various types of cloth, such as wool, cotton, and rayon. Give each student some of these pieces of cloth. Have all but two students dampen the cloth and place it in their plastic bag. Tie the bags closed with string. Have two students prepare the bags in the same manner, except that they are not to dampen the cloth. Have two or three students place their bags containing dampened cloth in sunlight. Place one bag containing cloth which has not been dampened in sunlight. Have the rest of the class place their bags in the dark.

Mildew

STEP 2. *Ask:* What do you think will happen to the cloth?

Which one do you think will change the most?

Have the class look at their bags each day. After several days:

Ask: What has happened to the cloth?

What are those black spots on the cloth?

Which bags had the spots appear first?

Do you think something is growing on the cloth?

How can we tell whether or not something is growing on the cloth?

Explanation: Allow the bags to remain in the room and have the students compare the size and number of spots that increase.

Ask: Does anyone know what we call this type of fungus?

From the experiments we did in class, can you make any conclusions about what mildew needs in order to grow well?

Why is it smart to hang your clothes up to dry when they are wet?

STEP 3. Have the class open their bags and smell them.

Ask: What does the bag smell like?

What produced this odor?

Take some of the cloth out of the bag and test its strength by tearing it. Compare how easily it tears with cloth which was not infected with mildew.

Ask: What does mildew do to clothing?

Explanation: The mildew is a fungus whose cells produce substances that actually change the chemicals which make the fiber of the cloth and weaken the cloth. Have the students look at the orange mold, bread mold, and mildew under a tripod lens or a microscope and draw what they see in space provided on the student activity sheet.

STUDENT ACTIVITIES

1. Record below what happened to the orange peeling.
   First Day   *Second Day*   *Third Day*   *Fourth Day*

2. Draw the orange peeling fungus.

3. What is the name of this particular kind of fungus?

4. Record what happened to the bread.
   a. Wet bread in dish.
   b. Bread kept in light and damp.
   c. Dry bread.
   d. Dampened bread in dark place.

5. Draw what each of the different fungi looked like under a tripod lens or a microscope.
   a. Orange peeling.
   b. Bread mold.
   c. Mildew.

6. Which of the bread molds grew the best?

7. How do you know that fungi are plants which grow?

8. Do fungi have any chlorophyll? (Are they green?)

9. Fungi are sometimes called parasites. Why are they called this?

10. What is mildew?

11. What harm can mildew, bread mold, or penicillium do?

12. Mark with an "x" those conditions fungi need in order to grow well.

_____ a. Lots of light.

_____ b. Very little light.

_____ c. Cold environment.

_____ d. Warm environment.

_____ e. No moisture.

_____ f. Lots of moisture.

_____ g. No air.

_____ h. Some air.

13. Why might it be desirable to keep oranges in the refrigerator?

14. Why isn't it smart to dampen clothes for ironing and roll them up in a bundle for several days?

15. Why might it be a good idea to keep bread in the refrigerator?

HOW DOES YEAST CHANGE SOME FOODS?
[7–8]

Concepts

Yeast is a fungus which causes fermentation.

A fungus is a plant which lacks chlorophyll and is dependent on other organisms for food.

Fermentation is chemical decomposition of starches or sugars by living organisms or by chemical agents to a simpler compound. *Example:* the souring of milk or the making of alcohol.

Yeast changes sugar to alcohol by fermentation. Carbon dioxide (CO_2) is given off in this chemical reaction.

An indicator, such as limewater, is a chemical that changes its appearance when carbon dioxide is present.

Procedure

STEP 1. Mix flour with water and place in a jar; sprinkle some yeast on top of the paste. Place some limewater in a graduate. Put a rubber stopper in the jar and a glass tube from the jar to the graduate (see illustration).

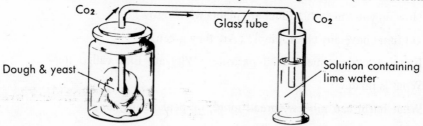

Ask: What is happening? Can you give a reason for this?

Explanation: CO_2 is given off by the yeast as a metabolic end product. All plants give off CO_2 as a waste product. The yeast plant uses the dough for its nutrition. Limewater, an indicator for CO_2, will turn milky in the presence of carbon dioxide.

Ask: What would happen if we added some sugar to the dough?

STEP 2. Add some sugar to the dough.

Explanation: When sugar is added, the action will be speeded up, because yeast lives on glucose and sugar contains glucose (see illustration of carbohydrate).

STEP 3. Prepare a similar jar, but mix the dough with the yeast. Place a glass rod in the stopper. When the dough rises, puncture it with the rod.

Ask: What happens when the dough is punctured?

Explanation: The carbon dioxide is trapped in the dough and is released by the punctures of the rod.

Ask: What are the practical ways we use yeast to work for us?

Explanation: Bread and baking.

STUDENT ACTIVITIES

Questions For Discussion

1. What is a fungus? Is it a plant or an animal? How do you know whether it is a plant or an animal?

2. Name a fungus that could be found in your home.

3. What is fermentation? Name some examples.

4. What does yeast produce in this experiment? Give the chemical symbol for it.

5. What did that substance do to the indicator? Give an example of an indicator. What is an indicator used for?

6. Name a waste product given off by plants.

7. What color did the limewater turn in the presence of carbon dioxide?

8. What does sugar contain? What did it do to the dough?

9. Why did the dough rise? Why was the dough punctured? Why was carbon dioxide released?

10. How did the second experiment differ from the first?

11. What color was the limewater before the dough was punctured? Why didn't the limewater change color before the dough was punctured?

12. What color did the limewater turn?

13. From this experiment, is there any indication that starch is more complex than glucose?

True or False

_____ 1. A fungus is a plant that lacks chlorophyll.

_____ 2. CO_2 is a gas.

_____ 3. Yeast is a fungus.

_____ 4. Starch is more complex than glucose.

_____ 5. When dough is punctured, CO_2 is given off.

_____ 6. Limewater is an indicator for CO_2.

STRUCTURE AND FUNCTION
OF PLANT LEAVES

PHOTOSYNTHESIS

The next three lessons "Do Leaves Breathe?" "When Do Plants First Get Green?" and "Do Plants Affect the Atmosphere?" can be used in one unit. They build concepts involving leaf structure and their function as a producer of food. These lessons strive to develop an understanding of photosynthesis — the process by which a plant makes food. Comprehending this process enables a child to see why plants must have water, air, and sunlight. Children then begin to see how the environment influences growth and why plants may not grow well in a house because of poor light. The lesson "What is Variation?" should be included in a unit on leaves to show diversity of life forms.

DO LEAVES BREATHE?
[2 – 6]

Concepts

Leaves have air in them.
Gas will expand when heated.

Because gases are lighter than water, they will go up through the water and escape.

Leaves have little openings (called stomates) through which air enters or leaves the leaf.

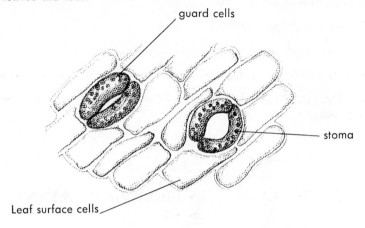

Procedure

STEP 1. *Ask:* Do you think leaves can breathe?

Do you think leaves might have air in them as you have air in you?

What happens in water when your head is under water and you let some air out of your mouth? What do you see?

What do you think will happen if we place some leaves under water?

Place some leaves under the surface of some cold water and determine whether or not they give off any bubbles. Have the class watch carefully for the presence of bubbles. You might have to squeeze the two sides of the leaf together in a fold in order to force the air out.

STEP 2. Repeat the above procedure, using warm water.

Ask: Did you notice more air escape from the leaves in cold water or warm water?

Explanation: The reason more air usually escapes from leaves in warm water is that the air in them expands more than it does in cold water. Peel off the outer layer of the under side of a leaf. Place this on a slide. Put a few drops of iodine solution on it and look at it through a microscope. You should be able to see the stomates. Show the students either a picture or a chart of the structure of the surface of a leaf, or make a diagram similar to the one above. Point to the stomates on the chart.

STUDENT ACTIVITIES

1. Do leaves breathe?

2. How do you know leaves breathe?

3. How does air get into the leaf?

4. Draw what the surface of a leaf might look like.

5. Why does the gas in the leaf go up in the water after it escapes from the leaf?

6. In which demonstration did you see more gas given off, the cold water or the hot water? Why?

WHEN DO PLANTS FIRST GET GREEN?
[K – 6]

Concepts

Light is necessary in order for chlorophyll to form.

A seed can produce chlorophyll in less light than is necessary for photosynthesis.

Photosynthesis is the process by which leaves in the presence of light make food.

Procedure

STEP 1. Take several seeds and sprout them in the dark. Plant several seeds, grains, or beans in milk cartons filled with soil. Water and care for these plants in a place where there is total darkness. After the plants have sprouted and grown for a few days, take some of them out of the dark environment and place them in a sunny area of the room. Let the rest of the plants remain in the dark.

Beans raised in the light   Beans raised in the dark

Ask: What color are the plants taken out of the dark?

How do the plants kept in the dark differ in appearance compared to those in the light?

What do you think will happen to the plants kept in the dark after they have been in the sunlight a few days?

Is there any difference between the growth of the plants grown in the dark and those grown in the light?

STEP 2. Continue to care for the plants for several days until those in the dark environment die.

Ask: Why do you think the plants in the dark died when the plants in the sunlight lived?

What color are the dead plants?

What color are the plants that grew in the sunlight?

What color is chlorophyll?

Did the plants in the dark make any chlorophyll?

How do you know they didn't make any chlorophyll?

Explanation: Light is necessary for the production of chlorophyll.

Ask: Do you think light is needed for chlorophyll formation?

Why did the plants in the dark environment eventually die while the plants in the sunlight lived?

How was it possible for the plants to grow and live for a while in the dark since they didn't have any chlorophyll?

Explanation: They received their necessary energy from the stored food in the seed.

STUDENT ACTIVITIES

1. Is light needed in order for chlorophyll to form?

2. How do you know a plant needs light?

3. Why did the plants live for several days in the dark?

4. In this experiment, why did we put some plants in the light and leave some in the dark?

5. From this experiment, how do you know that a seed has stored food in it?

6. How do you know that there was no chlorophyll formed by the plant in the dark?

7. What color is chlorophyll?

8. Some plants have red or purple leaves, but grow. Do you think that they must also have chlorophyll in their leaves but that you can't see it because the red or purple pigments are more intense?

9. If there is no chlorophyll, can a plant make food?

10. The scientist has a special word for the process by which plants make food. The word is called photosynthesis. It really is made up of two parts, "photo" and "synthesis." What does "photo" mean? What does "synthesis" mean? What does "photosynthesis" mean?

DO PLANTS AFFECT THE ATMOSPHERE?
[4–6]

Concepts

Light is necessary for photosynthesis.
Plants take in carbon dioxide and give off oxygen through the process of photosynthesis.
A candle will not burn when oxygen is not present.

Procedure

STEP 1. Attach a candle, by melting the wax, to the bottom of a pan. Place an inch of water in the pan. Light the candle and turn a glass jar over it. Place a sprig of mint to one side away from the flame, as shown in the picture.

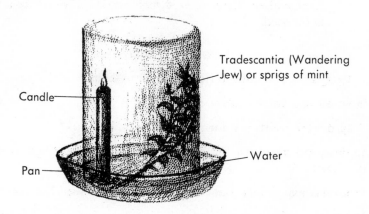

Candle

Tradescantia (Wandering Jew) or sprigs of mint

Water

Pan

Ask: What will happen to the flame? Why?
Why do you think we have placed the plant in the jar?

STEP 2. Add another inch of water to the pan. The stems of the mint sprigs must be in water and their leaves above the level of the water. Place this equipment in good light, but not in direct sunlight, for several days.

STEP 3. Set up a similar apparatus as before, and place it in a closet or dark place for an equal amount of time.

Ask: What do you think will happen? Why?
Why are we placing this apparatus in the dark?

STEP 4. After 10 days test the air in each jar. First, move the jar sideways enough to loosen the candle. Cover the mouth of the glass jar with a piece of glass while the jar is under water. Turn the glass and its contents right side up. Test the contents of both jars with a burning wooden splinter. Record results.

Ask: What was in the jar in the closet?
What was in the jar in the light?

STEP 5. Take two jars and fill them about half full with soil. Plant two or three bean seeds in the soil. Water the soil so that it is damp but not soaking.

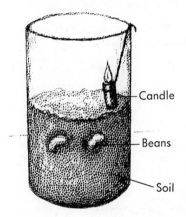

STEP 6. Hang a small candle down inside one of the jars, as shown in the diagram. Light the candle and let it burn until it goes out. Immediately take the candle out and cover both of the tops of the two bottles with waxed paper or Saran Wrap. Secure the tops with a rubber band or a piece of string.

Ask: Why do you think the candle went out in the bottle?
When the candle burned, what kind of gas did it need in order to burn and what kind of gas did it give off?

Explanation: The candle uses oxygen when it burns, and it produces carbon dioxide gas.

Ask: If the bottle has a lot of carbon dioxide in it and little oxygen, how do you think this will affect the growth of the seeds in it?
In which of the two bottles do you think the seeds will grow the best and why?

STUDENT ACTIVITIES

1. Was there any significant difference between the growth of the seeds in the jar with carbon dioxide and the one without carbon dioxide?

2. From these demonstrations, does it seem likely that:
   a. Plants can grow in air that is deficient in oxygen?
   b. Plants can grow in air with more than average carbon dioxide?
   c. Oxygen is not very necessary for plant growth?
   d. CO_2 is necessary for plant growth?

3. List the things you can conclude from the demonstrations done in class.

4. What assumptions are necessary for this activity?

5. Was this activity an experiment or a demonstration? How do you know?

6. Why was the mint sprig placed in the jars?

7. What are your conclusions from this activity?

8. What do you think would happen if we did not place any mint sprigs in the jar with the candle? How could you prove your assumption?

9. Can you think of any reasons why it is necessary to have green plants in the world?

WHAT IS VARIATION?
[1 – 6]

Concepts

There is tremendous variation in nature.
The structure of a plant is related to its
functions (e.g., thorns of a rose to
protect it).

Procedure

STEP 1. Collect several different types of leaves and twigs. The leaves may be pressed and preserved. Pin these on the bulletin boards.

Ask: What do you notice about the shapes of the leaves?
   Are they the same shape?
   Do you think that there are many more different kinds of leaves
      in nature than the ones we have here?

Show the class several different twigs from trees, rose bushes, etc.

Ask: What do you notice about the differences in the twigs?
   How does a rose twig protect itself against its enemies?

Explanation: Nature has many different types of life. Show the class a
shell collection.

Ask: What do you notice about the shells?
   Are there many different types of shells?
   Can you name other plants or animals which have several differ-
      ent types or varieties?
   Do all roses look the same?
   How about dogs, cats, horses, peaches?
   Are there variations in humans?
   Do you all look alike?

Bring in several different varieties of roses or other flowers and tell the
class that each one is a variety.

STUDENT ACTIVITIES

1. Draw or trace the shapes of different leaves.

2. Draw or trace the shapes of different shells.

3. Draw how a rose is constructed to protect itself.

4. What does "variation" mean?

REPRODUCTION AND
DEVELOPMENT OF PLANTS

The following lessons are designed to build concepts involved with reproduction, development, growth, and inheritance. The first two lessons "How Can We
Get Two Plants from One?" and "What is the Purpose of a Flower?" should be
used together to develop an understanding of how plants are reproduced.

   "Why Do We Have Plant and Animal Breeding?" and "Why Do We Have
Cross-Breeding?" should be included together in a unit. The purpose of these

lessons is to build an understanding of heredity and show that characteristics are transmitted from one generation to the next. The second lesson illustrates how the understanding of reproduction and inheritance can be used to produce better crops. Together these lessons illustrate how knowing scientific concepts helps an individual to operate more effectively in his environment. A farmer who understands heredity, for example, will certainly have an advantage over one who has no understanding of this study when selecting seeds to plant for the next year.

HOW CAN WE GET TWO PLANTS FROM ONE?
[1 – 6]

Concepts

Some plants can be grown by slipping them or growing them from stems.

Procedure

STEP 1. *Ask:* How can we make two plants from one plant without using seeds?

Cut stems off any or all of the following: coleus, geranium, begonia philodendron, wandering jew (tradescantia), or ivy. Take off some of the leaves from the lower part of the stems.

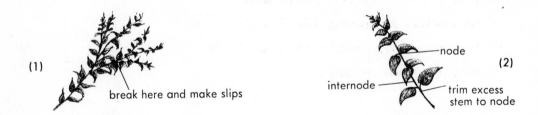

(1) break here and make slips

(2) node — internode — trim excess stem to node

Explanation: When one is making slips, it is always good to reduce the number of leaves. This is done because the plant at the first stage of slipping has no roots and cannot supply water as easily to the leaves. It is important, then, to balance the leaf surface with the amount of water the plant can easily supply. Don't cut off all the leaves, because the leaves make food necessary for cellular development and formation of roots. Explain to the class why it is important to take off some of the leaves of the plant. Cut off excess stem just below the first node. The nodes are the part of the stem where leaves or other stems are located. See Diagram 2. The young roots will develop from the node, not the internode.

STEP 2. Place these stems either in water or soil. If they are placed in soil, water them liberally, but do not keep the soil soaking wet.

Ask: What do you think will happen to our stems?

Hand each student a milk carton with some soil in it and have them make a small slip and care for the plant.

STUDENT ACTIVITIES

1. Record when you first saw roots appear on your plants grown in water.

2. Measure how much the plant grows each week. Does it grow faster or slower after the roots have developed?

3. If some of the plants die, discuss the possible reasons for this.

WHAT IS THE PURPOSE OF A FLOWER?
[4–8]

Concepts

The chief parts of most plants are the stem, leaves, flowers, and roots.
All plants that make seeds have either flowers or cones.
The flower contains the reproductive parts of the plant.
The flower is the seed-making structure of the plant.
Animals can help pollinate plants.
Pollination is the process of pollen falling on the pistil. Fertilization occurs when part of the pollen enters the ovule.

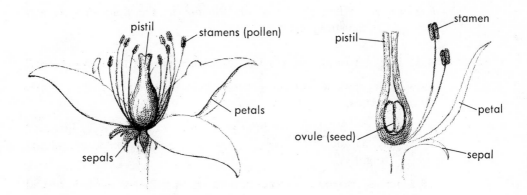

Procedure

STEP 1. Take some flowers or male cones. (The small male cones should be collected in the spring, when they are full of pollen.) Shake them so that the pollen falls on a piece of white paper.

Ask: What is this material that you see?
Where does the pollen come from?
Why does a plant produce flowers?
What part does the pollen play in the flower?

STEP 2. Place some pollen on a slide and have the students look at it through a microscope or a magnifying lens. (Prepared slides of pollen may also be purchased from a biological supply house.)

STEP 3. Give each student a flower. Have them separate as many different parts of the flower that they can find. After they have placed their parts in different piles:

Ask: How many parts of the flower did you find?
Can you name the parts of the flower?
From what part of the flower did the pollen come?

Put Diagram 1 on the board, but do not label it.

Ask: Can you label any of the parts?

Aid them in labeling those parts they do not know.

Explanation: A flower usually has many stamens. It may have one or several pistils. It is on the male part of the flower, the stamens, that you find the powdery pollen. Bees collect pollen on their legs as they visit flowers.

Ask: Look at your flower. Can you find the pistil?
Feel it. How does it feel? That's right — it's sticky.

Explanation: When the bee visits the flower, the pollen on its legs rubs off on the sticky pistil.

STEP 4. *Ask:* Does anyone know what purpose each part of the flower serves?

Show them some wheat or oats or other grains; then some brightly colored flowers.

Ask: Why do you think the grain plants are not colored very brightly?
Why do you think roses, carnations, and geraniums are colored brightly?

Explanation: Brightly colored flowers are pollinated by insects and birds. Flowers, such as grains, which are not brightly colored are pollinated usually by the wind.

Ask: Does anyone know what "pollination" means?

Explain that the pollen is the male part of the flower. The process of pollen from the stamen falling on the pistil is called pollination.

STEP 5. Draw Diagram 2 on the board.

Explanation: At the bottom of the pistil, some tiny things called *ovules* are located. When a pollen grain and an ovule join together, a seed is formed. Every seed that is made contains a baby plant with a food supply to nourish it until it is able to make its own food when it is planted in the ground. Have the students take a one-edged razor blade and see if they can cut the pistil as it was shown in the diagram.

STEP 6. *Ask:* Did anyone find the tiny ovules?
Look for them again and see if you can find them.
What do you think the ovules are?

Explanation: These will become seeds when part of the pollen joins each of them, causing fertilization. Explain that fertilization is the process of the male pollen joining with the female ovule to form a seed.

Ask: What will happen to the petals and stamens after the ovules have been fertilized?
Where will the seeds grow?

Explanation: Petals and sepals usually drop off after fertilization, and the seeds develop inside the lower part of the pistil.

Ask: What do you think the purpose of the sepals is?

Explanation: The sepals help to protect the flower before it opens. Have some students collect and press different types of flowers, labeling their various parts.

STEP 7. Raise some flowers, such as poppies, in the classroom. When they flower, immediately pull out of the plants the stamens, ovules, and upper part of the pistil. Leave some other flowers intact. After several days, have the students compare the ovules in the unfertilized flowers with those that were fertilized.

Ask: Why is there a difference between the two types of ovules?

STEP 8. Many insects help us make seeds. There are flies, beetles, wasps, mosquitos, butterflies, and other insects that visit flowers and help to carry pollen to make seeds. The wind also carries pollen.

STUDENT ACTIVITIES

Questions For Discussion

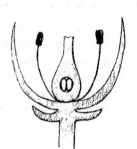

1. Give the names of the parts of the flower in the diagram.

2. What is the bee going to do?

3. Why are insects important to a plant?

4. What is inside the flower?

5. What does pollen look like?

6. Why is pollen important to plants?

7. Name three insects which help plants.

8. In what part of the flower do the seeds grow?

9. Of what use is a stamen to a plant?

10. How are seeds formed?

True or False

_____ 1. A pistil contains pollen.

_____ 2. A bee collects pollen on its wings.

_____ 3. The pistil is sticky.

_____ 4. The tiny particles in a pistil are called seeds.

_____ 5. Pollen is a fine yellow powder.

_____ 6. A flower does not need pollen.

_____ 7. The purpose of a flower is to help in the production of seeds.

_____ 8. A flower has only one stamen.

_____ 9. A seed contains a baby plant.

_____ 10. Fertilization occurs when part of a pollen grain and an ovule join.

_____ 11. An unfertilized ovule will produce healthy seeds.

_____ 12. Pollination is the process of the transfer of pollen from a stamen to a pistil.

_____ 13. The sepals protect the flower before it opens.

_____ 14. Pollen is made in the pistil.

WHY DO WE HAVE PLANT AND ANIMAL BREEDING?
[7 – 8]

Concepts

The offspring produced by plants or animals tend to inherit characteristics
    from their parents.
Some characteristics may be good, and some may be undesirable.

Procedure

STEP 1. Obtain one large and one small potato. Hold these up before the class.

Ask: Did you know that, if you plant a potato in the ground or any
        part of a potato containing an eye, it will grow and produce
        a potato plant?
    Which of these two potatoes or parts of them should I plant if
        I want to produce big potatoes?

Explanation: The larger potato would probably be more desirable,
since it would be more likely to produce large potatoes. Size is an in-
heritable trait. This assumes, however, that both of the above potatoes
were grown in the same environment.

Ask: Can I be sure that if I plant the large potato I will get large
        potatoes?
    Why not?

(See explanation above.)

STEP 2. Have two students of varying heights stand up.

Ask: Does anyone know why one of these two is taller than the other?

Explanation: Tallness may also be an inherited trait. Remind the class
that students have not yet matured and that the observed differences
may be caused by nutrition or age. Discuss influences of heredity and
environment.

Ask: Does anyone know what "heredity" or "to inherit" means?

Write the words "inheritance" and "heredity" on the blackboard.
Have a student look up the meaning of the words.
Write a definition of the words on the board.

Definition of "heredity": the transmission from parent to offspring of certain characteristics; tendency of offspring to resemble parents or ancestors.

Ask: Can anyone explain what the definition states in his own words?

If they are unable to explain it in their own words, explain that transmission means to send from one to another and that they are offspring. They are the offspring of their mothers and fathers. "Characteristic" means that there is something in them that is like their mothers, fathers or ancestors. The ancestors may be their grandparents or distant relatives.

Ask: Can anyone tell me the definition of "heredity" in his own words?
From whom do we inherit our characteristics?
From whom do our parents get heredity?

STEP 3. *Ask:* If you had to select a calf to keep for breeding to produce beef, what type of calf would you select?
If you wanted to grow flowers which had large blooms, what type of flower would you select to get seed?
Can you think of some things that you have inherited from your parents?

Have the two students who stood up before stand again.

Ask: Can anyone state some things which these students have inherited?

STUDENT ACTIVITIES

1. What determines our height?

2. From whom do we inherit our characteristics?

3. What is an offspring?

4. Give some reasons to explain why one of the students who stood in class was taller.

5. Do plants inherit as people do?

6. Why would you choose a large potato for seed?

7. If you wanted a calf to raise for a milk cow, what type of calf would you select?

8. If you were going to plant strawberry plants, from what type of parent plant would you select them?

9. Why is some knowledge of heredity important to farmers?

10. List some characteristics you have inherited from your parents.

11. What does "heredity" mean?

WHY DO WE HAVE CROSSBREEDING?
[7 – 8]

Concepts

Living things come only from living things.

We have plant and animal breeding to increase the production, to increase the quality of the product, and to increase resistance to certain diseases.

Plants and animals inherit certain traits.

Crossbreeding is the process of breeding or crossing two different pure lines.

Procedure

STEP 1. Obtain four sugar beets or potatoes, one very long and thin, the second of good shape, the third very soft and squishy (this could be made soft by alternating freezing and thawing rapidly two or three times), the fourth of good shape — not extremely long, but large, full, and firm. You may include other traits or select similar traits, using corn.*

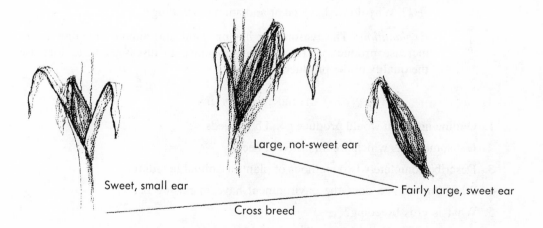

Large, not-sweet ear

Sweet, small ear

Fairly large, sweet ear

Cross breed

STEP 2. Tell students (and have cards with the information by each beet) that number one, although the shape is not desirable, grows best in this

---

*In potatoes the traits to consider would be size, shape, type of skin, whether it is resistant to scale disease, etc.

area. Point out that different soils, weather, and other environmental influences may affect growth of plants. Number two has good shape, but the sugar content (or starch in the potato) is very low. The third beet (the soft one) has the highest sugar content but is not compatible to these soil conditions. Do not show the fourth beet until later.

Ask: Where did these traits come from?

Draw out that these are natural characteristics of these beets (their genetic make-up), or that these traits are all inherited.

Ask: Would it be desirable to combine all of these good traits in one beet (show the fourth or ideal beet) and eliminate the defective traits?
How could we develop a good line of beets?
Would it be important to the farmer, the producer, and the consumer to have a good strain of beets? In what ways?

Explain the importance of breeding: breeding the disease-resistant strain with a beet or potato having some other desirable trait and then selecting those offspring that have the desirable characteristics for seed.

STEP 3. *Ask:* Does anyone know what crossbreeding is?

Explanation: Crossbreeding means to select some desirable trait from one plant and to breed it with another plant having a different desirable trait. For example, one corn plant has sweet but short ears. Another plant has long ears but not so sweet. Breed these together and you will get some long ears with sweet corn. You might have the students find and draw on the board a diagram of how hybrid corn seed are produced.

Ask: Why do we have plant and animal breeding?

Explanation: The reasons for having plant and animal breeding are to increase production, to increase resistance to disease, and to increase the quality of the product.

STUDENT ACTIVITIES

1. Outline how you would produce good beet seeds.
2. List some traits which are inherited in beets.
3. Describe completely two methods of plant or animal breeding.
4. What importance does the environment have in raising beets?
5. What is crossbreeding?
6. Explain how you would crossbreed corn.
7. Why do we have animal and plant breeding?
8. If you had excellent corn seed and you planted it but failed to water it, what would happen and why?

REPRODUCTION AND
DEVELOPMENT OF ANIMALS

The lessons "How Do a Cocoon and a Polliwog Change?" and "How Do Some Insects Develop from Egg to Adult?" involve reproduction and development of animals. The children in the process of seeing polliwogs and insects grow begin to understand some concepts involved in growth and development. The unfolding of the various stages in the development of the animal in these two sections presents fascinating lessons for children.

Procedure II of the lesson "How Does Your Body Grow?" covers the incubation of chicken eggs. These are cracked open at successive stages of development. This lesson can be integrated with the two preceding lessons in order to build a better understanding of the process of animal development. The teacher should point out that most higher forms of life start out as a small egg and through a process of development become mature forms of their species. The lesson "Why Do We Look Like Our Parents?" shows that animals also pass on traits to off-spring through heredity. Teachers should refer to children's books to compare plant and animal heredity and development.

HOW DO SOME INSECTS DEVELOP FROM EGG TO ADULT?
[1 – 6]

Concepts

Insects grow from eggs and change in body form into adult.
Insects pass through stages (metamorphosis) at different rates.
Flies lay their eggs on filth.

Procedure   I.   Flies

STEP 1. *Ask:* Where do insects come from?
How are they produced?
Are they born alive, or do they develop from eggs?

Make several small patties of hamburger. Put these in several jars. Have the students catch flies and put in the jars. Keep the jars covered with Saran Wrap and place outside the room. Put a small piece of soaked paper towel in the jars so that the meat will remain moist. After several days take a dissecting needle and move the spoiled hamburger and locate small fly eggs. After several more days, maggots will appear. Replace the eggs in the jars and wait.

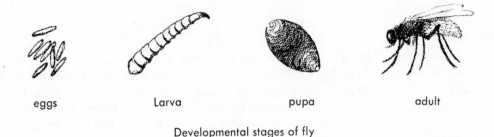

| eggs | Larva | pupa | adult |

Developmental stages of fly

STEP 2. *Ask:* Bring the jars into the class.
From where did the maggots come?

Leave the rest of the jars undisturbed for several more days. If the weather is fairly warm, the maggots will develop quickly into young flies.

Ask: How did the flies originate, and what happened to the maggots?

Summarize by stating that flies pass from the egg stage to the larvae (the maggot), to the pupa, and finally to the adult stage.

Procedure   II.   Moths

STEP 1. Have students collect caterpillars and place them in a jar with several fresh green leaves and a couple of twigs. The caterpillars will soon spin a cocoon on the twigs. Allow them to stay in the jar until they hatch into adult moths. Keep a moist blotter or paper towel in the bottom of the jar while the cocoon is developing.

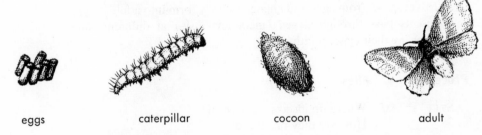

| eggs | caterpillar | cocoon | adult |

Developmental stages of moth

Ask: Why do you think it is necessary to keep the jar air moist?

STEP 2. Have the class catch several grasshoppers and bring them into class.
Place them in a small box with moist soil and cover the box with Saran
Wrap. Leave the adult grasshoppers there until they die. Have students
observe them over several days. They might be able to see the female
grasshopper deposit her eggs. Leave .the box in the classroom, maintaining the soil at a fairly moist level but not soaking. After several
months, have the students attempt to find any nymphs in the top of the
soil.

Ask: From where did these nymphs — young developing grasshoppers
— come?

STUDENT ACTIVITIES

1. Why did we put meat in the jar for the flies?

2. Why did the flies lay their eggs in the meat?

3. From where did the maggots come?

4. Why should we keep our garbage cans covered?

5. Into what does a caterpillar develop?

6. What did the cocoon change to?

7. How do grasshoppers reproduce?

8. Why did you have to leave a moist paper in the jar with the cocoons?

9. Grasshoppers, flies, and moths are called insects. From what you have
   observed in these demonstrations, do you think all insects develop from eggs
   and pass through different stages into adults?

10. Draw below the stages of a fly from egg to adult.

HOW DO A COCOON AND A POLLIWOG CHANGE?
[1 – 3, 2 – 4]

Concepts

Some animals change in shape and size as they mature.
Even a small animal may have a heart.
Growing and developing animals may not look like their adult parents.
Animals need oxygen in order to live.

Procedure

Step 1. Obtain some larvae or cocoons of the different moths.* Take a razor blade and very carefully cut through the outer skin of the larvae. Show the dissected larva to the class. [2 – 4]

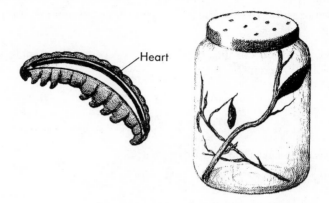

Heart

Ask: Can you see the heart beat?
Count the number of times the heart beats a minute.

Have the class feel their pulses and count the number of times their hearts beat a minute.

Ask: Does the larva's heart beat faster than your heart?

Step 2. Place some cocoons in a covered jar with some air holes in the lid. [1 – 3]

Ask: Why should we puncture the lid with holes?

Have some students keep a record of the number of days it takes for the animals to come out of the cocoons. When the moths metamorphose (change into adult form), have the class note the way they get out of the cocoons and the way the animals pump blood into their wings so that the wings take their shape.

Ask: How have our cocoons changed in appearance from the way they looked when we dissected them?
After watching a cocoon, what can we say about how moths grow and develop?

Step 3. Get some polliwogs from a pond or have some of your students bring them to class. Keep them either in a large mayonnaise jar or in an aquarium in which there are some green aquatic plants or algae. The polliwogs will eventually get shorter tails and their legs will begin to appear. [2 – 4]

*These can be obtained from Turtox Biological Supply House.

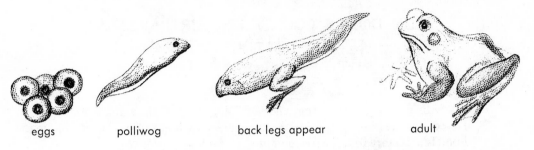

eggs   polliwog   back legs appear   adult

Metamorphosis of frog

Ask: When the legs appear, how are the polliwogs changed?
  Do you see any similarity in the way they develop and the
  way the cocoons developed?

An animal like the moth that changes into different stages during development is said to metamorphose.

Ask: Do you think the changes that a frog goes through could also be
  called metamorphosis?

STUDENT ACTIVITIES

1. Describe what you saw when you dissected the cocoon.

2. How many times a minute did the cocoon's heart beat?

3. Do developing animals necessarily look very much like their adult parents?

4. Why did you puncture the lid of the can with holes for the cocoon?

5. Do most animals have to have air to live?

6. How many days did it take the moths to metamorphose, or to come out of the
   cocoons?

7. What were the animals doing in the cocoon all that time?

8. How did the animal in the cocoon stage differ from the adult animal?

9. What is the reason for the difference?

10. Do polliwogs change their body shapes when they grow?

11. Do small animals have hearts?

12. Describe how your polliwogs changed in form as they grew.

13. Draw a cocoon of a moth and an adult moth.

14. Indicate by diagram some of the stages through which a frog goes during its
    development.

WHY DO WE LOOK LIKE OUR PARENTS?
[4 – 6]

Concepts

Every living thing comes from another living thing of the same kind.
Heredity is the passing on of traits and characteristics from parents to children.
Food is necessary for the growth of life.
At every stage of development the individual is an integrated organism. All
the cells, tissues, and organs are correlated and act together as a unit.

Procedure

Collect the following items: day-old chicken, hen (or pictures of the above),
box or cage, water, food, and a growth chart for each child. If you can't get a hen,
you can make a brooder to keep the chicken warm by obtaining a small cardboard
box about 18 by 18 inches square.

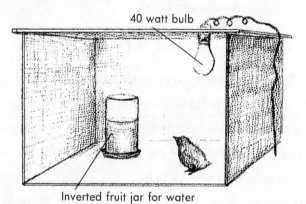

40 watt bulb

Inverted fruit jar for water

STEP 1. Insert a light socket with a 40 watt bulb in a piece of cardboard which
will be used to cover the top of the box. See Diagram 1.

Ask: Can you give me examples of living things that are alike?

Examples: Horse, colt; dog, puppy; cat, kitten; parakeet, baby parakeet.

Ask: How are these animals alike?

Show the cage with the hen and a chicken. (You may use pictures of a
hen instead.)

Ask: How is the chicken like the hen?

Hold the chick up to the class.

Ask: Where did this chicken come from?

Explanation: Students tend to answer that they come from eggs. Point out that eggs come from the mother hen.

Ask: Can something living come from something that is nonliving? Can something that is living come from something entirely different? For example, could a horse come from a cow?

STEP 2. Explain to the class that living things come only from other living things which are similar. Chickens come only from chickens.

Ask: Can you give me some examples of living things whose young look like their parents but are not identical to them when they are born?

List some of these on the board, such as horse, colt; dog, puppy; cat, kitten.

Ask: How are the young animals like their parents, and how do they differ?

Have the class compare the day-old chick with the adult chicken.

Ask: How does the chick look different?

STEP 3. Have the class keep a growth chart of the chicken for the next couple of weeks and mark everything on a chart that they notice about the growth of the chicken. Have them pay particular attention to specific features resembling the hen's, such as the feet, comb (feathers), wings, color, and what the chicken eats. Have them think of ways living things resemble their parents. They might cut out pictures at home of other animals and bring them to school. Discuss how the young are similar to their parents.

Ask: Are humans plants or animals?
How do babies resemble their parents?
Can you think of ways in which you resemble your parents?

Write on the board some examples of the ways in which parents and young are similar, such as hair, skin, eyes, facial features, etc.

STEP 4. *Ask:* (After several days) Have you noticed any changes in the chick? How has it changed as it grew?
Can you see any connection between how the chicken develops and the way you are developing to resemble your parents?

Explain to the class that all organisms inherit traits and characteristics from their parents. Also point out how the growth of the organism is balanced. The legs or head, for example, do not grow by themselves, but all parts of the chick grow in a balanced, integrated way.

STEP 5. *Ask:* Can you list any traits you have inherited from your parents?

Write some of these on the board, such as color of hair, eyes, skin color, facial features, etc.

Ask: What was necessary for the chicken to live?
Is good food and pure water also necessary for humans to live?
If you could find pictures of your parents when they were your age, do you think you would see a resemblance between them and you?
What did we decide made this resemblance?

We can all see why we look like our parents, as we have seen why the baby chicken grew up to look like its mother and father.

STUDENT ACTIVITIES

True or False

_____ 1. A chicken is an animal.

_____ 2. Food and water are not necessary for growth to take place.

_____ 3. Living things don't come from living things of the same kind.

_____ 4. The day old chicken looked exactly like its mother.

_____ 5. No animal or human resembles his parents.

_____ 6. The chicken looked more like its mother as it grew up.

Questions For Discussion

1. What causes us to resemble our parents?

2. Give some common traits and characteristics of the chick and of the hen.

3. What is the importance of food and water in the growth of the chicken or of living things in general?

4. What did you observe from your growth chart of the chicken?

5. Could a chicken come from a horse? Why or why not?

6. In what ways do you resemble your parents?

7. List five examples of living things that resemble other living things. *Example:* horse, colt.

8. What was the first change in the appearance of the baby chick that you noticed and recorded?

HOW DOES YOUR BODY GROW?
[K – 8, 7 – 8]

Concepts

When an animal or plant grows, its cells divide.

When a chicken develops in the egg, it passes through different stages.

A chick embryo needs a constant temperature and humidity in order to grow and develop.

A large part of the egg contains stored food for the young embryo to use in its growth.

Procedure   I.

STEP 1. Plant some bulbs or seeds. Have the students watch them and measure their growth with a ruler for a couple of weeks.

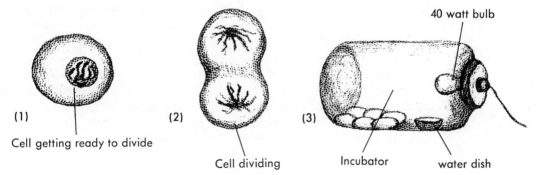

(1)

Cell getting ready to divide

(2)

Cell dividing

(3)

40 watt bulb

Incubator   water dish

Ask: How do you think a plant grows?

What happens in the plant when it gets bigger?

STEP 2. Show the students microscopic slides of cells, some pictures or charts of cells (see the experiment on the cell), or draw Diagrams 1 and 2 on the board. Explain that cells divide (mitosis) and that plants and animals are made of cells. Growth is caused by the old cells dividing and making two new cells.

STEP 3. Ask: Do you think you might also be made of cells?

What do you think happens to you when you grow?

When you cut or scratch yourself, do you scrape off millions of cells?

How do you think your body makes new skin?

Do you think your skin might fill in the cut by cell division?

Procedure II. *Chicken Embryo*

STEP 1. *Ask:* Where do chickens come from?

Have the class construct a simple incubator.* Explain to the class that in order for chickens to hatch they must be kept under a constant 37°C temperature for 21 days. Make the incubator with a 40 watt lamp, as shown in the diagram. Check the temperature for several days before you put in the eggs. You may have to change the size of the light bulb. Place a dish of water in the lower part of the box or glass container in order to prevent the air from becoming excessively dry. Turn the eggs every few days, but be careful to cover the eggs immediately so they don't become cool. In K–3 leave until the eggs hatch.

STEP 2. Obtain from a feed store fertile hatching eggs. Place six to eight eggs in the incubator. After three days of incubation, crack one of the eggs open. You should be able to see the little heart beat.

Ask: Can you locate the little developing heart?
How do you know it is the heart?

Crack another egg at the end of 18 days. Have the students note the difference in growth of the embryos. Have them draw a picture of the young developing chick.

STEP 3. When an egg hatches have the students note the way the chick gets out of the shell and the way it breaks the shell with its little egg tooth on the upper part of the beak. Draw or show some charts of how the chicken develops. Point out the environmental factors which are necessary for the embryo to develop, such as heat and humidity.

STUDENT ACTIVITIES

1. What happens to the cell in a plant or animal when it grows?

2. How do you think you grow?

3. When you lose blood, how is new blood made?

4. What part of the chicken seemed to develop first?

5. Do you think birds' body temperatures are higher or lower than our body temperature? Why do you think this?

6. Draw a picture or make a diagram of how cells divide.

7. From where do you think the chick embryo gets its food while it is growing and developing?

8. Why do you think the egg is such a nutritious food for us to eat?

---

*Some biological supply houses now have simple inexpensive incubators for sale.

9. Why do you think all of the eggs did not hatch?

10. Do you think air will pass through the chick's shell?

11. How do you think the chick breathes?

12. Draw the beak of the chick. What purpose or function does this beak serve?

13. Draw several pictures of how the chick embryo looked when it was developing.

ECOLOGY

INTERRELATIONSHIPS BETWEEN ORGANISMS AND THEIR ENVIRONMENT

The purpose of the following seven lessons is to develop an understanding that there are interrelations between organisms and their environment. Plants and animals can live and survive only if certain needs are met by the environment. Plants and animals in the process of living modify their surroundings. Plant cover, for example, protects the soil from erosion and provides food for animals. Animals may keep the plant population in check and provide fertilizer for plants. Any change that man introduces to a biological community may have wide effects upon the environment. For example, this is evident when one considers the effects of the indiscriminant use of insecticides. Their use may kill birds whose function is to keep insect population in check. Man as a result will be forced to use more insecticides in the future to replace the work formerly done by birds.

The first two lessons "What Is a Pond?" and "How Do Animals Affect Their Community?" introduce students to concepts related to biological communities. The lessons show that animals and plants are adapted to live in particular types of environments and their presence affects the environment. These lessons can be used to introduce a unit about biological communities. For example, study of how a pond changes and the variation of life in it might be continued throughout the entire year. A study of this nature could show the effects of such physical changes as temperature and light upon the community.

The lesson "Is Life Affected by Its Surroundings?" should be incorporated with the first lessons in a unit. This lesson advances the concept of biology communities and develops the idea of balance in nature between plants and animals. In comparing an aquarium with a desert-type terrarium community, children soon grasp that certain factors in the environment (temperature, water, food, and light) determine the kind and the amount of life able to survive in a community. The teacher should have the children make as many comparisons as possible between the two communities. Other communities, such as the forest, plain, sea, and mountain may also be studied and comparisons made of the type of life found in

each. "What Effect Does Temperature Have on the Activities of Animals?" and
"Is Life Affected by Temperature?" show how animals are affected by one specific
factor in their environment. They also develop concepts of dynamic change in any
environment and explain how the function of certain animals are dependent on
temperature.

"How Do Earthworms Change the Soil?" builds concepts related to changes
that animals make on the environment. It shows the interrelationships between
light, worms, and soil. This lesson also should be integrated with the other lessons
in this section to give a complete picture of the relationships between animals and
their environment and the effect each has on the other.

The lesson "Do Animals Need Oxygen?" introduces students to the fact that
any environment may have factors which limit life. One such factor for fish is
the presence of oxygen in water. If there is no oxygen in the water, the fish will
die. Emptying sewage and industrial waste into rivers reduces the oxygen available
to fish causing them to suffocate. The teacher should emphasize the importance of
understanding scientific principles in using good conservation practices.

WHAT IS A POND?
[1 – 6]

Concepts

> The purpose of color in animals or plants usually is to conceal (hide), dis-
> guise (fool), or advertise (show off).
> Every living organism possesses some body parts which are adapted for the
> life it leads.
> Each species (kind) is adapted (changed) or is in the process of becoming
> adapted (changing) to live where it is.
> A pond is a small body of water containing many different forms of life,
> which, if undisturbed, are in balance.
> Some forms of life are very small and can be seen only under a microscope.

Procedure

> STEP 1. *Ask:* What is a pond?
> > Is a pond nonmoving water?
> > Does a pond contain life?
> > Is there life around a pond?
>
> > Discuss pond life, vegetation (plants), sources of water, and the above
> > concepts. Pond life may include frogs, hydra, water skippers, aquatic
> > snails, crayfish, toads, spiders, flies, grasshoppers, turtles, snakes, sala-
> > manders, and snails. Vegetation: mosses, algae, cattails, water lilies,

pond scum (spirogyra), reeds, and grasses. Some examples of ponds are trapped rain water, dammed streams, sink holes, storage water, and trapped drainage water.

STEP 2. Take a planned field trip to a pond; include in your plans transportation, supervision, rules of conduct, safety rules, permission, and equipment. Equipment: dip nets (these can be made out of old stockings and coat hangers), jars with lids, containers for insects, and thermometers. Have students take temperature readings and water samples at different depths and record the data. Look for all of the different forms of life and vegetation. Gather a few specimens of the following, but replace most of what you see undisturbed: water samples, algae, mosses, insects, animals, and life from covered rocks. Have the student record any unusual examples of coloration they see.

STEP 3. *Ask:* What is the source of water that was in the pond?
What kinds of animals and insect life are there?
What kinds of plants did we find?
Could there be life in the water which we cannot see?
How could you examine the life?

Put a drop of water you collected from the pond on a slide and cover it with a coverslip. Place the slide on a microscope or microprojector.

Ask: What do you see under the microscope?
Can there be life we can't see?
What would happen if the pond dried up?
Is there any form of life on the rocks?
How could you examine it more closely?
What is the temperature of the water?
Does the temperature vary with depth?
Is the water temperature important to the life in the pond?
Why are algae and other plant life important?

Explanation: Temperature is important to life. If the pond is deep, there will be different types of life living at different depths. Algae and other plant life serve as food for fish and some water insects.

STEP 4. *Ask:* Did you see any examples of how life was colored so you could not see it easily?

Set up microscopes or use magnifying glasses for the students to observe the material of the wood, lichens on the rock, and the pond water more closely. Pour a glass of pond water and another of tap water.

Ask: After looking at the pond water under a microscope, why do you think you shouldn't drink pond water?
Why is it safe to drink tap water?

Explanation: City water has been purified by killing all these organisms. Summarize the lesson by reviewing what the purpose of each organism is in the pond, pointing out how the organisms are dependent on each other. For example, the fish eat the plants, but they also make fertilizer that plants need in order to grow.

STUDENT ACTIVITIES

1. If you were to put some soil, a few snails, and some water plants in a jar, would you have a small pond? Explain.

2. Do the above and record what happens to your pond over several weeks. See if you can explain the changes that occur.

True or False

_____ 1. Water lilies are plants.

_____ 2. The temperature of pond water has an effect on life in the pond.

_____ 3. Ponds are used in irrigation.

_____ 4. We can't see everything in a pond.

_____ 5. A pond has life.

_____ 6. Fish live on plant life.

_____ 7. A pond supports life.

_____ 8. Plants may benefit from animals.

_____ 9. Trees always grow near ponds.

_____ 10. A dip net is needed to gather specimens.

_____ 11. Rocks are never found in ponds.

_____ 12. Algae are not a food for pond life.

_____ 13. All ponds are safe to swim in.

_____ 14. Dammed stream water is one source of water.

_____ 15. Water gets colder as you wade deeper.

Questions For Discussion

1. Why did we use a microscope?

2. Why are algae important?

3. What happens to the life in the pond when the pond dries up?

4. What kind of life might we find on rocks and logs?

5. Where did the water in the pond come from?

6. What kind of life might we find in the water?

7. What is a pond?

8. Is a pond moving or nonmoving water?

9. What kind of life does a pond contain around it?

10. Where could you find life in a pond?

11. Name five types of life that you saw at the pond.

IS LIFE AFFECTED BY ITS SURROUNDINGS?
[4-8]

Concepts

Certain environmental factors determine community types.

Some of the types of communities are on land and some in water.

Land communities can be subdivided into forests, bogs, swamps, deserts, and others.

A community is a collection of living organisms which have mutual relationships among themselves and their environment.

All living things have certain requirements that must be met by their surroundings.

Habitat is a place where an animal or plant naturally lives or grows.

The main purpose of this study is to show that different environments are needed to sustain different types of life.

Procedure: Aquarium

STEP 1. Obtain several large commercial-sized mayonnaise jars or aquaria and terraria if they are available. Make a simple aquarium in the following manner (ask first if there is anyone in the class who knows how to set up and maintain an aquarium. If so, let him care for the aquarium):

Aquarium

a. Clean the aquarium thoroughly with soap and water and rinse well.

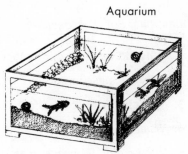

b. Wash the sand and gravel to be placed in the aquarium. Spread this over the bottom.

(1)

c. Fill the jar with water and let stand for several days before adding plants and fish. This allows the poisonous chlorine in the water to escape into the air.

d. Obtain several aquatic plants from a pet shop and place, as suggested by the salesman in the pet shop, in the aquarium.

e. Place one small fish and two snails in the aquarium and cover. Allow some air to enter the aquarium.

STEP 2. *Ask:* Why do you think it is necessary to clean the aquarium before we use it?

Why do we have to wash the sand and gravel before we put it in the aquarium?

What would dirty water do to the gills of the fish?

Why must the gills of the fish be kept clean?

How do fish breathe?

Why do you think the water was allowed to stand for several days before the fish was placed in the aquarium?

What does our health department add to the water that might be injurious to the fish?

Why were the snails added to the water?

Explanation: The snails will eat the small green algae, scummy plants, that collect on the side of the tank.

Ask: Why were plants added to the aquarium?

In this aquarium, why is it necessary to add fish food once in a while?

What would the fish eat in nature?

What do plants make that the fish can use, and what does the fish make that the plants can use?

Explanation: Plants make oxygen and food, and the fish produce carbon dioxide and waste products. The aquarium probably is not balanced, so food must be added to it from time to time for the fish.

Procedure: Terrarium

STEP 1. Obtain a terrarium or large commercial mayonnaise jar. If the jar is used, place it on its side. Fill it with sand, a few small cacti, a colored lizard, skink, chamelion, or horned toad. Place in the terrarium a small bottle cap filled with water for the animals or some twigs, and spray with water every day — lizards are more likely to take water this way. Water the entire terrarium thoroughly once every two weeks. Place a screen over the top of the container or puncture the lid.

Desert terrarium

(2)   sand

Explanation: The animals suggested above feed on insects, but will also eat live worms. The worms may be cut up to feed the animals. Reptiles will not generally eat dead material or meat. Food for feeding these animals can usually be obtained from a local pet shop.

STEP 2. Fill a terrarium as shown in Diagram 3. If a mayonnaise jar is used, place it on its side. Place in it some small ferns, mosses, lichens, liverworts, or tropical house plants, which can be purchased from the local dime store. Don't keep the water level too high. Place the plants in an area where the light is not too strong. Cover the terrarium or mayonnaise jar — if a mayonnaise jar lid is used, place a couple of holes in it. Place a turtle or small frog in the jar. Feed the animals live insects, meal worms, or parts of earthworms.

Bog terrarium
        moss
(3)
     gravel   water

STEP 3. *Ask:* How does the life found in the aquarium differ from that found in the desert and bog terrarium?

What kinds of conditions do the fish, the turtle, the frog, or the lizard have to have in order to survive in their particular habitats?

What kinds of conditions do the bog plants require in order to grow well?

What kind of food does the fish, the lizards, or the turtles eat?

What do you think would happen to the turtle if you left him in the desert habitat; to the lizard if you put him in the bog habitat?

STUDENT ACTIVITIES

1. From the three examples of communities, what would you say caused the difference in the kinds of plants and animals that grow in each?

2. Match the animals and plants in Column A with the communities they belong to in Column B.

	Column A		*Column B*
___ a. Cactus	___ d. Snakes	___ g. Moss	1. Desert
___ b. Toads	___ e. Birds	___ h. Ferns	2. Bog community
___ c. Lizards	___ f. Turtles	___ i. Water plants	3. Lake

3. In the above question you might have placed some of the animals in more than one community. Would you expect to find the same kind of snake, for example, in the desert as you would find in a bog community?

4. True or false.

    ___ a. The surroundings of an area determine what kind of life you will find there.

    ___ b. All living things have certain requirements that must be met by their surroundings.

    ___ c. In the demonstration communities we have in the room we have no examples of a water community.

5. What do you think would happen to the bog community if it became too dry?

6. What do you think would happen to the desert community if it were watered every day?

HOW DO ANIMALS AFFECT THEIR COMMUNITY?
[3 – 6]

Concepts

    Animals are dependent upon one another for food.

    The smaller the animals, the more likely it is that there will be a larger number of them present in a community.

    Larger animals may consume many small animals in order to satisfy their hunger.

    The fittest survive.

    When the supply cannot meet the demand, a change of some kind must occur in the community.

    Water plants are important to an aquatic community.

    "Pyramid of numbers" means that there are always more small animals in an environment which serve as food for the larger animals, who in turn are food for even larger animals.

Procedure

STEP 1. Set up an aquarium or use a mayonnaise jar (see previous demonstration on how to set up an aquarium). Obtain from a swampy region, a lake, or a stagnant pool some rather scummy water. Be sure to get some of the green plants (algae) which live in the water and place these in the aquarium. Also attempt to collect some snails, daphnia, and other organisms found in stagnant water. Include, if possible, some rocks and a small fish. You now have a microcosm, a small world. Use only water obtained from the stagnant pool.

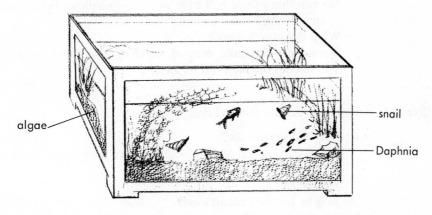

Stagnant-water aquarium

STEP 2. Place the microcosm on your desk.

Ask: What is this? What does it show?
Why did I bring this into class instead of just having a regular aquarium for you to see?
How many different kinds of life, organisms, do you see in the jar?
What is happening in it?
What change do you think will take place in the jar?
Could we call this a small world, a microcosm?
What part do the animals play in this microcosm?
What function do the plants have?
How many animals of each kind do you see in there?
What changes would you expect to take place in a day, a week, or a month?

STEP 3. Have the students record on their activity sheets the changes that they think will occur. Announce to the class that they are to observe and record on the data sheets what happens over a three week period.

Ask: What changes shall we look for?
Should we watch for water color change?

Should we watch for the change in the number of certain animals, or changes in the numbers of all animals?

Should we watch only for the general condition of the microcosm and record only noticeable results?

Explanation: During the first part of the experiment the students will not observe much of a change. The initial observation should be followed with the following questions.

Ask: Why hasn't there been much change?

Is the life in the aquarium balanced now?

Do you think there will have to be an imbalance before we detect any change?

What does the fish eat?

Does the plant take care of anything else other than itself?

Where does the plant get its food?

STEP 4. After some time the fish will die.

Ask: Why did the fish die?

What were some of the factors which contributed to the death of the fish?

Was he sick?

Was he getting enough food?

What did he eat?

If he ate smaller animals, how many did he eat at one time?

Do you think that there might have been a lack of oxygen and that this might have caused the death of the fish?

What will happen now to the fish if we leave him in the aquarium?

What effect will this have on the number of small animals in the aquarium since they will eat the fish?

STEP 5. After a few days:

Ask: How do you account for the rise in the population of the small animals?

What evidence do we have from the microcosm that one animal is dependent upon another for food?

Explanation: After some time there will be a definite change, owing to the fact that the organisms eating the dead fish multiply rapidly, but when the fish has been eaten they begin to die.

Ask: Why did the number of organisms first start to decrease?

Why did they later increase?

What caused them to decrease again?

Did the food supply have anything to do with it?

STEP 6. Keep the aquarium for several more days. Note any changes in the plants.

> *Ask:* Why are the plants changing?
> How did the plants contribute to the microcosm?

> *Explanation:* To make food and oxygen for the animals.
> What effect did the death of the animals have on the microcosm?

STUDENT ACTIVITIES

1. What is the word which means "small world?"

2. Why do we call it a microcosm?

3. Name the animals and their approximate numbers in the microcosm.

4. As the animals get larger in size, does the number in population increase or decrease?

5. Explain the principle of supply and demand.

6. Is the law of supply and demand evident in the microcosm? If so, how?

7. Give one main reason for the fish's dying.

8. What caused the smaller animals to decrease, rise, and then decrease in number during the time we kept the microcosm?

9. What were some of the factors leading to the fish's death?

10. How long would you expect the microcosm to last?

11. What purposes did the plants serve in the microcosm?

12. Animals are dependent on one another for food; that is, one animal serves as food for another animal. True or false? _____

13. What is the pyramid of numbers?

14. How does it work? Explain.

15. Is it evident in our microcosm? How?

16. Do you find evidence of the pyramid of numbers anywhere other than in our microcosm?

17. How would the water level be affected in the microcosm? Would it raise or lower?

18. Could we make a microcosm using a land environment instead of a water environment?

19. What would be some of the animals that we might use?

DATA SHEET

	Change in animal life	Change in plants	Change in water color	Any other noticeable changes
Monday				
Wednesday				
Friday				
Monday				
Wednesday				
Friday				
Monday				
Wednesday				
Friday				

Comments and observations or conclusions:

WHAT EFFECT DOES TEMPERATURE HAVE ON THE ACTIVITIES OF ANIMALS?
[1 – 6]

Concepts

Animals are affected by the temperatures in their environment.
The colder the environment, the less active cold-blooded animals will be.
The environment of living things changes continually.

Procedure

STEP 1. Obtain several goldfish. (This exercise may be done as a demonstration or in small groups.) They may be purchased from the local dime store. Place them in large jars and give each group a goldfish to study. Each should also have a thermometer or they may use one thermometer and pass it around the class. Have the class observe the fish and see if they can determine how the fish breathe.

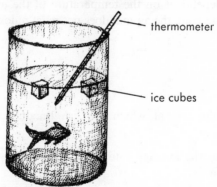

Ask: How does the fish breathe?

Can you tell how many times a minute it breathes?

Do you know of any way that we might slow down or speed up breathing of the fish?

Explanation: The number of times the gill covering (operculum) moves up and down is a rough indication of the rate of respiration of the fish. Have each group take the temperature of the water in the jars. Record the figures of each group on the board.

STEP 2. Have the students place a couple of ice cubes in the jars and see what happens. After several minutes have the groups take the temperature of the water and determine the rate of respiration. Record what happens.

Ask: What should we determine as the average rate of breathing of the fish?

Explanation: Add together all of the readings of the group at the same temperature and take the average of these.

Ask: What effect does the temperature of the water have on the rate at which the fish breathes?
What do you think would happen if we were to place the fish in fairly warm water?

Explanation: Explain to the class that the rate at which the body operates increases with the temperature. When the body is warm, the cells need more oxygen. The animal has to breathe more rapidly. A fish is a cold-blooded animal, which means that its body temperature is at the same temperature as its surroundings.

Ask: What do you think would happen to the fish if the water were extremely cold?
Do you think it would be possible for the fish to survive if they were frozen in water for a short time?
Are there any disadvantages to being cold-blooded?

Explanation: The disadvantage is that the rate of the body function is dependent on the temperature of the environment. If the surroundings are cold, the animal does not react quickly.

STUDENT ACTIVITIES

1. Record the rate at which the fish breathed at room temperature. At cold temperature.

2. What was the average rate at which the fish breathed, and how did you get this figure?

3. Why did you average the readings of several groups to get the rate?

4. How do fish breathe?

5. Why do they move their gill coverings up and down?

6. How are animals affected by their surroundings?

7. What have you noticed about the way the fish is built and how this aids him?

8. Why is a fish better able (adapted) to live in water than you are?

9. What is a cold-blooded animal?

10. Can you think of any disadvantage to being cold-blooded?

11. Why do horses and cows have a hairy coat, and fishes not?

IS LIFE AFFECTED BY TEMPERATURE?
[4−6]

Concepts

A warm temperature usually is more beneficial to life than a cold temperature.
There are maximum and minimum temperatures that living things can stand.
Most animals tend to be more active when the temperature is warm than when
it is cold.
Some animals are cold-blooded, and others are warm-blooded.
Fish and frogs are cold-blooded animals. Their body temperature is about
the same as the environment around them.

Procedure: *Reaction of Animals*

STEP 1. Take some goldfish or polliwogs and divide them into two different
jars. Place in one of these jars some ice cubes and keep the other at
room temperature. After 15 minutes note the temperature of each container and write this temperature on the board. Note the activity of the
two groups of animals.

(1)

Ask: Which of the two jars has the more active animals?
Do you think you would slow down in your reactions if you were
placed in cold water?
Is your body temperature more or less regulated, since it doesn't
change much, regardless of the surroundings?
From what you have seen in this experiment, do you think the
animals placed in the cold water have the same type of tem-
perature regulation as you have?
Are all animals generally more active in a warm environment?
What kind of animals are more active in a warm environment?

STEP 2. The experiment might be further developed by checking the reactions
of other animals, such as ants, worms, or insects. Some of these animals
might be placed in a jar and then deposited in a refrigerator. Keep the
control animals in another jar at room temperature.

Ask: From the experiments we have done so far, what would be your hypothesis as to what would happen if a jar with some ants in it were heated gently with a candle?

Take a jar with ants and heat it with a candle. Note their reaction.

Procedure   Reaction of Plants

STEP 1. *Ask:* Do you think plants might also be affected by temperature? What kind of experiment do you suggest might be done to determine whether plants are affected by temperature?

Obtain two jars. Place some well-soaked paper towels in the bottom of the two jars. Add some bean or pea seeds to each of these jars. Cover the tops of the jars with a lid or waxed paper. See Diagram 1. Put one of the jars in a refrigerator and leave the other one at room temperature. Have a student be responsible for reporting to the class when the seeds at room temperature first start to sprout. Have another student check the seeds in the refrigerator to determine whether they start to sprout. Report the results to the class and have each student record these data on the student activity sheet. In winter, place some plants outside and keep some inside. Note what happens. Plant some seeds outside and inside, and water them.

(2)

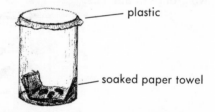

plastic

soaked paper towel

STEP 2. *Ask:* Why do we get a difference in the rate at which these seeds begin to sprout?

Allow the seeds to sprout for several days. After a week, take the two groups of seeds out of the jars and measure them to determine which group grew faster.

Ask: What is your conclusion about the effect of temperature on the sprouting of seeds and their growth? Can you give another example of how temperature may affect plants?

STUDENT ACTIVITIES

1. Are animals generally more active in a warm environment?

2. What kind of animals are more active in a warm environment?

3. Lizards and snakes are cold-blooded animals. Do you think they would be very active on cold days?

4. Record below your data on the planting of the seeds.
   Date you planted them: _____

   Cold Temperature Environment   *Room Temperature Environment*
   Date sprouted _____   _____
   Rate of growth _____   _____

5. Which plants sprouted first?

6. Which plants grew faster?

7. Why do you think some people grow plants in a greenhouse?

8. Do you think plants would grow very fast in a temperature of 200°F? Why not?

9. What other experiments can you think of to do with plants or animals which might show the effects of temperature?

HOW DO EARTHWORMS CHANGE THE SOIL?
[2 – 6]

Concepts

Earthworms help to aerate the soil.
They help to conserve water in the soil.
Earthworms are active in the dark and avoid the light. (They are photo-sensitive. "Photo" means light; "sensitive" means reacting to.)
Earthworms dig their way through the soil and thereby mix rich decaying organic material throughout it.

Procedure

STEP 1. *Ask:* What do earthworms do?
        Where do they live?
        Are they good or bad for the soil?
        Can you think of some way we might find the answers to some of these questions by doing some experiment?

STEP 2. Obtain three coffee cans, all the same size. Fill each of these about two-thirds full with loose loamy soil. To two of the cans add some earthworms. (These can usually be obtained at night on a lawn that has recently been watered or by digging in moist ground rich with decaying leaves.) To all three cans add about an inch of sand or saw-dust and on top of this place about a half inch of cornmeal.

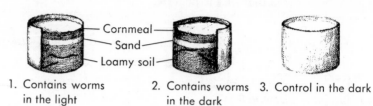

1. Contains worms
   in the light

2. Contains worms
   in the dark

3. Control in the dark

Earthworms help to mix air with the soil.

Ask: How could we tell whether earthworms react to light?

STEP 3. Place one of the cans with worms near a window. If possible, have a lamp near it which can be turned on at night. The lamp insures that light shines on the soil 24 hours a day. Place the other two cans in the dark. Have the students observe these cans each day and note in their notebooks what happens. Add to each container a small amount of water at room temperature each day.

STEP 4. After several days:

Ask: What is different about what occurred in the can we kept in the light compared with the cans we kept in the dark?
Why did we put one can in the dark with worms and one without worms?
Which of the three cans was the control?
Why should we moisten the soil with water?
Do worms need water in order to live?
What conclusion would you make about the sensitivity of worms to light and dark?
Which do they seem to like better?
Which of the cans seems to hold water better?
Why do you think the cans kept in the dark hold water better?

Explanation: The soil in the can kept in the dark appears to have been turned over more by worms.

Ask: Do you think water should be soaked up quickly in the soil containing the worms?

Explanation: Much of the water would be trapped in the loosely dug tunnels of soil the worm makes; therefore, the water will not evaporate easily.

Ask: How do worms help to conserve water in the soil?

How do worms help to mix the fertilizer and dead plants from the top of the soil into deeper part of the soil?

When you looked at the can kept in the dark with the cornmeal in it, did it look as if the worms had mixed it with the soil, or was it much the same as before?

STUDENT ACTIVITIES

1. Why don't we see many worms on the lawns during the daytime?

2. How do worms enrich the soil?

3. What happened to the cornmeal you put on the soil?

4. Why did we put that cornmeal there?

5. Which can was the control in the experiment?

6. How do worms help to conserve our soil?

7. Why was there less moisture in the soil without worms?

8. What caused the soil with the cornmeal to change in appearance?

9. Do you think the answer you just gave is a fact or an assumption?

10. If you were going to raise worms to sell to fishermen, how would you do it?

11. Suggested below are some experiments you might do with worms.
    Will worms grow better in:
    a. Acid soil?
    b. Basic soil?
    c. Dry, wet, or damp soil?
    d. Soil rich in humus (decaying organic material)?

HOW MAY THE UNWISE USE OF VARIOUS SUBSTANCES ENDANGER OUR HEALTH AND SAFETY?
[5 – 8]

Concepts

Sink and toilet cleaners contain strong burning materials which may injure the skin severely if used carelessly.

Some dry cleaning compounds are flammable (burn) and may give off dangerous fumes.

Skin poisoning may be caused by improper use of iodine and other antiseptics (germ killers).

Most germ killers are extremely dangerous if taken internally.

Most insect sprays are poisonous to humans as well as to insects.

Paint removers often burn or give off dangerous fumes.

Household ammonia has a poison label and should be kept out of the medicine cabinet in a safer place.

The poison label is a skull (skeleton head) with cross bones.

Bleaches should be used only with extreme caution.

All poisons should be kept "out of reach" in a medicine cabinet. They can be used by adults, but with caution.

Procedure

STEP 1. Bring into class several empty containers from home that have poison or warning labels on them.

Ask: Does anyone know the symbol they put on bottles to indicate that they contain poisons?

Point to the poison label and draw it on the board.

Ask: Does anyone know how to spell the word "poison?"

Write the word on the board and go over it with the class several times.

Ask: Why do you think I placed these bottles on my desk?

Point to the poison labels on the bottle. Pick up each bottle and explain the reason for the label.

STEP 2. Collect some live insects and place them in a jar. In front of the class spray the insects.

Ask: What do you think will happen to the insects now that I have sprayed them?

Do you think there is a poison in the spray that kills the insects?

Do you think this spray could poison you by making you sick or killing you?

Explanation: Most chemical sprays used in the garden or in the home to control insect pests are poisonous, and children should not play with these agents.

STEP 3. Pour some bleach on some cloth. Allow it to stand for a couple of days.

> *Ask:* What do you think will happen to the material that I put in the bleach?

> *Explanation:* The material will become weak and tear or look as though the chemical has ruined it. Explain to the class that bleach and other harsh chemicals used around the house may be very dangerous and should not be used in play. Adults know how to use them and are very careful when they use them.

STEP 4. Place some iodine several times on a leaf or the skin of a fruit for a few days.

> *Ask:* ·What do you think the iodine will do to the leaf?

> *Explanation:* After several days it will kill part of the tissue of the leaf and fruit. Explain that chemicals kept in the medicine cabinets may be dangerous if not used properly and that children should not use any medicines unless their parents are there to help them.

STEP 5. Point out the dangers of flammable chemicals that may cause explosions — especially paint thinners, gasoline for power mowers and boats, kerosene, and cigarette lighter fluid. Write the word "flammable" on the board and have students learn to spell and recognize it.

STUDENT ACTIVITIES

1. Draw the label you might see on a package to indicate that it is dangerous.

2. Write the word that might appear on a bottle if it is dangerous.

3. Why shouldn't you play with chemicals that you know nothing about?

4. From what you saw with the insect spray, why should your parents wash their hands after using an insect spray?

5. Mark T for true and F for false. (These may be read aloud.)
_____ a. Most insect sprays are poisonous.
_____ b. It is all right to get things from the medicine cabinet if your parents aren't there to help you.

_____ c. Bleach can be very harmful to your eyes.

_____ d. Bleach could kill you if you drank it.

_____ e. Gasoline may be very dangerous, especially if there is any fire around.

_____ f. Gasoline can explode and make you blind.

_____ g. All poisonous chemicals are always labeled "poisonous."

_____ h. "Flammable" means that it will burn and is very dangerous.

_____ i. It is all right to play with household paint and paint thinner.

_____ j. Medicines in the medicine cabinet should be kept out of reach of babies.

_____ k. Poison bottles and chemicals should be kept out of reach of babies.

_____ l. Insect sprays kill only insects.

_____ m. Garden sprays should not be left around where small children can get them.

6. Give the following spelling words to the class and explain them.
   a. flammable
   b. poisons
   c. antiseptics
   d. insects
   e. bleaches
   f. ammonia
   g. medicine

SECTION TWO
THE PHYSICAL WORLD

Structure of Matter, Energy Relations, and Change of Matter

Air and Water Pressure

- 1. How Can You Crush a Can with Air? [K–8]
- 2. Can Air Pressure Move an Object? [K–8]
- 3. How Does a Submarine Submerge? [4–6]
- 4. Why Are Suction Cups Hard to Pull Apart? [7–8]
- 5. How Does a Moving Stream of Air Differ from Resting Air? [4–6]
- 6. What Are Water Pressure and Cohesive Force? [4–8]

Heat

- 1. What Is Heat? [4–8]
- 2. How Is Heat Transmitted? [K–8]
- 3. What Is Convection? [5–8]
- 4. What Is an Insulator? [4–6]
- 5. What Happens to Metals When They Are Heated? [4–6]
- 6. What Happens to Gases When They Are Heated? [5–6]
- 7. Why Does It Take So Much Time to Boil Water? [4–6]
- 8. Can You Boil Water in a Paper Cup? [4–6]

Sound

- 1. How Does Sound Vary with the Length of the Vibrating Body? [2–6]
- 2. How Does Sound Vary with the Length of Air Column? [2–6]
- 3. How Does a Violin or Cello Work? [4–6]
- 4. What Causes Sounds to Be Louder? [4–6]
- 5. Do Solids and Liquids Conduct Sounds? [4–6]
- 6. How Can the Reflection of Sound Be Changed? [1–6]
- 7. Is Sound Possible in a Vacuum? [4–6]
  (Also see Student Experiment: "What Causes Sound?")

311

Light

1. Why Do You Need Two Eyes? [1–6]
2. How Do Convex and Concave Lenses Work? [6–8]
3. A Convex Lens Can Make Objects Larger [1–2, 3–6]
4. How Is Light Changed When It Passes Through Water? [1–6, 4–6]
5. How Is Light Reflected? [7–8]
6. How Does a Pinhole Camera Work? [4–6]
7. What Does a Prism Do to Light? [1–3, 4–6]

Mechanics: Simple Machines and Forces

1. Why Use a Single Fixed Pulley? [6–8]
2. Why Use Movable Pulleys? [6–8]
3. What Good Is a Lever? [6–8]
4. How Does a Second-class Lever Work? [4–6]
5. How Does a Third-class Lever Work? [4–6]
6. Why Use an Inclined Plane? [1–6, 7–8]
7. What Good Is a Jack? [1–6]
8. What Is the Advantage in Using a Wheel and an Axle? [K–5]
9. What Is Inertia? [4–6]
10. What Is Gravity? [4–6]

Magnetism and Electricity

1. What Is a Magnet? [K–2, K–6]
2. What Things Are Magnetic and What Is a Compass? [K–6, 3–6]
3. What Is a Magnetic Field? [K–6]
4. What Is Static Electricity? [4–6]
5. How Can You Make Electricity by Magnetism? [4–8]
6. What Is an Electromagnet? [1–6]
7. What Is a Parallel or a Series Circuit? [7–8]
8. How Are Objects Plated? [4–6]
   (Also see Student Experiment: "How Can We Make a Fleet Move Without Touching Them?")

AIR AND WATER PRESSURE

Air and air pressure are not well understood by the average person. Children do not grasp these concepts easily unless they see several demonstrations. For this reason include as many of the following lessons as possible for the grade level and time allowed in one unit. The lessons can be given in the order found in this section. Concepts related to the nature of air and pressure are stressed and, furthermore, build an understanding of the properties of a gas. Children can easily understand how a solid and liquid behave because they can see them, but they seldom have a good concept of the third, invisible state of matter — a gas.

A unit on air should be started by showing children that air exists even though it cannot be seen. This can be demonstrated by blowing up a balloon and asking children what is in it. They can see that air in the balloon, which is slightly modified because it has been exhaled from your lungs, exerts pressure and occupies space. Its presence can also be emphasized by releasing the balloon and letting the air escape. Ask the children what escaped from the balloon. A further development of the idea that air exerts pressure is illustrated in the first two lessons of this section.

In the first demonstration "How Can You Crush a Can with Air?" the difference of the force of the molecules of the air hitting the side of the can outside compared to those inside the can is sufficient to collapse it. It is important that children begin to develop the idea that air pressure is caused by the motion of the molecules which make up the air. The second lesson "Can Air Pressure Move an Object?" also emphasizes this principle.

The lesson "How Does a Submarine Submerge?" shows that the principle of air pressure is used in submarines. Embodied in this lesson also is the principle that air has weight, but that it is lighter than water.

The lesson "Why Are Suction Cups Hard to Pull Apart?" demonstrates again the force that air pressure can exert and that this force is exerted in all directions.

The lesson "How Does a Moving Stream of Air Differ from Resting Air?" introduces the idea that a moving stream of air may exert less force than the air around it. Several demonstrations are given in the development of this concept.

The last lesson "What Are Water Pressure and Cohesive Force?" introduces another aspect of pressure, namely, that water like air also exerts pressure. The greater the depth of the water the greater the pressure as is generally true for air. This explains why the air pressure usually found at sea level is greater than that found on top of a high mountain peak or in an unpressurized airplane.

HOW CAN YOU CRUSH A CAN WITH AIR?
[K – 8]

Concepts

> Air pressure (air weight) is strong enough to
>   crush a strong can.
> A partial vacuum is a space in
>   which the atmospheric pressure has
>   been lessened; in other words, the space
>   contains "thinner" air than the air
>   surrounding it.

Teacher's Note: A comparison of molecular structure of gases, liquids, and solids should be given first.

Procedure

STEP 1. Take an empty Ditto fluid can, add a little water to it, and heat it for several minutes with a Bunsen or alcohol burner.

STEP 2. When steam starts to rise from the can, cork it, and take it off the burner.

>*Ask:* What do you think will happen to the can now that it is slowly cooling?
>
>What do you think will happen to the cork?
>
>Will it be pushed out of the can or pulled deeper?
>
>How can I prove this? (Have some marking ink so that you can mark the cork where it enters the can.)

Explanation: As the can cools, its water vapor condenses, reducing the pressure on the inside of the can. The sides then will be slowly pushed in by the air pressure in the room.

>*Ask:* Why is the can being pushed in?
>
>What is happening to the air inside the can as it cools?
>
>What is now inside the can? (*Answer:* a partial vacuum.)
>
>Why doesn't the can just cave in immediately?
>
>How could the can be made to go back to its original shape?

Caution: Do not reheat the can with the cork in it in an effort to make it go back to its original shape, because the cork might get stuck and the pressure in the can might cause it to blow up.

Why wouldn't it be a good idea to heat the can?

STUDENT ACTIVITIES

1. When out camping, why wouldn't you heat an unopened can of soup in a fire?

2. What pushed in the sides of the can?

3. Why did the teacher put a little water in the can before she heated it? (*Answer:* Water vapor requires room and has considerable pressure when hot. It expands and pushes the air out of the can.)

4. After the teacher took the can off the flame, why did she put the cork in it?

5. What would have happened to the can if she had not put the cork in it?

6. After the can was corked, what happened to the water vapor inside?

7. What could you have done to speed up the rate at which this can was crushed?

8. What is a partial vacuum?

CAN AIR PRESSURE MOVE AN OBJECT?
[K – 8]

Concepts

Air exerts pressure.

In order for paper to burn,
there must be oxygen present.

When oxygen is burned in a
closed container, the air
pressure will be less in that
container; i.e., there will be less air (gas)
in the container.

Heat causes air to expand and
reduces the air in the bottle.

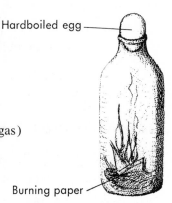

Hardboiled egg

Burning paper

Procedure

Obtain a milk bottle and a peeled hard-boiled egg.

STEP 1. *Ask:* How do you think I could get this egg into the bottle without
pushing it?

Place some paper or a candle in the bottle and light it. After the paper
has burned for several seconds, place the egg in the bottle.

Ask: Why did the egg go in the bottle?

Why did I put paper in the bottle and light it?

What does the paper need from the air in order to burn?

If we use some of the oxygen of the air in the bottle, do you
think the air pressure will remain the same?

Explanation: The pressure exerted by the gases alone would be the
same, since the oxygen would combine with carbon from the paper to
make another gas, carbon dioxide.

Ask: When we light the paper in the jar, what will the heat do to the
air in the jar?

Does warm air rise or fall in a room?

If warm air rises, would we have more or less air in the jar after
we burned the paper?

If there is less air in the bottle, how will the air pressure in the
bottle compare with the air pressure in the room (after the air
in the bottle cools)?

What, then, pushes the egg into the bottle?

Explanation: The air pressure in the bottle would be less, because the
burning paper would cause the gases in the bottle to expand and escape
before the egg was placed on the bottle.

STEP 2. *Ask:* How can I get the egg out of the bottle?

Invert the bottle so that the egg falls into the opening. Blow hard into the bottle so as to increase the pressure inside the bottle. Quickly take the jar away from your mouth and step aside. The egg usually will fly out with considerable force.

Ask: Why did the egg come out of the bottle?
What pushed it out?

STUDENT ACTIVITIES

Questions for Discussion

1. Since you can't see air, how do you know there is air pressure?

2. Why did the egg go into the jar?

3. Why was it necessary to blow hard in the jar in order to get the egg out?

4. Why did we burn paper in the jar?

5. What did the burning paper take out of the air?

6. What do you think would happen to an egg if we placed it over a bottle in which the pressure was the same as the air?

7. What causes the tires on your parents' car to hold their shape?

True or False

_____ 1. Hot air rises.

_____ 2. When paper burns, it uses some of the gases in the air.

_____ 3. Oxygen is in the air.

_____ 4. Air pressure can move objects.

_____ 5. Air has weight.

_____ 6. Cold air rises.

_____ 7. In order for the egg to enter the bottle, the pressure inside the bottle had to be less than the air pressure outside.

HOW DOES A SUBMARINE SUBMERGE?
[4-6]

Concepts

Air has pressure.
Air is lighter in weight than water.

Procedure

STEP 1. Explain "vacuum" and "partial vacuum." Place a bottle, as indicated in the diagram, in a half-full aquarium.

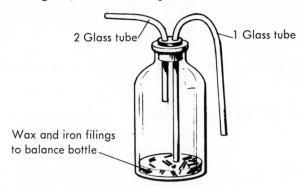

Ask: What do you think will happen when you suck on tube 2 while tube 1 is dipped in water?

STEP 2. Suck tube 1. Water will move into the jar.

Ask: Why does the water move into the jar?

Explanation: When you sucked out the air from the jar, a partial vacuum was produced. The air pressure exerted on the surface of the water then pushed water through tube 1 into the jar.

STEP 3. *Ask:* Why did the jar sink?

STEP 4. *Ask:* How do you think you could get the jar to float again?

STEP 5. Blow hard through tube 1.

Ask: Why do water and some air bubble out through tube 1?

STUDENT ACTIVITIES

1. Why did the "submarine" sink?

2. Why did it float later?

3. Draw how our submarine looked when it was sunk.

4. Draw how it looked when it floated.

5. Why do you have to have two glass tubes to make the glass submarine work?

6. After seeing this, how do you think the big naval submarines work?

7. What do you think would happen if you continued to suck on the tube after the submarine sank?

WHY ARE SUCTION CUPS HARD TO PULL APART?
[7 – 8]

Concepts

A partial vacuum is a space where there is less air pressure because there is less air.

Teachers Note: Use after students know $2\pi r^2$ or with math assignment where this is developed.

Procedure

STEP 1. Obtain two hemispheres, rubber vacuum cups (suction cups), and a spring scale.

STEP 2. Take two rubber vacuum cups, moisten them around the edges, and squeeze them together.

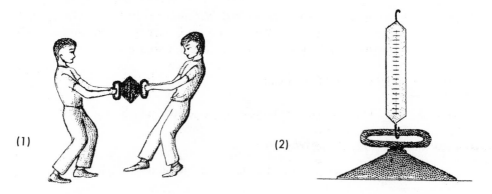

(1)   (2)

Ask: What do you think about the ability of two people to pull these apart (see Diagram 1)?

Explanation: They are difficult to pull apart because of the partial vacuum created within the cups. Air on the outside presses against the cups and holds them together.

STEP 3. Moisten one of the cups and push it against the blackboard. Take a spring balance and pull as indicated in Diagram 2. Do not pull hard on the balance — only use it to show that a great amount of force is required to pull the cup from the board. With a spring scale you can measure the pull required to loosen the cup.

Ask: How much force do you estimate will be needed to pull the hemisphere free from the wall?

Explanation: The area of a half a sphere may be determined by using the formula $2\pi r^2$, where the radius of the sphere is the distance from its center to the edge. If this is figured in square inches of area on the sphere, the total force applied to the sphere can be calculated by multiplying each square inch by 14.7 lb of air pressure for each square inch of surface on the sphere. The result will be slightly incorrect, because the 14.7 lb of pressure is for sea level at standard temperatures.

STUDENT ACTIVITIES

1. Von Guericke originally took two copper hemispheres, stuck them together, and pumped the air out of them. He then attached horses to each side of the globes, as shown in the Diagram 3, and tried to get the horses to pull them apart. Less than eight teams of horses could not separate the globes. Why?

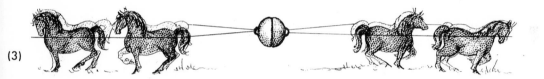

(3)

2. What did Von Guericke do to the hemispheres so that the horses could pull them apart easily?

3. About how many pounds of air pressure per square inch is there exerted on your body?

4. On the moon there is no air pressure. What would happen to your body on the moon if you walked out of a rocket ship and forgot to put on your pressurized suit?

(4)

5. A balloon is this size at sea level:
   Draw about how big this balloon would be at the top of a mountain 15,000 ft high.

6. Sometimes when people fly, their fountain pens leak. Why do you think this happens?

HOW DOES A MOVING STREAM OF AIR DIFFER FROM RESTING AIR?
[4–6]

Concepts

When a liquid or gas is flowing steadily, its pressure will be low if it is moving fast and will be high if it is moving slowly.
This principle is called Bernoulli's principle.

Teacher's Note: Before this demonstration is done, an explanation of "potential" and "kinetic" should be given. Explain about gravity.

Procedure

STEP 1. Take a piece of paper and fold the two sides as shown in Diagram 1. Blow a stream of air under the paper.

(1)

Ask: What do you notice about the way the paper top moves?
Why does the paper top sink down more when you blow under the paper?
Since the top of the paper sinks down, what do you know about the air pressure under it compared to the air pressure in the room?

Explanation: When you blow under the paper, the air moves much faster beneath the paper. The air before you blow under the paper has part of its energy in a potential form. When you blow the air, you increase its speed, or kinetic energy (energy due to movement), at the expense of its potential energy. The increase in kinetic energy is achieved at a loss of potential energy. The air, therefore, exerts less pressure.

STEP 2. Take a Coca Cola bottle and place a small piece of wadded paper in it, as shown in Diagram 2.

(2)

Ask: What do you think will happen to the paper if I blow across the front of the bottle (as indicated in Diagram 2)?

Blow across the front of the bottle.

Explanation: The paper will come out of the bottle, because the air will be moving at greater velocity across the front of the bottle, causing a lowering of air pressure. The paper is then pushed out by increased pressure inside the bottle.

Ask: What do you think will happen if the experiment is repeated, but this time I blow directly into the bottle?

STEP 3. Take a spool and a small card. Place a needle in the center of the card and stick the needle into the hole of the spool. Hold the paper with your hand at first and blow from the top of the spool. Release your hand after you have started to blow (see Diagram 3).

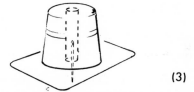

(3)

Ask: Why doesn't the paper fall?
What is holding the paper up?
Why doesn't the air I am blowing through the hole make the card fall?
Why do I need the pin in the middle of the paper?

Explanation: The pin is placed in the card to hold the card in the center of the spool. This allows for the air to escape more or less evenly on all sides of the spool. If the air didn't escape evenly, one side of the card would be tilted more than the other and would then fall, because of the pull of gravity. When you blow into the spool, the air moves rapidly between the spool and the card — causing less pressure. The air pressure holds the card up against the spool.

STEP 4. Place a ping pong ball in a thistle tube.

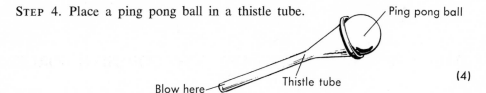

Ping pong ball

Blow here

Thistle tube

(4)

Ask: What do you think will happen to the ball when I blow through the tube?

Blow through the tube.

Ask: Why does the ball remain above the tube?

STEP 5. Take a piece of paper; hold each corner with a hand. Blow across the top of the paper (see Diagram 5).

(5)   Blow paper

Ask: Why does it rise?

Why wouldn't it be wise to stand close to a moving train?

Explanation: The paper rises because the moving air over the top causes less air pressure on top. The air pressure under the wing of a plane causes it to rise. The rapid motion of the train causes air to pass by it rapidly. This causes less pressure near the train. Air pressure farther out would then push a person into the train.

STUDENT ACTIVITIES

1. Explain what happened to the paper when the teacher blew under it.

2. Draw the Coca Cola bottle and explain what happened to the paper when the instructor blew across the mouth of the bottle.

3. Draw the Coca Cola bottle and explain what happened to the paper when the teacher blew directly into the bottle.

4. Explain what happened when the instructor blew into the spool.

5. Why didn't the card fall?

6. Was the air between the spool and the card moving faster or slower?

7. In order to have Bernoulli's principle work, decrease the air pressure. How must the air be moving? _____

8. Do you think Bernoulli's principle might also work with water?

WHAT ARE WATER PRESSURE AND COHESIVE FORCE?
[4−8]

Concepts

The deeper the water, the greater the pressure.

Water has cohesive force.

A force is defined as a push or pull on an object.

Molecules of the same substance tend to stick to each other, because they are attracted by an invisible force.

Each molecule of the substance pulls other atoms to it.

The force of attraction between molecules of the same kind is called *cohesive force.*

Teacher's Note: Molecular structure should be explained first.

Procedure   I.   Water Pressure

STEP 1. Take a tin can or a milk carton and puncture holes in the side of it at varying heights as shown in Diagram 1.

> *Ask:* What do you think will happen when the can is filled with water? Do you think the water will come out faster if it is filled closer to the top?

STEP 2. Fill the can.

(1)

> *Ask:* What can you say about how water pressure varies with depth?

Procedure   II.   Cohesive Force between Water Molecules

STEP 1. Puncture holes in a can as shown in Diagram 2.

(2)

> *Ask:* What is your hypothesis as to what will happen when water is poured into this can?
> How many jets of water will you get coming out of the holes in the can?

Pour water into the can.

> *Ask:* How many jets of water come out of the can?

What would I have to do to the water pouring out of the can so that I got only one jet?

List their hypotheses on the blackboard.

STEP 2. Pour water in the can and pinch the jets of water together with your fingers just as you would pinch someone. The jets will form one stream.

Explanation: If the water comes out in one jet, there must be some kind of force holding the water together. The force that holds similar molecules to each other is called cohesive force. Each molecule of water has cohesive force which pulls and holds other molecules of water to it (see Diagram 3, which is supposed to represent how a water droplet is being held together by cohesive force).

 Water molecules held together by cohesive forces

(3)

STUDENT ACTIVITIES

Part I

1. The deeper the water, the greater the _____.

2. In the diagram mark where the pressure is the greatest.

3. Air pressure is similar to water pressure. Knowing this, where do you think the air pressure would be more likely to be greater — on a mountain or at the beach?

4. Why do you think a dam must be built with very thick walls at the bottom and thinner walls at the top (see Diagram)?

5. Why do your ears sometimes hurt when you dive down deep in a swimming pool? What pushes in on your ears as you go deeper?

6. Why are the walls of a submarine so thick?

7. What would happen to the water escaping from two of the holes of a can if you stopped one hole?

8. What will happen to the water coming out of the bottom hole as the water gets lower in the can?

Part II [7–8 only]

1. What is a force?

2. Why do the water particles (molecules) tend to stick to each other?

3. When water comes over a waterfall, why doesn't it form several streams rather than one big fall?

4. Draw below how the water looked coming out of the can before the teacher pinched it and after the teacher pinched it.

HEAT

The following lessons can be included in one unit involving an understanding of heat and energy transfer. Whenever heat is applied to a substance, there is involved a transfer of energy from the source of the heat to the object receiving the energy. The way heat is transferred and the results of such transfer are outlined in the following lessons.

The first two lessons "What Is Heat?" and "How Is Heat Transmitted?" build concepts that relate heat to the motion of molecules. The lessons show that heat may be transmitted in three ways and explain how these vary. Children do not understand heat transfer easily unless they have seen several demonstrations; for this reason the third lesson "What Is Convection?" should be done soon after the preceding lessons.

"What Is an Insulator?" involves demonstrations related to the transfer of heat by conduction. Children see that some objects conduct heat better than others and that man uses this information to his advantage. It is desirable to supplement the lesson by bringing into class several building materials used in insulating homes. These should be tested to see how well they keep things cold or warm. This can be done by wrapping ice cubes in the insulating material and measuring the time they take to melt compared to ice cubes left at room temperature.

The next two lessons "What Happens to Metals When Heated?" and "What Happens to Gases When They Are Heated?" show the effects of the transfer of heat on materials. The instructor should explain that the transfer of energy always involves the motion of molecules. For example, in heated metals, the molecules vibrate more than when unheated. As a result of this vibration, a greater distance between molecules occurs. The metal will then expand or become larger. Gas molecules, when heated, increase their energy and vibrate even more vigorously than metals causing expansion.

The last two lessons "Why Does It Take So Much Time to Boil Water?" and "Can You Boil Water in a Paper Cup?" show that water can absorb large amounts of energy. The first lesson also develops concepts showing that the change of a state of matter requires a large amount of energy transfer. For example, to change ice from $0°C$, the solid state, to water at $0°C$, the liquid state, 80 calories of heat must be added. However, it takes only 10 calories of heat to change 1 gram of water $10°C$.

The children should gain the idea that whenever a change of state occurs there is a relatively large transfer of energy involved. Ice to water and water to steam require that heat be added while steam to water and water to ice require that heat be given off.

The last lesson incorporates many of the concepts found in the previous lessons and in addition introduces the idea of the kindling point, the temperature at which a substance will first start to burn. Involved in this lesson is the transfer of energy from the flame to the water, convection of the water in the cup, and the change of the state of water to water vapor.

WHAT IS HEAT?
[4 – 8]

Concepts

When a body is heated, its molecules move faster or vibrate more.
When a body is cooled, its molecules are moving more slowly.
Heat is the total energy a body has because of the motion of its molecules.

Teacher's Note: Explain molecules.

Procedure

STEP 1. Hit a nail several times with a hammer.

Ask: What do you think the nail head will feel like?

STEP 2. Let several students feel the nail. Have another nail present at room temperature so that students can compare it with the one hit with the hammer.

Ask: Why do you think the nail feels warm?
What happened to the molecules of the nail when I hit them with the hammer?

Explanation: When you hit the nail with the hammer, the nail and the hammer become warm. A theory of matter explains this fact by stating that by hitting the nail you made its molecules move faster. According to this theory, heat is the total energy a body has because of the motion of its molecules. The faster the molecules move, the more heat it has.

STEP 3. Rub some sandpaper very quickly over a board.

THE PHYSICAL WORLD

Sandpaper ⎯⎯

Board ⎯⎯

Ask: What do you think the board will feel like after I rub it very rapidly with sandpaper?

After sanding the board rapidly, have several students feel the board.

Ask: What do you note about the warmth of the board?
Why does the board feel warmer?
What do you do to the molecules in the board when you rub it quickly with sandpaper?

STUDENT ACTIVITIES

1. How do scientists explain heat?

2. Why do you rub a match against the side of a match box?

3. Why don't matches catch fire sitting in a match box?

4. When you bend a wire back and forth several times, why does it get warm?

5. Put your hands together and rub them back and forth several times. What happens to your hands? Why do they feel the way they do?

6. A man tried to strike a match against a piece of glass in order to light it. The match wouldn't light. Why?

7. If you feel the tires of your car before you take a trip and then just after you get out of the car, they will not feel the same. How do you think they will differ?

8. How would you explain the above difference?

9. A man was chopping wood with an axe. After chopping very hard for about ten minutes, he felt the axe. How do you think the axe felt and why?

10. When people are cold, they often jump up and down. Do you think this helps to warm them? Explain your answer.

Teacher's Note: The following are questions to use in testing for background understanding of molecular structure.

1. All matter is made of _____.

2. Molecules (never, always, sometimes) move or are moving.

3. The molecules in metals, gases, liquids move. (True, False)

4. When a body is heated, the molecules move (faster, not at all, more slowly).

5. Heat is energy caused by moving _____.

HOW IS HEAT TRANSMITTED?
[K – 8]

Concepts

A candle gives off radiant heat.

Heat can be transmitted from one body to another by conduction, convection, and radiation.

A candle gives off radiant energy.

Liquids and gases transfer heat by convection.

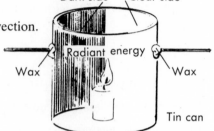

(1)

Procedure I. [K–6]

STEP 1. Obtain a large tin can like that indicated in Diagram 1. Paint one half of the inside with black paint and leave the other side the natural metal.

STEP 2. Place one stick in some wax on the outside of the dark side of the can. Place another stick on the unpainted side (see diagram).

STEP 3. Light a candle and place it in the can. Don't let the students know that one part of the inside of the can has been painted. Have the students time how long it takes for the sticks to fall.

Ask: Why do you think one of the sticks on one side fell first?

Repeat the experiment, if you have time, so that the class can see that the stick on one side always falls first.

STEP 4. *Ask:* Since you have noticed that the stick on one side of the can always falls first, what do you suspect about the inside surfaces of the can?

When you look at a piece of aluminum foil in sunlight, what happens to your eyes?

When you look at a piece of black paper, what happens to your eyes?

Why doesn't the black paper seem to bother your eyes as much as the aluminum foil?

Explanation: The aluminum foil reflects radiant energy, whereas the black paper does not.

Ask: Knowing this, what do you suspect the inside surfaces of the cans might look like?

STEP 5. Show the class the inside of the can.

> *Ask:* What is the candle giving off that is being absorbed by the black
> side of the can and being partially reflected by the light side
> of the can?

> *Explanation:* The candle is giving off radiant energy in the form of
> light and heat waves. These heat waves are absorbed by the black side
> of the can. This process of transferring heat by means of heat waves
> is called radiation. Radiation is the means by which the sun's energy
> is sent to the earth.

Procedure   II.   Conduction   [7–8]

STEP 1. Take some aluminum foil and roll it tightly to make an aluminum
rod. Place some wax and tacks on it, as shown in Diagram 2. Obtain
a copper wire or tube and a silver knife and do the same thing.
Attempt to get the three pieces of metal the same length.

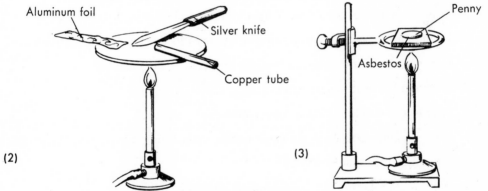

(2)   (3)

> *Ask:* What do you think will happen when I light the burner and
> heat the tips of these metals?
> Will the tacks all fall at the same time?

Heat the tips of the metals, as shown in Diagram 2.

> *Ask:* Why didn't the tacks all fall at the same time?
> What can you conclude about the rate of conduction of these
> different metals?
> Why do the tacks closest to the flame fall first?

STEP 2. Place a piece of asbestos on a ring stand and a penny on top of it,
as shown in Diagram 3. Place a burner or candle below the asbestos.

> *Ask:* Which of these, the penny or the asbestos, do you think will
> feel warmer?

Touch the penny, then the asbestos.

> *Ask:* Why does the penny feel warmer?

Explanation: The asbestos and the penny are nearly the same temperature, but the penny can conduct heat much more rapidly than the asbestos, so it feels much warmer.

Explanation of Conduction: Conduction is the process of the transfer of heat by collisions of molecules against each other. A frying pan gets hot because when it is heated the molecules in the bottom of the pan move faster and they collide with other molecules. This process continues until all the molecules of the pan are moving faster. As a result, the pan becomes hot.

STUDENT ACTIVITIES

1. When you stand in front of a fireplace and the front of you is warmed by the fire, how is the heat transferred?

2. How does heat energy come from the sun?

3. What colors are more likely to absorb heat?

4. Why do people generally wear lighter colored clothes in the summer?

5. In the can experiment, what kind of energy did the black surface absorb?

6. How was the heat transferred from the black surface to the wax?

7. What kind of heat was transferred in the wax?

8. Why is it desirable to have a copper-bottomed tea kettle?

9. Why wouldn't you want a copper handle on a frying pan?

10. What metals conduct heat well?

11. Why would asbestos be a good insulator against heat loss?

12. What are the three ways heat is transferred from one place to another?

WHAT IS CONVECTION?
[5–8]

Concepts

Convection is the process whereby warm liquids or gases rise and colder liquids or gases fall.

Warmed liquids and gases expand and occupy more space. As a result they have fewer molecules per volume than when they are cold.

They are, therefore, less dense.

The warmer liquids and gases rise because they are less dense than they would be if they were cold.

Procedure

STEP 1. Open a window from the top down. Take some newspaper, wad it, and light the tip. Hold the paper near the window.

Ask: What do you notice about the movement of the smoke?

STEP 2. Leave the top part of the window open and open the bottom part slightly as well.

Ask: What do you notice about the way the smoke moves now?

Explanation: If the room is warmer than the air outside the room, the warm air in the room will pass out of the top window. The smoke then will move out of the room. The reverse is the case for the lower window. The cold air will move into the room through the lower window This shows that warm air rises and cold air falls.

STEP 3. Set up apparatus as shown in Diagram 1. Obtain some twine, or purchase from a scientific supply house some special smoke paper. Place it in the bottom of the chimney. Light the twine or paper so that it gives off smoke.

(1)

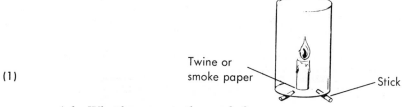

Ask: What happens to the smoke?
   Why is it rising?
   Is the smoke warmer or colder than the air around it?
   What can you say from this experiment about the movement of warm air?
   Do you think that this process of warm air rising and cold air falling, called convection, might also be true with liquids?

STEP 4. Take a small ink or paste bottle and place two glass tubes in its cork as indicated in Diagram 2. Fill the bottle with hot colored water.

(2)

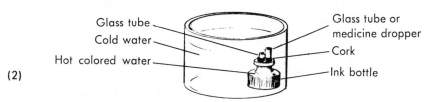

Ask: What do you think will happen if I drop this bottle in a tank of cold water?

STEP 5. Drop the bottle in a large glass jar filled with cold water.

Ask: Do you think there may also be convection currents in the ocean?

STEP 6. If possible, obtain from a scientific supply house a convection tube like that shown in Diagram 3. Place a drop of colored water in the opening.

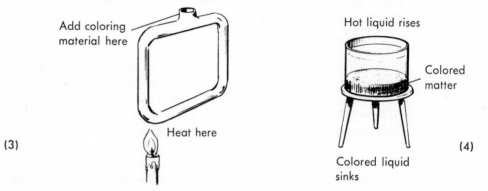

Add coloring material here

Heat here

Hot liquid rises

Colored matter

Colored liquid sinks

(3)

(4)

Ask: How can I make this colored water move to the right without moving the tube?

Where should I heat the tube so that it will move in this direction?

Heat the tube as indicated in the diagram.

Ask: As I heat the left side of the tube, what happens to the water in that side of the tube?

Why does the water in the right side of the tube fall?

Fill the beaker with water. Place small coloring crystals in the bottom of the beaker. (Potassium permanganate will work and can be obtained cheaply from a druggist.)

Ask: What will happen to this coloring matter as I heat the solution?

STEP 7. Heat the solution on one side of the beaker.

Explanation: As you heat the glass, the water on the bottom of the beaker receives heat by conduction and is warmed. Water is a poor conductor of heat, so heat is not conducted to other parts of the glass. The warmer solution in the bottom of the glass expands and becomes less dense. Therefore, it moves above the colder, denser water above it.

STUDENT ACTIVITIES

1. Why does smoke rise?

2. Why are chimneys high?

3. Why do some people wad newspaper, light it, and hold it high in the fire-place, directly below the opening of the chimney, before they light the main part of the fire?

4. What proof have you seen from the experiments that there are convection currents in liquids?

5. What is the warmest part of the school room?

6. What is the coldest part of the school room?

7. Why do warm liquids or gases rise above colder ones?

8. If you wanted to have good air circulation in your room at home, how would you arrange your windows?

9. Draw below how the convection currents looked in the experiments we did with the colored water.

10. Draw below how the smoke moved in the glass chimney. Indicate where the cold air enters the chimney.

WHAT IS AN INSULATOR?
[4 – 6]

Concepts

Water is a poor conductor of heat.
Wood, cork, glass, asbestos, and air are poor conductors of heat.
Heat from a burner rises.

(1)

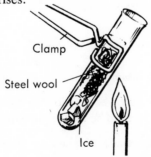

Clamp

Steel wool

Ice

Procedure

STEP 1. *Ask:* Do you think water is a good conductor of heat?

Set up the demonstration as indicated in Diagram 1. Heat the solution above the ice cube for several minutes after the water has boiled.

Ask: What can you conclude about water being a good or a bad conductor of heat?

Can you conclude from this experiment whether heat rises or falls?

Why do you think the deeper part of a lake is often colder than the surface?

Why did we put steel wool in the top of the tube?

Explanation: The steel wool is to keep the ice down.

STEP 2. Obtain a piece of asbestos from your local hardware store. Place the asbestos on a stand as shown in Diagram 2 and some matches on the upper surface. Heat the lower surface.

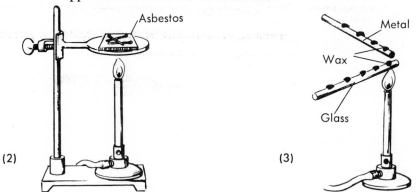

(2) (3)

Ask: Why didn't the matches immediately burst into flame?

Do you think asbestos is a good conductor of heat?

STEP 3. Take a glass rod and a metal rod (a brass curtain rod can serve for the metal rod). Place wax on the two rods as shown in Diagram 3. Heat gently over a candle.

Ask: On which rod did the wax melt first?

Would you say that metal is a better conductor of heat than glass?

Do you think glass is a very good conductor of heat? Why?

STUDENT ACTIVITIES

1. Name some poor conductors of heat.

2. If glass were a good conductor of heat, and you lived in a glass house, what do you think your heating bill would be like in the winter?

3. Why are coffee cups usually made of glass or china instead of metal?

4. Why do frying pans often have wooden handles on them?

5. Why do builders sometimes install asbestos around stove pipes and chimneys?

6. If you have a glass coffee pot, why don't you have to worry too much about the handle being hot?

7. How could the handle be made better to protect you against burning your hand?

8. If you left a brass poker in a fire in the fireplace for a long time, what would you do before you picked up the poker?

9. Houses are often built with an outside wall, an air space, and an inside wall. It would be cheaper to build a house with only one wall and no air space. What purpose do you think the air space serves in the wall?

10. Do you think air is a very good conductor of heat?

11. Draw the apparatus we used to show that water is not a particularly good conductor of heat and tell how you can conclude this fact from the experiment.

12. When the test tube with the ice was heated in class, why was it held fairly high above the flame instead of directly on the flame?

WHAT HAPPENS TO METALS WHEN THEY ARE HEATED? [4–6]

Concepts

Metals expand when heated.
Different metals expand at different rates.
Solids transfer heat by conduction.

Procedure

STEP 1. Obtain two wires: one copper and one steel (piano wire will do). They should preferably be the same diameter. Suspend the wires as shown in Diagram 1, hanging equal weights on each wire. Measure the height of the weights so that each weight is the same distance from the top of the demonstration desk.

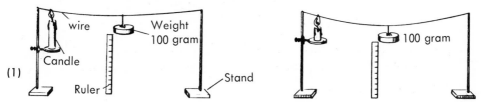

(1)

Ask: What do you think will happen to the wire when I heat it with a candle or Bunsen burner?

STEP 2. Heat the wires as indicated in the drawing. Place the candles the same distance below the wires. After heating for several minutes, measure the distance the weights have moved toward the desk top. Touch the end of the wire opposite the end you heated.

Ask: How do you think the wire feels?

How was the heat transferred to that end of the wire?

Explanation: When you heat one end of the wire, the molecules in that end are excited and vibrate more, exciting the molecules next to them. Thus, by successive bombardments the molecules hit each other until the other end of the wire is reached. This transfer of heat by means of collisions of molecules is called conduction.

Ask: Why did the weights move closer to the desk?

What happened to the length of the wire as we heated it?

Which wire lengthened or expanded more?

Would you say from this experiment that different metals expand at different rates?

How could we get the metals to expand more?

Which expands faster, copper or steel?

STEP 3. Obtain some copper wire, a ring stand, newspaper, paper clips, a small stick, and a weight. Tie one end of the wire to a stand and attach the weight to the other end. Wrap the wire around a stick to be used as a pointer (see Diagram 2). Place next to a pointer a card with equally distant marks on it. Draw in red a line next to where the stick points before you begin the experiment.

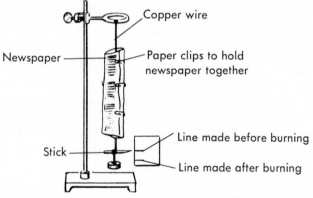

(2)

Caution: When you light the paper, be certain the equipment is so arranged that it will not burn the desk. This can be insured if you have the apparatus hanging away from the desk and do not use excessive paper.

Ask: What do you think we are going to do with this apparatus?

What do you think will happen to the wire when I light the paper?

Explanation: When the paper burns, the heat released causes the wire to expand, and the pointer will move downward. When the wire recools, the pointer will move upward. It might be advisable to put one end of the pointer between some books in order to give it stability.

STEP 4. Light the paper and watch the pointer move.

> *Ask:* Why did the pointer move?
> Which way did it move?
> What can you conclude about a metal when it is heated?
> Why did we use copper wire in this experiment?
> If we had used aluminum wire, would you suspect that the wire would move as much?

STUDENT ACTIVITIES

1. What happens to metals when you heat them?

2. Your mother has a jar lid that she can't open. What would you suggest she do in order to open the lid more easily?

3. From the demonstrations you have seen, do you think all metals expand at the same rate?

4. What happens to telephone wires in the winter compared with the summer?

5. When engineers build a bridge, they leave spaces in the road at specified distances. These are called expansion joints. Why do you think they do this?

6. A man is said to have measured the San Francisco Bay Bridge in the winter and in the summer. He found that the bridge was actually eight inches longer in the summer than in January. Does this seem possible? Why?

7. In the demonstration with the two wires and weights, how was the heat transferred from one end of the wire to the other?

8. How do solids transfer heat?

9. When both are heated in the same way, which expands more — copper wire or steel wire?

10. How was heat conducted along the wire when we held the candle at one end?

WHAT HAPPENS TO GASES WHEN THEY ARE HEATED?
[5 – 6]

Concepts

> Gases expand when heated
> Gases contract when cooled
> Gases are less dense than water.
> When gases are heated, the molecules move farther apart and exert greater pressure on the walls of the container.
> Glass is not a very good conductor of heat.

Procedure

STEP 1. *Ask:* Using a balloon, how could I determine if a gas will expand
when heated or contract when cooled?

Obtain four balloons. Blow them up so that they are all about the
same size, and tie them closed. Place one of them near a radiator or
room heater. Tie it to a chair. If your school has an infrared lamp,
place another one about two feet away from the lamp. (These lamp
bulbs can be purchased fairly inexpensively from the local hardware
store.) A large regular light bulb may be substituted for this purpose.
Take a third balloon and immerse it in ice-cold water over its surface.
Leave the fourth balloon at room temperature on your desk (See
Diagrams 1, 2, and 3).

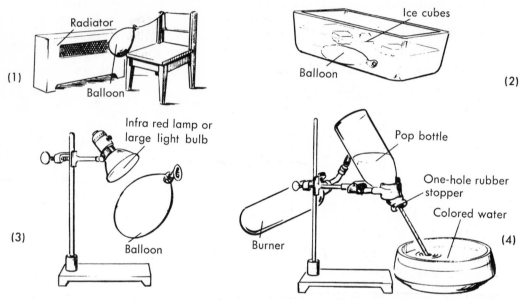

Ask: Why did I leave one balloon at room temperature?

Which balloons expanded?

What do you think happened to the molecules inside the expanding balloons?

Do you think the molecules are moving faster and hitting the sides
of the balloon with greater force than the molecules in the
cold balloon?

STEP 2. Assemble the equipment shown in Diagram 4 by inserting a glass tube
in a one-hole rubber stopper. Place the stopper and tube in a pop
bottle. Support the pop bottle with a clamp. Be sure that the open end
of the glass tube is under water.

Ask: What do you think this apparatus will be used to demonstrate?

STEP 3. Start heating the flask slowly.

> *Ask:* What will happen to the air in the bottle when I heat it?
> Why don't bubbles immediately escape from the tube?
> Knowing that the thickness of the wall of the bottle is not very great, do you think glass is a very good conductor of heat?
> Why do the bubbles continue to escape from the tube?
> Why do the gas bubbles go up? Is the gas less dense than the water?
> What do you think will happen when I take the heat away from the bottle?
> What do I have in the tube?

> *Explanation:* When you heat the bottle, the gas molecules move faster and with greater energy. The gas, as a result, expands down the tube and escapes. The bubbles go to the surface because water is more dense than air. Since there is less air in the bottle than there is in the same volume of air in the room, you have a *partial vacuum* in the bottle.

STEP 4. Take the burner away from the bottle and let it cool slowly.

> *Ask:* What will happen to the air in the flask as it cools?
> Since the gas will exert less pressure when it cools, what will happen to the water in the glass tube?

> *Explanation:* Since the air pressure will be greater than the pressure in the cooled bottle, water will be forced up the tube into the bottle until the pressure inside the flask is equal to room air pressure.

STUDENT ACTIVITIES

1. What evidence do you have that gases expand when heated?

2. One hot day you drove a car. You stopped and checked the tires and found that there were 40 lbs of pressure per square inch instead of the 35 lb of pressure suggested by the car manufacturer. Why wouldn't you necessarily want to let air out of the tires?

3. What time of day would be the best time to check your car tires?

4. Some boys were camping. They had some canned beans. They decided that they would heat them by placing the unopened can in the hot embers of the fire. Knowing what you do about air pressure and gases, tell why this would be a very dangerous idea.

5. What happens to gases when you cool them?

6. What happens to the gas molecules when you heat them?

7. What do you mean when you say gases expand when heated?

8. Why do you think steam boilers are constructed with such thick walls?

WHY DOES IT TAKE SO MUCH TIME TO BOIL WATER?
[4–6]

Concepts

To change the state of matter requires heat to be added or taken away from a substance.

Water absorbs a considerable amount of heat before it will be changed into water vapor.

Water at sea level boils at 100°C or 212°F.

Boiling water will not rise above this temperature, no matter how fast you heat it, except in a pressure cooker.

It takes 540 calories of heat per gram to change water to steam.

Procedure: Different Substances Contract or Expand at Different Rates

STEP 1. Obtain the following equipment and assemble it as shown in the diagram: ring stand, flask or beaker (flask is better), Bunsen burner, two thermometers.

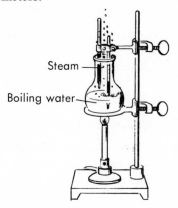

Ask: How can you change water into water vapor or steam?
     Why do you think I have two thermometers?

STEP 2. Ask: Why do the thermometers go up when heat is added?
        What makes the mercury metal in the thermometer move up?

Explanation: Develop the concept that when a metal is heated it will expand and when cooled it will contract. Mercury is a metal, so it expands and moves up the tube when heated.

Ask: What do you think will happen to the metal in the thermometer when it is cooled?

What would happen to the thermometer if you took it out of the hot water and plunged it into ice-cold water?

Explanation: It would probably crack, because the outside layer of glass would contract at a much faster rate than the inside layer of the tube used in the thermometer. The outside section of the glass tube would, therefore, contract faster and pull apart from the inside section. The stress would be too great and the tube would then crack.

STEP 3. Heat the water.

Ask: Which thermometer do you think will get the hotter, and why?

Explanation: The experiment shows that water requires a lot of heat to change its state. When the flask is heated, both the thermometers will have the same reading after the water reaches its boiling point. The temperature will be the same for both steam and water. Take several readings and post them on the blackboard. Continue the process for several minutes after the water has begun to boil.

Ask: Why does it take so long for the water to boil after it has reached 100°C.?

Explanation: One cubic centimeter of water (this is about the same volume of water as one cube of sugar occupies) requires one calorie to go up one degree. When water reaches the boiling point, however, it takes 540 calories of heat per cubic centimeter to change the state of water into water vapor. This 540 calories of energy is used just to change the state, liquid to gas. Emphasize to the class that a large amount of heat is necessary to change the state of any matter.

STUDENT ACTIVITIES

1. What happens to metals when they are heated?
2. Record the temperatures taken during the experiment.
3. How hot did the water get? What do you think would happen to the water if you heated it more rapidly?
4. After water reaches the boiling temperature, does it do any good to turn up the heat on a stove?
5. At what temperature does water boil?
6. Did you lose any water from the flask by heating it?
7. Where did the water go?
8. Why did it take so long for the water to boil?
9. What was the water absorbing from the flame?

10. Why did it take so long for the water after it got to 99° or 100° before it changed into steam?

11. For what reason did we use two thermometers in this experiment?

12. Why does hot tea poured in a glass containing ice cubes crack the glass?

CAN YOU BOIL WATER IN A PAPER CUP?
[4 – 6]

Concepts

A flame can be the source of radiant heat.

Water, when heated, will expand and will give off water vapor.

Water can absorb a considerable amount of heat.

Before a substance will burn, its kindling temperature must be reached.

The kindling temperature is the temperature at which a substance will first start to burn.

Procedure

STEP 1. Obtain a nonwaxed paper cup and place it on a stand as shown in the diagram. Place a burner with low heat not too close to the bottom of the cup. Heat gently. The cup should be supported on top of a piece of wire screen over a ring clamp.

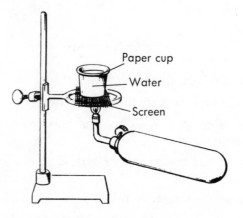

Ask: What do you think will happen to the cup?

Explanation: The ring and screen serve as support and as a conductor of heat. They help to spread the heat over a greater area. Have the class note the boiling of the water. The experiment, however, will work without a screen if the heat is kept low. Take the temperature of the water to show that it is boiling. An alcohol burner works well.

Ask: Why doesn't the paper burn?
What is the water taking away from the bottom of the cup?
What is happening to the heated water at the bottom of the cup?
When the water escapes from the cup as a vapor, what does it carry away with it?
When do you think the paper cup will burn?

Explanation: There is an equilibrium reached between the heat the water absorbs and from the flame and the amount of heat released by vapor.

Show an example of an equilibrium by dropping one drop of green and one drop of yellow food coloring in still water. When blue is achieved, equilibrium is reached. The food colors must be dropped at opposite ends of the container.

STEP 2. Heat the cup until all of the water has evaporated.

STEP 3. *Ask:* Why did the paper cup finally burn?
Do you think the kindling temperature of the paper cup is higher than the temperature it takes to boil water?
How do you know that this is true?

STEP 4. Explain that different substances have different kindling temperatures.

Explanation: The kindling temperature of gasoline is lower than wood, and that of wood is lower than coal.

STUDENT ACTIVITIES

1. Explain what happened to the water in the paper cup.

2. Would you say that water is capable of absorbing a lot of heat?

3. Why did the paper cup eventually catch fire?

4. How could you have prevented the cup from catching fire?

5. What portion of the water heated first in the cup?

6. What is happening to the molecules of the water as they absorb heat?

7. Why did your instructor place a ring or a wire screen below the cup?

8. What is the kindling point?

9. Place the following substances in order, listing the one with lowest kindling point first and with the highest last: wood, paper, coal, gasoline, steel.

SOUND

The study of sound involves the transfer of energy. No sound is produced unless some thing is vibrating. The lessons that follow develop this concept. Most of the lessons in this section can be included in one unit, grade level permitting.

The first two lessons "How Does Sound Vary with the Length of a Vibrating Body?" and "How Does Sound Vary with the Length of an Air Column?" introduce the idea that vibrating bodies produce sound and that the sound varies depending upon the length of a vibrating body or a column of air. The third lesson uses these principles to explain how string instruments produce various sounds. A visit to a band room introducing children to various instruments can do much to complement a unit on sound. The class should also be shown tuning forks. The concept that each fork vibrates at a definite frequency and that frequency is the number of vibrations a body makes per second should be explained.

The fourth lesson "What Causes Sound to Be Louder?" shows how an object vibrating with a greater energy but not a greater number of times per second produces a louder sound. Here again the concept of a body in motion producing a sound is actively depicted by the vibrating drum.

The lesson "Do Solids and Liquids Conduct Sound?" unfolds the idea that not only air but solids, such as wood and metal, and liquids can conduct sound.

The lesson "How Can the Reflection of Sound Be Changed?" outlines how sound energy may be absorbed or reflected.

The last lesson "Is Sound Possible in a Vacuum?" complements the preceding lessons by showing that sound must have a medium in order to be transmitted. The teacher should explain what a vacuum is and how it was produced in flask. An application of this principle to space science may be given by asking: "Why couldn't an astronaut hear a loud speaker on the moon?" The answer would be that the moon lacks an atmosphere to provide a medium to carry the sound across the space.

HOW DOES SOUND VARY WITH THE LENGTH OF THE VIBRATING BODY?
[2−6]

Concepts

Bodies in vibration make a sound.
The longer the vibrating body, the lower the tone.

Teacher's Note: This can be used in K-6; however, a visit to the band room during rehearsal and an explanation by the band teacher is necessary, helpful, and motivating.

Procedure   I.   A Pin Board Demonstration

STEP 1. Obtain a piece of balsa or soft wood, and place several pins in it at varying depths, as shown in Diagram 1.

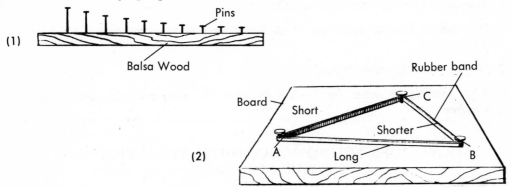

(1)

Pins

Balsa Wood

(2)

Ask: What do you think will happen if I vibrate the pins with my fingers?

Will we get the same sound from each of the pins?

Which pin do you think will give the highest tone when it is vibrated?

STEP 2. Vibrate the pins.

Ask: What is your conclusion about how the length of the pins determines the pitch of the tone?

Procedure   II.   Rubber Band Demonstration

STEP 1. Obtain a flat board and place three tacks or nails in it as shown in Diagram 2. Place a rubber band around the three tacks.

Ask: Where do you think I should pluck the rubber band in order to get the deepest tone?

STEP 2. Pluck it between points A and B.

Ask: Where do you think I should pluck it to get the next deepest tone?

Pluck it between A and C; then between C and B.

Ask: How does the tone vary with the length of the rubber band?

What instruments in an orchestra use this principle of sound?

How do musicians shorten the length of a string to get a higher pitch?

STUDENT ACTIVITIES

1. The longer the vibrating sound, the _____ the sound.

2. Draw two strings on a harp and label which one would give the higher tone.

3. Sound can be produced only if something is _____.

4. Why did the pins make sound?

5. Why did the rubber band make sound?

6. Why does a violinist move one of his hands up and down the strings when he plays?

7. Why does a piano make sound?

8. What vibrates to make sound when the cymbals in an orchestra are brought together?

HOW DOES SOUND VARY WITH THE LENGTH OF AIR COLUMN?
[2 – 6]

Concepts

The higher the pitch of a note, the more rapid the vibrations of the producing body.

Pitch can be varied by adjusting the depth of an air column.

The higher the water level, the shorter the air column, and the higher the pitch.

Procedure

STEP 1. Obtain eight pop bottles and place water in each so that there is a successive graduated depth of water from one bottle to the next. See the diagram. Blow across the tops of the bottles to check the tone. A little water may have to be added in order to get the tone desired.

Air

Ask: Which bottle do you think will give the highest tone and which one will give the lowest tone?

Blow across the tops of the bottles to demonstrate that the sound varies with the air column.

Ask: Using the pop bottles, how would you play a chord?

Have students blow simultaneously different combinations of the tubes, such as 1, 3, 5, or 1, 3, 5, and 8. Try to discover others. Play "Mary Had a Little Lamb."

STUDENT ACTIVITIES

1. Draw a bottle with water in it which would produce a high tone.

2. Draw a bottle with water in it which would produce a low tone.

3. What is vibrating in the bottles?

True or False

_____ 1. All the bottles had the same level of water, but thicker glass made the different pitches.

_____ 2. It was the length of the column of air in the bottle that made the difference in the pitch.

_____ 3. The longer the column of air in the bottle, the lower the pitch.

_____ 4. The shorter (or the less the amount of air in) the column, the higher the pitch.

HOW DOES A VIOLIN OR CELLO WORK?
[4 – 6]

Concepts

Tension of a string determines its pitch.
If the tension is increased, the pitch is raised.
The length of the string determines the pitch.
A thick string will give a lower tone than a thin string if both are the same length.
The longer the string, the lower the tone.

Procedure

STEP 1. Obtain a cardboard box (a shoe or cigar box will do). Place three pins or small nails at one end of the box. Attach a piece of thick string to one nail and thin string to each of the other nails. Attach equal weights to the other ends of the strings.

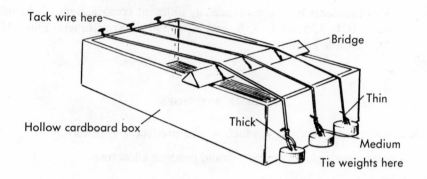

Ask: What do you think I am going to demonstrate with this box? Which of these strings do you think will give the highest tone when it is vibrated?

STEP 2. Pluck the strings.

Ask: Which one gave the lowest tone? The highest tone?

Take a weight off of one of the thin strings, and attach a heavier weight to it.

Ask: What do you think this heavier weight will do to the string?

Pluck it and have the students compare its sound with that of the other string.

Ask: What does increased tension on a string do to the sound?

STEP 3. Place a small board or ruler under the strings across the width of the box. Pluck the strings again. Move the board back and forth as you pluck in order to show how sound is varied.

STUDENT ACTIVITIES

True or False

_____ 1. Sound is caused when an object vibrates.

_____ 2. Air has to be present before we can hear sound.

_____ 3. The thickness of a string affects the tone.

_____ 4. A thick string will give a low tone.

_____ 5. A short string will give a high tone.

_____ 6. A tight string will give a high tone.

_____ 7. Sound is always absorbed and never reflected.

_____ 8. Sounds differ according to the quality of the object making the sound.

_____ 9. Sound is not a form of energy since it can never be used to make something else move.

Questions for Discussion

1. What evidence do you have from the demonstrations done in class that sound is made by vibration?

2. How would you make your voice produce a higher pitch, assuming that the vocal cords were similar to strings?

3. How would you get a vibrating string to make a louder sound?

4. What did the board do to the sound when we placed it under the strings on the cigar box?

5. How could you stop the sound on a string you had just plucked?

6. Why does a bass violin usually give deep tones?

WHAT CAUSES SOUNDS TO BE LOUDER?
[4 – 6]

Concepts

Sound is made when an object vibrates.
Loudness of a sound is caused by an object vibrating with greater energy, but not a greater number of times per second.
The pitch is not changed by a stronger vibration.

Teacher's Note: Background necessary for this lesson: molecular structure, vocal cord function, terms such as "pitch" and "vibration."

Procedure   I.   Vibration of the Drum

STEP 1. Obtain a drum or make a drum out of a large tin can over which you have stretched a balloon or piece of rubber tubing. Place a cork on the drum.

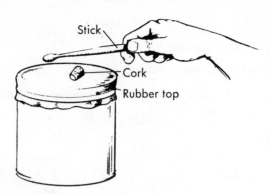

Ask: What do you think will happen to the cork if I hit the drum?

STEP 2. Hit the drum lightly.

  Ask: Does the cork bounce up and down only once or does it bounce
          several times?
          What do you think will happen to the cork if the drum is hit much
          harder?

Hit the drum harder and note what happens to the cork.

Ask: Did I change the pitch of the drum by hitting it harder?

Explanation: No. The sound was only made louder. A stronger vibration does not affect the pitch or quality, but it causes more molecules in
the air to move, which, in turn, strike our ear drums with greater force,
giving us the sensation of loudness.

Procedure II. Vibration of the Voice Box

STEP 1. Have the students place the palms of their hands over the front of
         their necks. Tell them to whisper hello.
         Now tell them to shout hello.

  Ask: How did your throat feel when you whispered compared to when
          you shouted?
          Did you make the same sound each time?
          Did the word sound like "hello" each time?
          Did your voice box seem to vibrate harder when you shouted
          than when you whispered?

Explanation: Tell the class that the drum on the can is similar to the
vocal cord in the voice box. The vocal cords probably vibrated the
same number of times when the students whispered as when they yelled,
but the vibration muscles moved farther up and down when they
shouted, making a louder sound as a consequence.

STUDENT ACTIVITIES

1. From the experiment with the can and cork, what do you conclude about how sound is made?

2. When the drum or the can was hit, did the cork bounce several times or just once?

3. Why did the cork bounce higher the second time the teacher hit the drum?

4. Did the pitch of the sound change because the drum was hit harder?

5. Where is your voice box?

6. Does your voice box vibrate with greater force when you shout?

7. How can you make a sound?

DO SOLIDS AND LIQUIDS CONDUCT SOUNDS?
[4 – 6]

Concepts

Sound can travel through solid substances.
Sound can travel through liquid substances.

Procedure   I.   Can Phones

STEP 1. Have the students make tin can telephones by using two cans and some string. Cardboard containers will also work. If possible, it is better to replace the tin end of a can with an old drum head. Soak it and stretch it over the end of the can. Cut a hole in it and attach the string by knotting it inside the can. A rubber drum head may also be used.

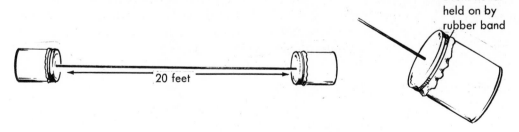

Drum head held on by rubber band

20 feet

STEP 2. Have the students hang the string loosely and note the difference in the transmitting of sound.

Ask: When is the sound best transferred from one phone to the other? How is the sound conducted?

Have some other students make similar phones, using steel or copper wire instead of string.

Explanation: When you talk into the telephone, the air in it vibrates the back of the can. This causes the string to vibrate, which, in turn, moves the drum at the other end. The air in that can moves back and forth so that a sound is produced.

Step 3. Take a board and hold it to a student's ear. Scratch one end of the board with a pencil or some other object. Repeat the above experiment but do not place the board next to the ear of the student.

Ask: Do you hear the scratching as well as you did when the board was against the ear?
Can sound pass along solid objects?
Is sound carried better in a solid than it is in the air?

Procedure II. Wood Can Produce Sound

Step 1. *Ask:* Can wood make sound?

Hold up a board and hit it with another board.

Ask: What did you hear?
What vibrated to produce the sound?

Step 2. Take a wood ruler or some other thin board. Hold it firmly with one hand against a desk. With the other hand pluck the overhanging part of the stick, causing it to vibrate.

Ask: What causes the sound to be produced?
Does anyone know how we could produce a high pitch by vibrating the stick?

Explanation: A low-pitched sound will be produced when the part overhanging the desk is long. A high-pitched sound will be produced when the overhang is short. By assembling eight sticks with various overhangs it is possible to produce a scale.

Procedure III. Liquids Carry Sound

Step 1. *Ask:* Do you think that liquids might also carry sound?
How could we prove that liquids carry sound?

Fill a large jar, bucket or aquarium with water. Take two pieces of metal or two rocks and hit them together under water.

Ask: Did you hear any sound when I hit them together under water?
What do you conclude about the ability of liquids to carry sound?

STUDENT ACTIVITIES

1. What did you do to the air in the can phone when you talked into it?

2. What happened to the end of the can when you talked into it?

3. When is the sound carried best by the can phones?

4. Will solid substances carry sound?

5. What solid substance transmitted the sound in the can phones?

6. Describe in detail how the sound is transmitted from one can phone to the other.

7. Why do the can phones work better if the string is held tightly?

8. What causes the backs of the cans to vibrate?

9. In your electrical telephone at home, what vibrates to produce the sound?

10. How do you know that liquids will conduct sound?

11. What is the purpose of making so many instruments out of wood?

12. Why are expensive radios or stereo phonographs usually made of wood?

HOW CAN THE REFLECTION OF SOUND BE CHANGED?
[1 – 6]

Concepts

When sound waves hit a hard surface, they may be thrown back.
Sound waves may be taken in and held in much the way a sponge holds water.
Some things absorb sound waves better than others.

Procedure   I.   Reflection of Sound

STEP 1. Obtain two large tin cans; the larger the better.

   Ask: What do you think will happen if I have someone yell into one of these cans?

STEP 2. Have several students yell into a can while the rest of the class notes what happens.

Ask: What did you hear?

What do you think happened to the sound waves when they hit the end of the can?

STEP 3. Take another can the same size and make several nail holes in the end of it.

Ask: What do you think will happen to the sound when a student shouts into this can?

Have several students shout first into the unpunctured can and then into the punctured can.

Ask: Why do you think the sound wasn't the same in the perforated can?

What happened to some of the sound waves in the can with holes?

Procedure II. Sound Absorbers

STEP 1. Take a cloth and place it inside the can without holes.

Ask: What do you think will happen to the sound when a student yells into this can?

Have a student yell into the can.

Ask: Why did the sound seem different?

Repeat the experiment, using other substances such as paper, steel, and wool, and note the difference in the sound.

Explanation: When sound waves hit a hard, smooth, solid surface, they are easily reflected, but when they hit a soft substance, such as cloth, they are absorbed.

STEP 2. Take an alarm clock and some wool cloth.

Ask: What will happen to the sound of the alarm if I wrap the clock in the wool cloth?

Turn the alarm clock on and wrap it in the cloth.

Ask: What happened to the sound of the alarm when the clock was wrapped with cloth?

STEP 3. Repeat the experiment, using cotton cloth, silk, newspaper, a coat, and a sweater.

> *Ask:* What is the difference in the sound for each of the above substances?

STEP 4. Turn on the alarm and place the clock inside a shoebox and cover the box with its top.

> *Ask:* What happens to the sound?
> Why doesn't the sound seem as loud?

STUDENT ACTIVITIES

Questions for Discussion

1. What is sound that is thrown back called?

2. What kind of surface do you need to have sound reflect well?

3. What happened to the sound when it hit the can with holes in it?

4. Why does a room without any furniture or drapes in it make a sound different from that which it does when it is furnished?

5. What suggestions would you make for building an auditorium so that there would be no reflected sound or echoes?

6. Do all substances absorb sound equally well?

7. Which of the substances tested in the demonstration in class absorbed sound the best?

8. Why did the alarm make less sound inside the box?

9. List the things which you have in your schoolroom to help reduce noise or reflection of sound.

True or False

_____ 1. Woolen cloth is good at throwing back sound.

_____ 2. Curtains help to absorb sound waves.

_____ 3. Sound waves are absorbed when they hit a hard, smooth surface and reflected when they hit a soft surface.

_____ 4. Some things absorb sound waves better than others.

_____ 5. A vast empty auditorium will produce a reflected sound.

_____ 6. Rough surfaces are good reflectors of sound.

_____ 7. All substances absorb sound equally well.

_____ 8. Some of the sound waves that hit the end of the can were absorbed.

_____ 9. The sound of the alarm in the shoebox was less than that of the alarm outside the box.

_____ 10. Wall-to-wall rugs will help to absorb sound.

IS SOUND POSSIBLE IN A VACUUM?
[4 – 6]

Concepts

Sound is produced by moving matter and is transmitted by matter.
Air transmits sound.
A vacuum doesn't transmit sound, because there is no substance present to transmit it.

Procedure

STEP 1. Partially fill a florence flask or large milk bottle with water. Boil the water for several minutes.

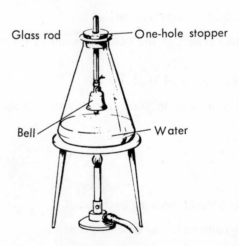

Glass rod — One-hole stopper

Bell — Water

Ask: What happens to the air in the flask when it is heated?

STEP 2. After boiling for several minutes take the burner away from the flask and immediately insert a one-hole cork stopper. A solid glass rod should be pushed through the hole and a small bell attached to the one end. See diagram.

STEP 3. Let the flask cool for several minutes.

Ask: What happens to the water vapor in the flask when it cools?

Shake the flask in order to ring the bell.

Ask: Can you hear the bell?
Is it very loud?
Why isn't the bell very loud?
What would I have to do to the flask so that you can hear the bell?
Is there a partial vacuum in the flask?
How do you know this?

Explanation: When you heat the flask, the water is changed to water vapor. It expands, pushing out the air. When the stoppered flask cools, the water vapor is condensed into water, so there is very little air or gas present in the container. There is produced, therefore, a partial vacuum in the flask.

STEP 4. Remove the stopper from the flask and allow some air to enter. Ring the bell again.

Ask: What does the bell sound like now?
Why is it louder?
Do you need air in order to transmit sound?
Did you hear the air rush in when I unstoppered the bottle?
Would you say that there is more air in the flask now?
Does the bell ring louder with air in the flask?
Would you say from this demonstration that air transmits sound?

STUDENT ACTIVITIES

Questions for Discussion

1. How did the bell sound when there was air in the flask?

2. How did it sound when there was little or no air in the flask?

3. Why was the flask heated in the demonstration?

4. After the flask was heated, stoppered, and cooled, what was present in the flask?

5. Will sound pass through a partial vacuum?

6. On the moon there is no atmosphere. If one astronaut shouted at another on the moon, what would the shout sound like?

7. Heat is used to change water into _____.

True or False

_____ 1. There was absolutely no air left in the stoppered flask after heating.

_____ 2. There was a partial vacuum in the flask.

_____ 3. Air is the only matter that can transmit sound.

_____ 4. In this experiment the bell wasn't heard because there wasn't enough water in the flask to transmit sound waves.

_____ 5. Water vapor pushed out the air when the flask was heated.

LIGHT

Most of these upper elementary grade level lessons on light should be grouped together in order to give children more experiences with the subject. Some of the concepts included in this section are not easily understood unless the children have several experiences using them.

"Why Do You Need Two Eyes?" is an elementary lesson used to make children aware that they are not able to judge depth and distance easily without the use of both eyes.

The next two lessons "How Do Convex and Concave Lenses Work?" and "A Convex Lens Can Make Objects Look Larger" can be given together in the upper grades. The lessons compliment each other in that they both have individual concepts involving lenses. The difference between convex and concave lenses in structure and function is developed plus some understanding of how light waves may be changed by lenses.

The fourth lesson "How Is Light Changed When It Passes Through Water?" shows that the direction of light waves can be altered by passing them through water or glass. The lesson "How Is Light Reflected?" shows that light is reflected in certain definite ways. The diagrams immediately following the lessons should be held up to the class or drawn on the blackboard. The class should be asked to explain what each diagram shows in order to see how well the children have gained the concepts presented in the preceding lessons.

The lesson "How Does A Pinhole Camera Work?" explains how a box camera works and how the light waves move to form an inverted image.

The last lesson "What Does A Prism Do to Light?" shows that visible white light is really made of several different wave lengths of colored light. This lesson can be used to introduce a study of the physical nature of color. The lesson shows further that a prism can refract or spread out light producing a visible spectrum or rainbow and can change the direction of light as is done in a periscope.

WHY DO YOU NEED TWO EYES?
[1 – 6]

Concepts

To judge the third dimension well (depth and distance), you need two eyes;
i.e., two eyes are needed to see well, especially to see how far away
things are and how low they are.

Procedure

STEP 1. Place a pop bottle on a table below eye level. Stand a nickel coin on
edge in the bottle. Walk ten to fifteen feet away from the bottle. Cover
one eye with your hand. Walk toward the bottle *and without hesitation*
try to flip the nickel out of the bottle with your other hand. (Hold hand
at waist height and flip coin. Don't just push it off.)

Ask: Why was the coin missed?

Explanation: Most people will not flip the coin out of the bottle, because they don't see with one eye how far below their fingers the
nickel is located. One cannot judge depth and distance as well with
one eye as with two eyes.

STEP 2. Have several students try this and note their responses. Repeat the
experiment without covering the eye.

Ask: What do you conclude about the necessity of using both of your
eyes to see how deep and how far away a thing is?

STUDENT ACTIVITIES

Questions for Discussion

1. How did most students miss the coin?

2. Why did they miss the coin?

3. After a student did the trick several times, why did he get better at hitting the nickel?

4. Do you think it would make much difference if the room were partially darkened when you did the experiment? Explain your answer.

5. If you walked more slowly toward the bottle, do you think you would be able to hit the coin more easily?

6. What happens when the experiment is done without covering the eyes?

7. What do you lack when just one eye is used?

8. Why must the nickel be flipped without hesitation?

9. If we see differently with each eye, why don't we see two images when both eyes are open?

10. Can a basketball player with one eye still make baskets? Explain your answer.

True or False

_____ 1. Distance and depth can be judged with one eye.

_____ 2. The nickel is not where it appears to be when one eye is used.

_____ 3. The third dimension is red and blue.

_____ 4. A nickle can be flipped out of a bottle just as well with one eye as with two if you have practice.

HOW DO CONVEX AND CONCAVE LENSES WORK?
[6 – 8]

Concepts

When light is passed from a denser to a less dense medium or vice versa, it
    may be refracted (bent).
A convex lens may magnify near objects and invert objects far from the lens.
The thicker the lens, the more the light rays will be bent.
Convex lenses converge light rays.
Concave lenses diverge light rays.
Concave lenses make objects look smaller.

Procedure

STEP 1. Take a cardboard box and cut the top and one end of the box as shown in Diagram 1. Cut a slit at *A* for the light to pass through. Place a projector or strong light source in front of the slit. A good flashlight might serve for this purpose. Obtain some convex and concave lenses and a prism.

(1)

Ask: Is it possible to bend or change the direction of light?

Hold up a convex lens.

Ask: What is this object called?
What does a lens do to light?
What do you think this lens will do?

STEP 2. Have a student draw on the board a side view of the lens.

(2)

Convex converges light

Explanation: Explain to the class that the edges of a convex lens are always thicker than the center. Have three or four students draw on the board how they think the light rays will be altered as they pass through the lens. Place the lens at position *B* as shown in Diagram 1.

Ask: What is your conclusion about how a convex lens bends (refracts)?

STEP 3. Hold up a concave lens. Have a student draw a side view of the lens on the board.

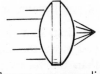

(3)

Concave diverges light

Ask: How does the shape of this lens differ from the convex lens?
Does anyone know the name of this type of lens?

Explanation: This is a concave lens. Its center is always thinner than the edges. Have several students go to the board and draw how they think this lens will refract light. Place the lens in position *B* as shown in Diagram 1.

Ask: Which of the students who did the drawings on the board had the right idea?

How does a concave lens refract light?

Explain to the class that a convex lens converges light and a concave lense diverges light.

STEP 4. Hold a convex lens up to your eye. Look at the class through the lens and have the class look at you. Move the glass slowly away from the eye.

(4)

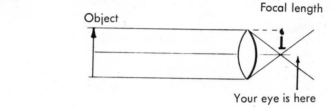

Object

Focal length

Your eye is here

Ask: What happened as I moved the lens away from my eye?

Why do you think you became inverted (upside down)?

Explanation: When you first look at the class, the students look right side up. But as you move the lens away from the eye so that it is a greater distance than the focal length of the lens, they become inverted. See Diagrams 3 and 4.

STEP 5. Draw Diagrams 4 and 5 on the board and explain what happened. Take a concave lens and place it near the eye and move it slowly away from the eye.

(5)

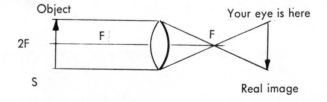

Object

Your eye is here

2F

F

F

S

Real image

Ask: What happened when I moved the concave lens away from my eye?

How do things look through a concave lens compared to a convex lens?

Summarize: Draw on the board how convex and concave lenses refract light.

THE PHYSICAL WORLD

STUDENT ACTIVITIES

1. Draw a convex lens and tell how you can tell a convex lens from a concave lens.

2. Draw a side view of a concave lens.

3. Show how a convex lens might invert an image.

4. If you wanted to start a fire and had no matches but some lenses, which lens would you use and why?

5. What proof is there that light can be refracted by lenses?

6. Draw how a concave lens refracts light.

7. What kind of lens do you think you have in your eyes?

8. Why do you think people sometimes have to wear glasses?

9. Why do biologists say that our eyes see things upside down?

A CONVEX LENS CAN MAKE OBJECTS LOOK LARGER
[1–2, 3–6]

Concepts

A convex lens inverts the image of a distant object.
A convex lens can be used to magnify near and far objects.

Procedure   I.   [1 – 2]

STEP 1. Set up the equipment as shown in Diagram 1. Darken the room if possible.

(1)

Ask: What do you think will happen to the image if I move the lens close to the candle? See **Diagram 2.**

STEP 2. Move the candle back and forth several times so that the students can see how the image varies with the distance of the lens from the source of light.

Procedure II. [3]

STEP 1. Take a convex lens and focus the sun's rays on a piece of paper.

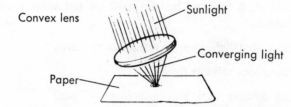

(2)

Ask: What do you think will happen when all of the sun's rays are concentrated at one point on the paper?

Explanation: The paper will catch fire, because all the sun's rays, energy, are concentrated at one point. This is similar to taking a little heat from several places and adding it all to one point.

Ask: Does anyone know what the name of the point is called where all the light rays come together?

Explanation: This is called the focal point.

Procedure III. [3 – 6]

STEP 1. Draw on the board a diagram of the microscope except for its lenses.

Ask: How is the light bent by the convex lenses in the microscope? Why is the image larger?

The magnification of a convex lens can be illustrated by taking a milk carton or tube and placing a transparent substance with a figure attached or drawn on it over one end. Use your lens to show magnification as indicated in the diagram.

STEP 2. Move the lens close to the carton, then far from the carton.

Ask: How does the magnification vary with the distance the lens is from the carton?

STUDENT ACTIVITIES

1. Draw how an object may be magnified by a convex lens.

2. Show how the magnification varies when you move to or from the candle by drawing the image in the space provided.

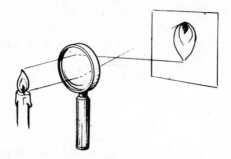

3. Draw how a refracting telescope works.

4. Draw how a microscope works.

5. Draw how a magnifying glass works.

True or False

_____ 1. The eyeball has a convex lens in it.

_____ 2. A convex lens may invert the image of a distant object.

_____ 3. A convex lens makes objects appear smaller.

_____ 4. The focal point is the point where all rays spread out.

_____ 5. If an object is placed close to a convex lens, the magnification will be larger.

_____ 6. If all the sunlight is focused by a convex lens into one point on a piece of paper, the paper will burn.

_____ 7. Light is not bent by a convex lens in a microscope.

_____ 8. "Magnification" means to enlarge an object.

_____ 9. A convex lens is thicker in the center than on the edges.

_____ 10. A convex lens can both magnify and reduce an object.

HOW IS LIGHT CHANGED WHEN IT
PASSES THROUGH WATER?
[1 – 6, 4 – 6]

Concepts

A substance that is curved and transparent can be used as a lens.
Light may be refracted (bent) when it passes through water or glass.

Procedure I. [1 – 6]

STEP 1. Water may serve as a lens. Fill a glass with water.

(1)

Ask: How do you think a ruler would look when I place it in water?

STEP 2. Place the ruler in the water.

Ask: How has the ruler changed in appearance?
Does it look bent?
Does the size of the ruler appear to have changed in the water?
Since the ruler is enlarged, the glass of water must be serving as what kind of lens?

Explanation: A convex lens is thicker in the center and thinner on the edges. When we look through a glass of water, the center is much thicker than the edges in appearance. It therefore magnifies the ruler.

STEP 3. Light can be refracted (bent). Put a small coin in the bottom of a pan. Have a student back away from the pan until he just can't see the coin.

(2)

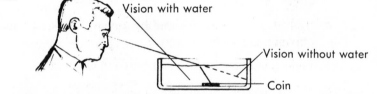

Vision with water

Vision without water

Coin

Ask: How can we make it possible for our classmate to see the coin without moving him or the coin?

STEP 4. Gradually fill the pan with water and have the student state when he sees the coin.

Ask: How was it possible to see the coin after I placed water in the pan?
What must the water have done to the light rays coming from the coin to our classmate's eyes?
How was the light bent?

Procedure II. [4 – 6]

STEP 1. Draw Diagram 2 on the board and explain how the light was refracted. Take a glass and add a little powdered milk, flour, or fluorescin; fresh milk may be used as a substitute. Add just enough so that the light beam will be visible. Two or three drops usually will do.

STEP 2. Make a small hole in a piece of cardboard or preferably black paper. Pass a light beam from a flashlight or candle through the hole, as shown in Diagram 3.

(3)

Ask: How is the beam of light refracted when it enters the water?

STEP 3. Now reverse the process by passing the light through the hole from the bottom of the solution (see Diagram 4).

(4)

Ask: How is light refracted when it leaves the solution?

Draw Diagrams 3 and 4 on the board.

Explanation: When a light ray passes obliquely from one medium **into** another of greater optical density (heavier) it is refracted away from the normal, or perpendicular. See Diagrams 3 and 4.

STUDENT ACTIVITIES

1. What happened to the ruler when it was placed in water?

2. Draw below how the ruler was bent.

3. How is a glass of water similar to a lens?

4. What kind of lens did the glass of water make, and how do you know it was that type of a lens?

5. In the coin demonstration, draw how it was possible for the student to see it in the pan.

6. Draw how light is bent when it goes from air into water.

7. Draw how light is bent when it is coming from water into air.

8. A boy saw a fish in a pool; he tried to spear it several times, but each time he missed. Can you give one explanation as to why the boy might have missed so many times?

DISCOVERY LESSON PLANS

HOW IS LIGHT REFLECTED?
[7–8]

Concepts

When light is reflected from a mirror, it is reflected at the same angle as the angle of light hitting the mirror.

The physicist says: The angle of incidence equals the angle of reflection.

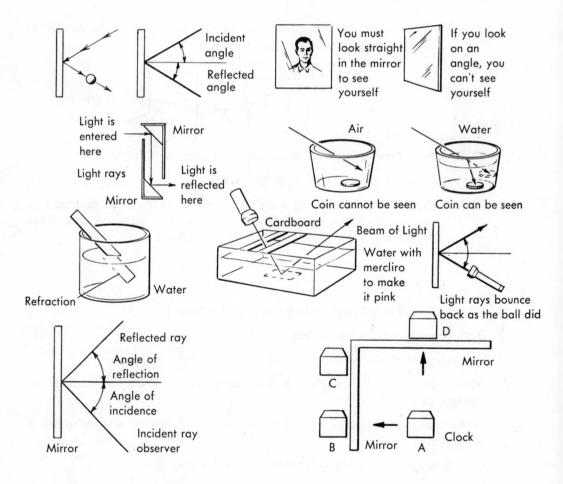

Procedure

STEP 1. Bounce a rubber ball on an angle against a wall. Notice how it bounces away from the wall.

Ask: How does the ball bounce back from the wall when I hit it against it at various angles?

What do you think will happen to light if I do the same thing?

Do you think the light will be reflected away from a mirror like the ball?

STEP 2. Hold a mirror so that you can see yourself. Now move the mirror so that you can see another person or another part of the room.

Ask: When you see yourself, how must the mirror be held?

Explanation: The mirror will or should be directly in front of you. When you see another person in the mirror and you are looking in the mirror on an angle, you usually can't see yourself.

Ask: How is the mirror held when you see another person?

How does the angle (how the mirror is slanted) vary?

STEP 3. Would you say that the way light is reflected from a mirror is similar to the way a ball bounces off a board? Hit the ball straight on, and it will bounce straight back to you. When you hit the ball against the wall on an angle, the ball bounces off it in a similar angle but in the opposite direction. Now see if this is true with light. Does it bounce off like a ball?

STEP 4. Draw Diagrams 2, 3, and 4 on the board to summarize the lesson and to show what "angle of incidence" and "angle of reflection" mean.

STUDENT ACTIVITIES

1. Draw how light bounces off a mirror when it hits the mirror head on.

2. Draw how the light would bounce off a mirror if it were coming from a light held by a person and hitting the mirror as shown in the following diagrams.

   Light comes from the person _____.

3. What is the name of the angle at which the light hits the mirror?

4. What is the name of the angle at which light is reflected from the mirror?

5. A periscope made from mirrors is shown in the diagram. Explain how it works.

A Quiz on Light Using Charts

To summarize what the children have discovered about light. Draw the following on posterboard by using a felt pen. Hold the charts up and ask the children to explain what is taking place.

HOW DOES A PINHOLE CAMERA WORK?
[4-6]

Concept

Light travels in a straight line.

Procedure

STEP 1. Obtain a round Quaker Oats box or an empty tin can. Puncture a small hole in the middle of the can or in the cardboard end of the box. Cover the other end of the box or can with waxed paper. Secure the paper with a rubber band. (see Diagram 1).

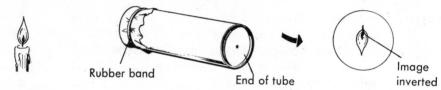

(1) Rubber band End of tube Image inverted

STEP 2. Place a candle in front of the can and light it.

Ask: What do you think I am going to do with this equipment?

STEP 3. Darken the room. Have some students watch the waxed-papered end of the container, while you move the small-holed end back and forth in front of the candle.

Ask: What kind of image is made on the waxed paper?
Why do you think the image is upside down?

STEP 4. Draw Diagram 1 on the board.

Ask: From what you have seen in the demonstration and the drawing on the board, do you think light travels in a straight line?

STEP 5. Move the can back and forth and have the students note how the image of the candle on the waxed paper changes.

Ask: How do you think a picture of an object appears on the film in the back of a camera?

STUDENT ACTIVITIES

1. In Diagram 2 there is a pinhole camera placed near a flower. Draw how the flower would look on the film when it was developed.

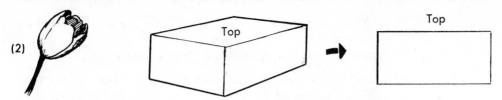

(2)

2. Show how the candle looked on the back of the waxed paper.

3. Why did the teacher move the can back and forth in doing the demonstration?

4. Why don't you get an image you can recognize on the waxed paper if you move the can two or three feet from the candle?

5. How does light travel?

WHAT DOES A PRISM DO TO LIGHT?
[1 – 3, 4 – 6]

Concepts

White light, when passed through a prism, may be dispersed to form a continuous spectrum similar to a rainbow.
White light is a mixture of many colors.
Each color in the spectrum has a different wave length.

Procedure   I.   A Prism Can Produce a Spectrum [1–3]

STEP 1. Hold a prism* up to the class.

Ask: What is this called?
What does it do to light rays when they pass through it?

STEP 2. Place a prism in the path of a strong beam of light, as shown in Diagram 1.

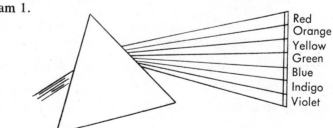

(1)

Ask: What happens to the light after it passes through the prism?
Which colors seem to have been bent the most?
Which colors have been bent the least?

---

*If a prism is not available, use a jar of water. Place white paper behind the jar to show the rainbow.

What do you know about the way the different colors of light are refracted (bent) in the prism?

Which are refracted the least and which the most?

Explanation: White light is composed of many colors. When these colors, in their proper proportion, enter our eyes, we see white. Each color is produced by a different wave length. When light passes through a prism, the different wave lengths are bent in varying degrees. The dispersed white light then forms the color band called the visible spectrum. The long wave lengths, reds, are slowed down the least, whereas the short wave lengths, the violets, are slowed the most. Refraction is caused by an increase or a decrease in the speed of light through a new medium. This difference in refraction of the different wave lengths causes the production of the spectrum.

Procedure   II.   A Prism Can Change the Direction of Light Waves [4–6]

STEP 1. Hold the prism as shown in Diagram 2. Look into the *AB* side and point the *AC* side toward some student. Tell the class what the student is doing.

(2)

Ask: Does anyone know what else a prism can do to light?

Can you see through a prism?

How can I tell what the student is doing if I am not looking directly at him?

What happened to the light entering the prism that made it possible for me to see the student?

STEP 2. Draw Diagram 2 on the board and explain how the light is almost totally reflected off the back of the prism.

Explanation: A prism is a better reflector than a mirror because it absorbs less light than a mirror.

Ask: How would you make a periscope out of two prisms?

STUDENT ACTIVITIES

1. Diagram how white light is refracted when it passes through a prism.

2. If the red wave lengths were represented by this length _____ and the violet by this wave length _____ draw the intervening wave lengths in the space provided:

Red
Orange
Yellow
Green
Blue
Indigo
Violet

3. Draw what happens to light when it enters a prism as indicated.

4. Many wave lengths such as X rays cannot be seen with our eyes. What do you think would happen to these wave lengths if they were passed through a prism or a crystal?

.5. What is another common name for a visible, continuous spectrum?

6. Which wave lengths are refracted the most?

7. Which wave lengths are refracted the least?

8. Draw below how a prism may change the direction of light.

9. Draw below a periscope made from prisms.

10. Draw below how you would make a periscope with two mirrors.

11. Why are prisms used as expensive optical equipment instead of mirrors?

MECHANICS: SIMPLE
MACHINES AND FORCES

This section contains demonstrations on the function of simple machines, the advantages in using them, and the forces involved in doing work.

The first two lessons show the mechanical advantages in using pulleys and should be incorporated together in one unit. The next lessons "What Good Is a Lever?" "How Does a Second-class Lever Work?" and "How Does a Third-class Lever Work?" should be given together with several applications of each. A successful activity to complement these lessons is the placement of several examples of each of the three types of levers on cards. Hold these up to the class or let individual children look at the front of the cards and write down what type of lever they see. The children can use these in small groups and learn science by playing a card game if the type of lever is placed on the back of the cards.

The next two lessons "Why Use an Inclined Plane?" and "What Good Is a Jack?" should be used together. A jack is a circular inclined plane. This second lesson, therefore, complements the first. These lessons show that the exertion of force requires work or the output of energy. For example, if a 50 pound barrel is lifted straight up two feet, it takes 100 foot pounds of work to accomplish this task. If the barrel is rolled up an inclined plane 10 feet long, the same amount of work is performed. In the latter case, however, the individual is not exerting as much effort at any one time. He must, nevertheless, pay for using less effort by working longer. Children grasp this principle easily if a weight too large to be lifted straight up is given to them as a problem, and they are asked to suggest ways of moving it up several feet. Most children have observed ramps around railroad yards and truck loading platforms. A discussion of why there are ramps in these areas aids in developing the concepts included in these two lessons.

The lesson "What Is the Advantage in Using a Wheel and Axle?" explains how a wheel works. Some mention of the development of the wheel and the role it played in making modern civilization can be included to show the relationship between technological advances and their effects on society.

The last two lessons "What Is Inertia?" and "What Is Gravity?" involves concepts and principles related to space flight, an area extremely interesting to children. The pull of gravity is part of the reason so much energy is needed to shoot a satellite into orbit around the earth. This pull must be overcome by the thrust exerted by the escaping gases and fuel from the satellite as it leaves the earth. Inertia is also involved. The law of inertia states that "a body in motion tends to stay in motion and resists any effort to stop. A body at rest tends to stay at rest and resists any effort to move." To get a satellite off the ground its inertia of rest must be overcome. Once, however, it is in motion in its orbit it tends to continue in its orbit needing no fuel. The pull of gravity causes the satellite to turn and circle the earth. It would continue off into space in a straight line if there were no gravity to pull it and make it take an elliptical path around the earth. The satellite would circle the earth forever except that it encounters friction from the atmosphere and is thereby slowed down. When it is slowed enough, gravity is not only able to turn it but also to pull it toward the earth where it will burn up as it passes through the atmosphere.

WHY USE A SINGLE FIXED PULLEY?
[6 – 8]

Concepts

A single fixed pulley has no positive mechanical advantage, but it can be used to move an object in one direction while pulling in the opposite direction. If a pulley is attached to a beam and does not move, it is called a fixed pulley. The mechanical advantage of a pulley is computed by using the formula

$$\text{M.A.} = \frac{\text{Resistance}}{\text{Effort}} \quad \text{or} \quad \text{M.A.} = \frac{\text{Number of strands holding up the resistance}}{\text{Number of strands holding up the effort}}$$

The mechanical advantage of pulleys is equal to the number of strands holding
up a resistance.

Teacher's Note: SRA Math introduces the above equation in the sixth grade.

Procedure

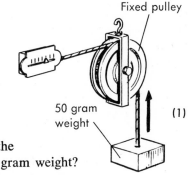

Fixed pulley

STEP 1. Assemble the apparatus as shown
in Diagram 1. Place weights on the
right-hand side of the pulley and
attach a scale to the other end.

50 gram
weight   (1)

Ask: How much force do you think
I shall have to pull down on the
scale in order to raise the 50 gram weight?

STEP 2. Pull sideways on the scale and raise the weight.

Ask: Why did I have to pull slightly more on the scale than the weight?

Explanation: In a single fixed pulley there is no mechanical advantage.
The only advantage in using the pulley is that you can change direction.
Ideally, you should have to pull as much as the resistance you move.
Actually, you will have to pull more than 50 grams because part of
your effort is lost as friction.

STEP 3. Repeat the experiment several times, noting the reading on the scale.
Record these on the blackboard. Take an average of three or more
readings on the scale before you determine the mechanical advantage.
Use the formula

$$\text{M.A.} = \frac{\text{Resistance weight}}{\text{Effort weight}}$$

The use of every machine involves two forces, the effort and the
resistance. The force exerted by man in using the machine is called the
effort, and the resistance is the weight of the object being moved. The
ratio of the resistance to the effort is called the mechanical advantage.
For example, if an object weighs 60 lb and is moved by pulleys with
only 6 lb of effort being applied to the rope, the ideal mechanical
advantage is figured: $\text{M.A.} = \dfrac{60 \text{ lb}}{6 \text{ lb}} = 10$. In reality, friction causes
the actual mechanical advantage to be less than the ideal mechanical
advantage because part of the effort must be used to overcome the friction of moving parts.

Explanation: A scientist usually repeats his experiments several times
and reads his instruments several times. He averages his results so that
he may average out any errors he made either in operating the apparatus or in making faulty readings from the instruments. In this way
he insures greater accuracy.

STEP 4. Rearrange the apparatus as shown in Diagram 2.

(2)

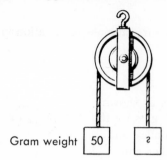

Gram weight | 50 | 2

Ask: What effort does it take to keep the resistance in place?
Is there any mechanical advantage in using this pulley?

STEP 5. Arrange the apparatus as shown in Diagram 3. Raise the weight by
pulling the string down.

(3)

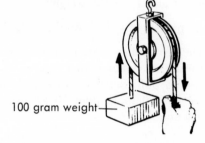

100 gram weight

Ask: Since there is no mechanical advantage in using this pulley, why
would anyone want to use it?

Explanation: The only reason to use a fixed pulley is to change the
direction. By pulling down on the string the weight is raised.

STUDENT ACTIVITIES

1. Diagram how a single fixed pulley might be used.

2. What would have to be the weight in Diagram 3 in order to keep the other
weight in place?

3. What would you have to do to the effort in order to make the resistance
represented in Diagram 4 move?

4. What is the mechanical advantage of a single fixed pulley?

5. If the resistance of a pulley is 10 lb and the effort is 10 lb, what is the mechanical advantage? Is this good? Why?

6. For what purpose would you use a single fixed pulley?

7. Why do you always have to pull just a little more on a single fixed pulley than
the weight you are lifting?

WHY USE MOVABLE PULLEYS?
[6-8]

Concepts

Pulleys which move with the resistance are called movable pulleys.

Movable pulley systems will always have a mechanical advantage greater than one.

The mechanical advantage of movable pulley systems is equal to the number of strands holding up the resistance.

Procedure

STEP 1. Assemble the apparatus as shown in Diagram 1.

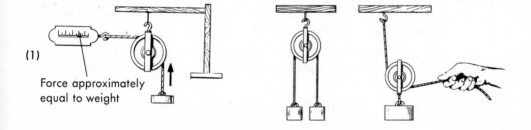

(1)

Force approximately equal to weight

Ask: How much do you think I shall have to pull on the spring balance in order to raise the 100 gram weight?

Raise the weight on the scale with a slow steady rate.

Ask: How much effort did I have to apply?

Repeat the process several times, checking your results.

STEP 2. Assemble the apparatus as shown in Diagram 2, except for attaching the 50 gram weight or a scale.

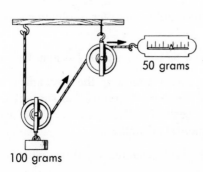

50 grams

(2)

100 grams

Ask: What weight do you think I shall have to apply in order to move the 100 gram weight?

Attach the 50 gram weight.

Ask: What happened to the resistance and why?

Explanation: This arrangement has the advantage of showing immediately to the student that a 50 gram weight can suspend a 100 gram weight. The mechanical advantage of a pulley system can be computed easily by counting the strands holding up the resistance.

Ask: What is the advantage of using this type of pulley system?

Explanation: The advantage is that you can move a large resistance with a small force.

Ask: When I raise the resistance two inches, how far will the 50 gram weight be moved?

STEP 3. Raise the 100 gram weight with the 50 gram weight. Measure how high the weight moves with a yardstick. Also measure how far the 50 gram weight moved. Record these on the board.

Ask: In using this type of a pulley system, we can move a heavy object with a light force, but what do we have to pay for doing this?

Explanation: You pay in distance what you gain in force. In using this system of pulleys you have to exert a light force over a greater distance in order to lift a heavier weight.

STUDENT ACTIVITIES

1. To raise the 100 gram weight using a single fixed pulley, how much force did you have to pull with the spring balance?

2. What is the name of the type of pulley used in these demonstrations which made it possible to move a large weight with a small force?

3. Draw the kind of pulley system that you would construct if you had to raise a piano that weighed 300 lb.

4. Draw how you would use a single pulley in order to obtain ideally a mechanical advantage of two.

5. Where will some of your energy be lost in a pulley system because of friction?

6. In class it was stated that you could determine the mechanical advantage of a pulley system by counting the number of strands that support a resistance. In the diagrams below there are several pulley systems. Under each one in the space provided mark the mechanical advantage.

7. If a pulley system has a mechanical advantage of three, what does that mean?

8. Why do you always have to pull or use a force just a little greater than the object you are moving?

9. Name some points in a fixed pulley where there is friction.

10. In order to move an object one foot higher by using a single movable pulley, how much rope would have to pass through your hands? (a) 1 foot; (b) about 2 feet; (c) about 3 feet.

WHAT GOOD IS A LEVER?
[6 – 8]

Concepts

A lever is a simple machine.

A lever cannot work alone.

A lever consists of a bar which is free to turn on a pivot called the fulcrum.

By using a first-class lever it is possible to increase a person's ability to lift heavier objects. This is called the mechanical advantage.

The mechanical advantage of a lever is determined by the formula

$$\text{M.A.} = \frac{\text{Effort Arm}}{\text{Resistance Arm}}$$

The weight times the distance on one side of the fulcrum must equal the weight times the distance on the other side if the lever is balanced.

A first-class lever has the fulcrum between the resistance and the effort.

Procedure

STEP 1. Assemble the apparatus as shown in Diagram 1. Do not attach a weight to the *B* side of the yardstick until later.

Teacher's Note: If a metric stick is available, use it to measure the distance in centimeters rather than in inches.

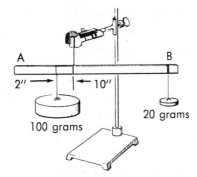

(1)

Ask: What kind of a machine do you think I have here?

Explanation: Explain to the class that a first-class lever consists of a bar which is free to turn on a pivot point called the *fulcrum*. The weight moved is called the resistance. The end of the lever where a force is exerted is called the effort. Draw Diagram 2 on the board to illustrate this point. State that in a first-class lever the fulcrum is always between the resistance and the effort.

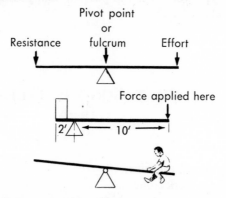

(2)

Ask: Where should a 20 gram weight be placed in order to balance the 100 gram weight?

STEP 2. Apply the weight as shown in Diagram 1.

Ask: Can you see any relationship between the weight and distance on one side of the fulcrum compared to the weight and distance on the other side?
What is two inches times 100 grams?

Write the answer on the board (200 inch grams).

Ask: What is 10 inches times 20 grams?

Write the answer on the board (200 inch grams).

STEP 3. *Ask:* Now can anyone state the relationship between one side of the lever arm and the other side?

Explanation: The distance times the weight on one side of the fulcrum must equal the distance times the weight on the other side of the fulcrum if the arm is to be balanced.

STEP 4. Repeat the experiment several times, but change the weights and calculate where the weight on the *B* side of the fulcrum would have to be placed in order to make the lever balance.

Ask: Does anyone know the advantages gained in using a lever of this type?
How much weight did you have to apply in the first experiment in order to balance the 100 gram weight?

Explanation: You needed only 20 grams. The advantage of the lever in that case is five. The mechanical advantage of the lever could be calculated in the following manner:

$$\text{M.A.} = \frac{\text{Effort Arm}}{\text{Resistance Arm}} = \frac{10 \text{ in.}}{2 \text{ in.}} = 5 \quad \text{or} \quad \frac{100 \text{ grams}}{20 \text{ grams}} = 5$$

This means that because you used the lever you could move an object that weighed 100 grams with an effort of 20 grams.

STUDENT ACTIVITIES

1. Make a diagram of a first-class lever. Label it with *F* for fulcrum, *R* for resistance, and *E* for effort.

2. In a first-class lever the fulcrum is between the resistance (the weight) you are trying to lift and the _____.

3. What is another word for pivot point?

4. If you had a weight of 200 grams on one side of a lever and it was one inch away from the fulcrum, and if you wanted to balance it with a 100 gram weight, where would the 100 grams have to be placed?.

5. What does "mechanical advantage of four" mean?

6. What mechanical advantage is indicated in the diagram below?

7. Give some examples of a first-class lever.

8. In the diagram below, a heavy boy is teeter-tottering with a boy that weighs much less. Mark an X where you think the small boy would have to sit in order to balance the heavy boy.

9. What type of simple machine are crowbars, pliers, and a seesaw or teeter-totter?

HOW DOES A SECOND-CLASS LEVER WORK?
[4−6]

Concepts

In a second-class lever the weight is located between the effort and the fulcrum. The closer the resistance is to the fulcrum, the less effort required to move the lever.

Teacher's Note: This lesson should follow the first-class lever demonstration.

Procedure

STEP 1. Draw Diagram 1 on the board.

(1)

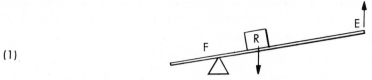

> *Ask:* What type of machine does this diagram represent?
>
> What is different about this lever compared to the first-class lever?
>
> Does anyone have an idea how much force would be required to move the rock?
>
> Do you think the same principle of resistance $\times$ resistance arm = effort and effort arm will work for this type of lever as it does in a first-class lever?
>
> Where are the resistance and the effort in this diagram?

STEP 2. Have the class calculate the force required to lift the rock. Verify the equation by assembling the apparatus as shown in Diagram 2. Place a rock an inch or two from the fulcrum and have the class determine how much they will have to pull on the scale. Repeat the demonstration, but vary the rock's distance from the fulcrum.

(2)

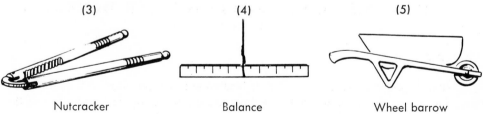

> *Ask:* What happens to the amount of effort needed to move the rock when it is placed farther away from the fulcrum?

STEP 3. Draw Diagrams 3, 4, and 5 on the board or a chart.

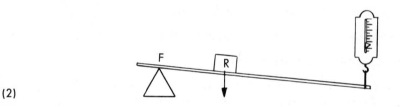

| (3) | (4) | (5) |
| Nutcracker | Balance | Wheel barrow |

> *Ask:* What type of levers are these?

STUDENT ACTIVITIES

1. Mark in Diagrams 6, 7, and 8 the fulcrum, effort, and resistance.

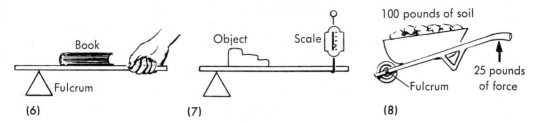

(6)   (7)   (8)

2. Circle in Diagrams 6, 7, and 8 the examples of second-class levers.

3. In a second-class lever, what is always in the middle?

4. Draw diagrams of some useful second-class levers.

5. Explain why you might want to use a lever.

6. Place in front of each of the following the number which stands for its class, first or second:

      a. _____ a crowbar

      b. _____ a nutcracker

      c. _____ ice tongs (use only if third-class levers are known to the class)

      d. _____ a bottle opener

      e. _____ a balance

      f. _____ a teeter-totter

HOW DOES A THIRD-CLASS LEVER WORK?
[4–6]

Concepts

In a third-class lever the effort is always between the resistance and the fulcrum.

Third-class levers make it possible to multiply distance at the expense of force. In other words, you always have to use a greater effort than the resistance.

The mechanical advantage of a third-class lever is always less than one.

Procedure

STEP 1. Assemble the apparatus as shown in Diagram 1.

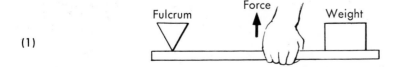

(1)

Ask: What type of simple machine do I have here?

What is different about this lever from the others we have studied?

Does anyone have any idea of how much force will be required to lift the weight?

Let's use the principle

$$\text{Resistance} \times \text{resistance arm} = \text{Lever} \times \text{lever arm}$$

to calculate how much force we would have to use to support the weight.

Ask: If we want to raise the weight, will we have to use more or less effort than the weight?

Explanation: You will have to apply more weight, but you gain in distance. You raise the effort arm slightly, and this causes the resistance arm to raise much more.

STEP 2. Raise the weight with the scale.

(2)

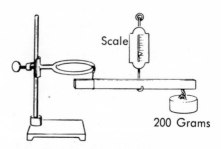

Ask: What did you notice about the force I had to supply?

How does this lever differ from the others we have used?

Since we must use more effort to raise a weight than the weight weighs, why use this lever?

When you move your shoulder muscles and your arm rises, how far does your shoulder move compared to how high your arm moves?

What kind of lever is your shoulder?

Explanation: Draw a diagram on the board showing the arm muscles. Explain that the muscles contract a short distance in the shoulder compared to how far the arm moves.

STEP 3. Take some ice tongs and hold something in the tongs.

(3)

Ask: What kind of a lever is this?

Why is it desirable to use this type of a lever?

THE PHYSICAL WORLD

STUDENT ACTIVITIES

1. Diagram below an example of a first-, second-, and third-class lever. Label in each the fulcrum, resistance, and effort.

2. For what purpose is a third-class lever used?

3. Mark in front of each of the following what class lever it represents.
   a. _____ sugar tongs   e. _____ crowbar
   b. _____ tweezers   f. _____ nutcracker
   c. _____ scissors   g. _____ wheelbarrow
   d. _____ human forearm

4. Figure out the mechanical advantage of the third-class lever if the effort arm is 5 inches and the resistance arm is 10 inches (sixth grade only).

5. What do you find often in school yards which is an example of a first-class lever?

6. Name a machine which may consist of two levers.

7. What advantage is there in using pliers?

8. What advantage is there in using a rake?

9. List one example of each of the three types of levers as they are found in the human body (seventh and eighth grades).

WHY USE AN INCLINED PLANE?
[1 – 6, 7 – 8]

Concepts

Inclined planes are used for moving objects which are too heavy to lift directly.

The work done by moving an object up an inclined plane is equal to the weight of the object times the height of the plane.

Resistance $\times$ Height of plane = Effort $\times$ length of plane.

An inclined plane is one example of a simple machine.

Procedure   I.   [1 – 6]

STEP 1. *Ask:* What is an inclined plane?
Why use an inclined plane?

Arrange a board as shown in Diagram 1. Gradually pull the weight with the scale up the board. Note the amount of force needed to pull the weight on the scale.

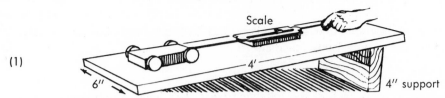

(1)

STEP 2. Repeat the experiment several times, and record your readings on the board. Take an average reading to determine the average force required to move the object. Repeat the above process, but increase the height of the plane by making it steeper.

Ask: What happens to the amount of force needed when the plane's height is increased?

STEP 3. Lift the weight straight up, as shown in Diagram 2. Repeat the experiment several times and record the readings on the blackboard.

(2)

Ask: How much more effort is required to lift the weight straight up compared to using the inclined plane?

From seeing this demonstration, what is the advantage in using an inclined plane?

What is the disadvantage in using an inclined plane?

Explanation: The steeper the plane, the greater the force required to move an object up it. However, when an object is pulled straight up, as indicated in Diagram 2, the force required to lift the object is the same as its weight. The disadvantage in using an inclined plane is that the effort must be exerted over a greater length than to lift an object straight up.

Procedure II. [7 – 8]

STEP 1. Write the following formula on the board:

Resistance × resistance distance = Effort × effort distance

Ask: If a piano weighed 300 lb and it was moved up an inclined plane 10 feet long and 1 foot high, how much effort was necessary to move the piano?

Why would it be necessary actually to push more than 30 lb to move the above piano?

Explanation: The formula used to determine the work done in using an inclined plane does not take into consideration the amount of work required to overcome friction. There is always energy lost in every machine due to friction.

STUDENT ACTIVITIES

1. When a board gets steeper, the amount of force required to move an object _____ .

2. Why don't roads go straight up and down mountains?

3. Why is it sometimes easier to lift an object on a ladder than straight up?

4. Mark an "x" in front of each of the following examples of inclined planes.
   a. _____ ramp   d. _____ stairway
   b. _____ hill   e. _____ wedge
   c. _____ gangplank   f. _____ head of an axe

5. In the diagram below there is a log being split by a wedge (a double inclined plane). What would be the advantage in using a wedge?

6. A man moves a 200 lb safe up an inclined plane 20 ft long and 2 ft high. How much effort does he have to use to move the safe?

WHAT GOOD IS A JACK?
[1 – 6]

Concepts

A screw is an inclined plane wrapped around a rod.
As with an inclined plane, force is gained at the expense of distance.
A large weight can be moved by a small force if the smaller force is applied over a greater distance.

Procedure

STEP 1. Place in front of the class some bolts and a small jack if available (an auto jack will do).

Ask: What are these objects called?
What kind of simple machine are these objects?
What is the advantage of a bolt or screw over a nail?
Does anyone see what kind of machine studied thus far a screw resembles?

Explanation: A screw is a circular inclined plane.

STEP 2. Take a small piece of paper and cut it in the shape of a triangle, as shown in Diagram 1. Place a pencil on the paper and roll it as indicated in the diagram. The paper will wind around the pencil to give the appearance of a screw.

(1)

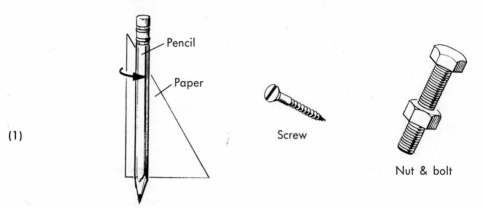

Ask: How can you see the relationship between a bolt and an inclined plane?

STEP 3. Take a ring stand clamp and insert a pencil as shown in Diagram 2.

(2)

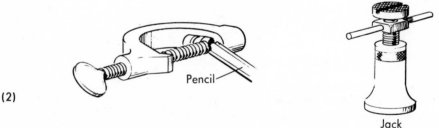

Ask: What will happen to the pencil when you move the screw inward?

Do you think very much effort will have to be exerted in order to break the pencil?

Since it would normally take a lot of effort to break the pencil without the screw, what advantage is there in using a screw?

Can you name some other types of screws?

What is a jack?

What is the purpose in using a jack on a car?

How is it possible for a man who weighs 150 lb to lift a car that weighs 3000 lb with a jack?

Would the man have to exert a force for a relatively long time to raise a car a small distance?

STUDENT ACTIVITIES

Questions For Discussion

1. What is a bolt?

2. What other simple machines does a bolt resemble?

3. When a jack is used, how is it possible to lift such heavy objects as a car or a house?

4. A jack increases your force at the expense of _____.

5. Why does a metal bolt usually have so many more turnings on it than a wood bolt?

6. Would it be easier or harder to lift a car with a jack that had just a few threads on it?

7. The more threads on the bolt, the (harder, easier) it would be to move the bolt into a block of wood.

8. Why does it take a considerable time to jack up a car?

9. Draw how you could make a screw from a triangular piece of paper and a pencil.

10. What are some examples of an inclined plane?

11. What is the advantage of a screw?

12. Give some common uses of screws.

True or False

_____ 1. The inclined plane is a simple machine.

_____ 2. In an inclined plane, distance is gained at the expense of force.

_____ 3. The pencil in the ring clamp breaks because the screw exerts force by itself.

_____ 4. A screw may be regarded as a rolled inclined plane.

_____ 5. A jack is a type of screw.

_____ 6. Some screws are used as fasteners to hold objects together.

_____ 7. A jack is commonly used to lift automobiles.

_____ 8. A jack is never used to lift a house.

_____ 9. There is only one type of jack.

_____ 10. A screw is an example of a simple machine.

_____ 11. A simple machine is one that is driven by two forces.

_____ 12. A screw always offers a certain amount of resistance.

WHAT IS THE ADVANTAGE IN USING A WHEEL AND AN AXLE?
[K – 5, 6 – 8]

Concepts

Kindergarten: Every wheel has an axle to help turn it around or the wheel turns the axle.

The work obtained from a simple machine is always equal to the work put into it less the work used in overcoming friction.

A small effort applied to a large wheel can overcome a large resistance on a small wheel.

A wheel and an axle usually consists of a large wheel to which a small axle is firmly attached.

The mechanical advantage is equal to the radius of the wheel divided by the radius of the axle.

Procedure   [3 – 5]

STEP 1. Construct a small wheel and axle as shown in Diagram 1, or use a pencil sharpener or meat grinder.

(1)

Wheel & axle

Pencil sharpener

Meat grinder

Ask: What is the advantage of using a wheel and an axle?

STEP 2. Hook a weight to your axle as shown in Diagram 2.

(2)

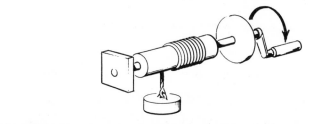

Ask: What do you think we will gain if we turn a large wheel and a small axle moves?

Explanation: A small force applied to a large wheel can make a large resistance attached to the axle move. This is done, however, at the expense of distance, since we actually have to move the large wheel much farther in distance to raise the resistance a small distance.

STEP 3. Attach a small scale as shown in Diagram 2. Pull the scale so that you move the sharpener or windlass handle from a bottom position to a top position, as shown in the diagram.

> *Ask:* What did you note about how much force I had to apply to the scale in order to raise the weight (resistance)?
>
> How much does the weight weigh?
>
> How is it possible to move a heavy resistance by applying a small force?

Repeat the procedure several times with different weights.

Procedure   [6 – 8]

STEP 1. Have the class calculate the mechanical advantage of using a wheel and an axle.

> *Explanation:* The formula is
>
> $$\text{M.A.} = \frac{\text{Resistance}}{\text{Effort}}$$
>
> You may also calculate the mechanical advantage by taking the radius of a large wheel over the radius of a small wheel.
>
> $$\text{M.A.} = \frac{6 \text{ in.}}{3 \text{ in.}} = 2$$
>
> If a wheel and an axle have a mechanical advantage of two, this means that you can move an object two times as heavy as your applied effort. For example, if you applied an effort of 100 lb, not allowing for friction loss, you could lift a weight of 200 lb.

Procedure: *In Some Wheels and Axles the Effort Is Applied to the Small Axle in Order to Gain Speed*

STEP 1. Draw on the board a chain and a wheel of a bicycle, as shown in Diagram 3, or have a student bring into class a bicycle.

(3)

> *Ask:* Where are the wheels and axles on the bicycle?
>
> When we ride the bike, where do we apply force?
>
> Why do we apply the force to the small wheel?

> *Explanation:* The effort is applied to the small wheel in order to gain speed. You move the small sprocket with a great force a short distance, and it, in turn, moves the large wheel a greater distance but with less force.

STEP 2. Show the class diagrams of the following, or the actual objects: a door knob, a steering wheel, a screwdriver, wheel and axle of cars, wagons, and bicycles.

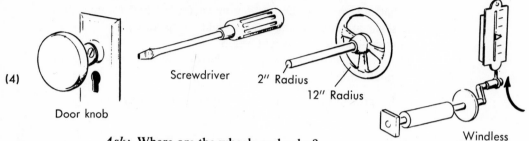

(4)

Door knob

Screwdriver   2" Radius   12" Radius

Windless

Ask: Where are the wheels and axles?

Do they increase ability to move heavier objects, or do they increase the speed?

STUDENT ACTIVITIES

Questions for Discussion

1. Name some examples of wheels and axles.

2. Describe in the diagram below how a wheel and axle work to give you a mechanical advantage.

3. Explain how a bicycle works.

4. If a large wheel has a radius of ten inches and is connected to a small wheel with a radius of five inches, what will be the mechanical advantage?

5. In the rear end of a car there is a small axle which is turned by a shaft connected to the engine. This axle turns the wheels of the car. What do we gain by this arrangement?

6. A man is lifting a bucket of water weighing 4 lb with a windlass. He is, however, applying only 2 lb of force to the handle of the windlass. What is his mechanical advantage?

True or False

_____ 1. A simple machine requires less work than would be the case if the machine weren't used.

_____ 2. All machines have some friction involved with them.

_____ 3. The mechanical advantage of the wheel and axle is determined by multiplying the radius of the wheel by the radius of the axle.

_____ 4. A door knob is a wheel and an axle.

_____ 5. A spring scale is an example of a wheel and an axle.

_____ 6. If a wheel and an axle have a mechanical advantage of two, this means that an object two times as heavy as the applied force can be moved.

_____ 7. If a 100 lb resistance is moved by applying only 50 lb of force, the machine must have a mechanical advantage of 3.

_____ 8. The work obtained from a simple machine is always exactly equal to the work put into it.

_____ 9. To raise a large resistance a small distance, we have to move a large wheel a much greater distance.

_____ 10. In a bicycle, we apply effort to the small axle to gain speed.

_____ 11. A wheel and axle may be used either to increase the ability to move heavier objects or to increase the speed.

Multiple Choice

Write the letter of the phrase that correctly completes each statement.

_____ 1. To find the mechanical advantage of a machine, we divide the resistance by the (a) weight; (b) friction; (c) effort.

_____ 2. What is one advantage of using a wheel and axle? (a) We get more force; (b) we get less friction; (c) we move a shorter distance.

_____ 3. If you apply an effort of 50 lb using a wheel and axle with a mechanical advantage of 2, how heavy an object can you move, not allowing for friction loss? (a) 50 lb; (b) 100 lb; (c) 200 lb. [6 – 8]

_____ 4. In a screwdriver, the principle of the wheel and axle is used to (a) increase the speed; (b) increase the distance; (c) increase the ability to move heavier objects.

WHAT IS INERTIA?
[4 – 6]

Concepts

A body in motion tends to stay in motion and resists any effort to stop it.
A body at rest tends to stay at rest and resists any effort to move it.
This process of a a body's tending to stay in motion or at rest is called inertia.

Procedure

STEP 1. Place a small thin board under some newspaper, as shown in Diagram 1.

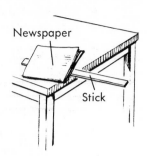

(1)

Ask: What do you think I am going to
do with this paper and the board?

Move your hand rapidly and hit the board, attempting to break it with
the side of your fist.

Ask: Why did the board break?

STEP 2. Repeat the experiment, but this time move your hand slowly.

Ask: Why didn't the board break?

Explanation: When you moved your hand rapidly, it had considerable
inertia. It was moving and tended to keep moving. The board, however,
was at rest and tended to remain at rest. When your moving hand hit
the board, its inertia of movement was such that it overcame the
resistance of the board and broke it. When you moved your hand
slowly, it did not have as much inertia and as a result did not break
the board.

STEP 3. Take a glass or a bottle and place a card over it, as shown in Diagram
2. Place a coin on top of the card. Pull the card suddenly from under
the coin.

(2)

Ask: Why does the coin fall into the bottle?
Why do you have to pull the card rapidly?
What could you say about the inertia of the coin?

Explanation: When the card is pulled rapidly from under the coin, the
inertia of the coin at rest tends to cause it to remain at rest. After the
card is pulled from under it, the force of gravity pulls the coin into
the bottle.

STEP 4. Place a piece of paper on a desk and pile some books on top of the
paper (see Diagram 3). Pull the paper rapidly.

(3)

Ask: Why doesn't the paper move the books?

> *Ask:* Why doesn't the paper move the books?
> What would have to be done to the paper in order to move the books?

Repeat the experiment, but pull the paper slowly.

> *Ask:* Can you explain why the books moved the second time but remained more or less still the first time?

STEP 5. Obtain the apparatus shown in Diagram 4 from a scientific supply house. Place a small card under the ball, as shown in the diagram. Pull back the spring and release it so that it moves forward.

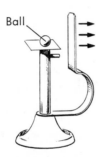

(4)

> *Ask:* Since there is a projection to stop the spring from hitting the cardboard (see point *A* in Diagram 4), why did the cardboard fly out from beneath the marble?
> What object in this demonstration was at rest?
> Where was there inertia owing to motion?

STUDENT ACTIVITIES

1. Why is it that when you are in a train that starts forward, your back sinks into your seat?

2. Explain what would happen if you were in a car moving rapidly and the brakes were suddenly applied.

3. Why does the upper part of your body tend to move forward when you wade through water?

4. Why is it so dangerous to have a collision of cars traveling at high speeds?

5. What function do seat belts serve in a car?

6. What is the principle of inertia?

WHAT IS GRAVITY?
[4−6]

Concepts

Every particle of matter has gravitational attraction for every other particle
of matter.

The gravitational force between two objects increases as two objects approach
each other.

The earth has a great mass and has, as a result, a large force.

At any point on the earth's surface, the gravitational attraction is directed
toward the earth's center.

The closer an object is to the center of the earth, the greater the gravitational
pull.

Heavy and light objects accelerate toward the earth at the same rate.

Air has resistance.

Teacher's Note: Find a picture of the Leaning Tower of Pisa and review the
structure first.

Procedure   I.   Falling Objects

STEP 1. Hold a book and a piece of paper above the floor.

Ask: Which of these objects will hit the floor first?

Drop both the paper and the book at the same time.

Ask: Why didn't the paper hit the floor first?

Explanation: The air resistance interferes more with the paper falling
than it does with the book.

Ask: What pulled the paper and the book down?

How can I get the paper and book to fall together without tieing
them?

STEP 2. Place the piece of paper on top of the book and drop the book.

Ask: Did the paper fall at the same rate as the book?

Does the weight of an object necessarily have anything to do
with the speed at which an object falls?

What force pulls the object toward the earth?

Why must a rocket have so much fuel in it in order to get away
from the earth?

What pulls the rocket toward the earth?

If a person is weightless, would he have any gravitational force
acting upon him?

Procedure   II.   The Center of Gravity

STEP 1. Balance a card on the end of your finger.

Explanation: The point where the card is perfectly balanced is where the center of gravity is located. Take a round card and stick in it a pin to which a string is tied holding a weight (see Diagram 1). Draw a line down the edge of the string. Move the pin and string to another part of the disc and turn the card as shown in the diagram. Draw another line down the edge of the string.

(1)

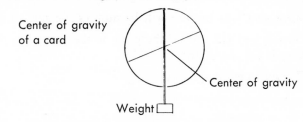

Center of gravity
of a card

Center of gravity

Weight

Ask: Why did you think I made these two lines?

Explanation: The point where the line intersects the other is where the center of gravity is located, and the entire weight of the object is thought to be concentrated at that point. A body will stand erect if a line drawn from its center of gravity falls within the base of the object. Draw the Leaning Tower of Pisa on the board (see Diagram 2).

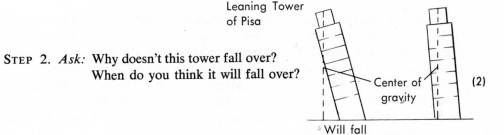

Leaning Tower
of Pisa

STEP 2. *Ask:* Why doesn't this tower fall over?
When do you think it will fall over?

Center of gravity   (2)

Will fall

It will fall over when a line drawn perpendicularly from the center of gravity to the base falls outside the tower.

Ask: Where is the center of gravity of a yardstick?

Hold a yardstick on two index fingers, as shown in Diagram 3. Move the hands toward each other. The fingers will come together at the center of gravity.

(3)

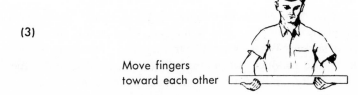

Move fingers
toward each other

STUDENT ACTIVITIES

1. What pulls an object to the earth?

2. Mark on the diagram where the center of gravity is located.

3. Draw the Leaning Tower of Pisa and explain when it will fall.

True or False

_____ 1. Every particle has a center of gravity.

_____ 2. An object falls to the earth because of the pull of gravity.

_____ 3. Objects will fall toward the earth at the same rate of speed if air resistance is not considered.

_____ 4. The moon has no gravity.

MAGNETISM AND ELECTRICITY

Magnetism and electricity are related. Magnetism can be used to produce electricity, and electricity moving in a wire can produce around it an area which acts like a magnet. The lessons on electricity should follow those given on magnetism because they assume in some instances an understanding of magnetism.

The first three lessons "What Is a Magnet?" "What Things Are Magnetic and What Is a Compass?" and "What Is a Magnetic Field?" build concepts concerning fundamental properties of magnetism and magnetic fields showing its importance to industry and navigation.

The next lessons concern electricity. The teacher should have no fear in doing these lessons because the amount of current used is so little that there is no danger of being shocked. This should be explained to the children. At the same time it should be emphasized that the electrical outlets at home have far more current and are highly dangerous.

The lesson "What Is Static Electricity?" introduces the student to the ways in which electricity can be produced by friction. Concepts related to the fundamental electrical nature of matter, electrical force, insulators, and conductors are developed.

The next lesson "How Can You Make Electricity by Magnetism?" shows that electricity can be produced by using wire and a magnet. This lesson should be incorporated with the next lesson "What Is an Electromagnet?" The latter shows that electrical current in a wire produces magnetism. Thus, magnetism under the right conditions makes electricity, and electricity can make magnetism.

The lesson "What Is a Parallel and a Series Circuit?" demonstrates the characteristics of a circuit and the varied ways in which it can be constructed.

The last lesson "How Are Objects Plated?" shows how man's understanding of electricity may be applied. It also introduces such concepts as batteries; for example, they have negative and positive poles, and a solution can conduct electrical current.

WHAT IS A MAGNET?
[K – 6]

Concepts

A magnet has two poles: one end
 is called the north, and the
 other is called the south.
Like magnetic poles repel.
Unlike magnetic poles attract.
Around every magnet there is an
 area called the magnetic field
 made up of magnetic lines of
(1) force.

Repel

Procedure I. A Magnet May Repel (Push Against) or Attract (Pull Together)

STEP 1. Obtain two round bar magnets as shown in Diagram 1.
Place one of the magnets on the desk.

Ask: What do you think will happen if I bring the other magnet toward
this one?

STEP 2. Bring the other magnet near it.

Explanation: The magnet will either attract or repel the other magnet.
If it attracts the other magnet, flip the ends of one of the magnets so
that like poles are facing each other. The magnets will repel each other
and roll along the table owing to the repulsion of the magnetic fields.

Ask: Why is it that when I place one magnet close to the other it
either repels the magnet or attracts the magnet?

STEP 3. Take a bar magnet, tie a piece of string around it, and suspend it as
shown in Diagram 2. Bring one end of your magnet close to the suspended magnet and then change the poles as indicated in Diagram 3.

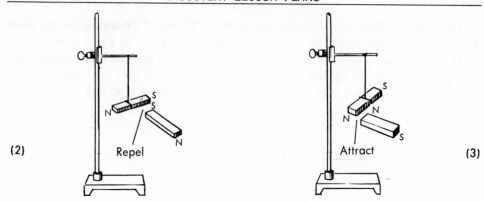

(2) Repel   Attract   (3)

Ask: What happens when a magnet is brought close to the suspended magnet?

Why do you think the magnet moves?

Are both ends of the magnet the same?

Can you see the force that is attracting or repelling the other magnet?

What is a force?

Explanation: A force is a push or a pull. Magnetism is an invisible force. We know it is there because we can see it pull or repel objects.

STEP 4. Stroke some needles and stick them in corks as shown in Diagram 4. Bring a magnet near the corks. Reverse the poles.

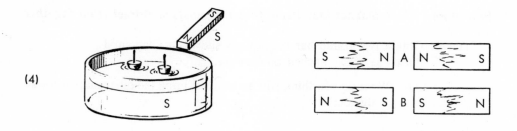

(4)

Ask: Why do the corks move in the way they do when I bring a magnet close to them?

Draw on the board Diagram 3 and explain that unlike magnetic poles attract and like magnetic poles repel.

STUDENT ACTIVITIES

1. Draw a magnet showing its poles, and label them.

2. Draw how two magnets would have to be arranged if they were to attract each other.

3. Draw how two magnets would have to be arranged if they were to repel each other.

4. How do you know there is such a thing as a magnetic force?

5. Do you think that the bar magnet that was suspended with a piece of string could be used as a compass? Explain your answer.

6. How could you move a magnet without touching it?

Completion

1. Like magnetic poles of magnets _____ each other.

2. Unlike magnetic poles of a magnet _____ each other.

3. If there has been a push or pull on an object, there must have been a _____ present.

WHAT THINGS ARE MAGNETIC AND WHAT IS A COMPASS?
[K – 6, 3 – 6]

Concepts

Cobalt, nickel, and iron are strongly attracted to magnets.
Not all substances are capable of being attracted by magnets.
A piece of steel stroked several times with one of the poles of a magnet will
become a permanent magnet.

Procedure   I.   [K – 6]   What Things Are Magnetic?

STEP 1. *Ask:* What things are magnetic?

Take some iron filings, paper clips, pieces of glass, cloth, tin cans, sawdust, and paper. If possible, obtain from the high school chemistry instructor some pieces of nickel metal, or use a Canadian nickel (an American nickel won't work) and some cobalt. These are also magnetic. Pass them out to groups of the class and give them some magnets to test the substances for magnetism.

Ask: What things did you find were magnetic?
What things were not magnetic?
What conclusions can you make about the magnetic properties of some substances?

Explanation: American nickels are made of copper and nickel. Copper is not magnetic.

Procedure II. [3 – 6] How Can You Make a Compass?

STEP 1. Take a needle and stroke it with a magnet several times in the same direction, using the south pole. Lift the magnet each time. Do not stroke the needle back and forth. Place the needle on a very small piece of cork in a glass of water. Change the direction of the needle several times with your hand. See Diagram 1.

(1)

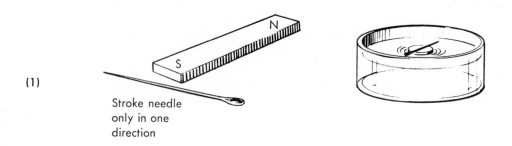

Stroke needle
only in one
direction

Ask: What do you notice about the way the needle points?
Why is it that when I push the cork with my hand, the needle
eventually will move so that it points in the same direction?
What have I made out of this needle?

Explanation: When you stroke the needle, you induce magnetism into it. A freely suspended magnet such as the one you have made out of the needle and placed on the cork is a compass. The needle magnet is attracted by the earth's magnetic field, so the needle points north (see the next demonstration on the magnetic poles).

STUDENT ACTIVITIES

1. List the things which you found to be magnetic.

2. List the things which you found not to be magnetic.

3. How would you make a compass out of a needle?

4. Why did the cork and needle move and point in a certain direction?

5. If one end of the needle points toward the north, where does the other end of the magnet point?

6. What is a compass?

7. Draw a compass. Label it.

WHAT IS A MAGNETIC FIELD?
[K – 6]

Concepts

Around every magnet there is an area where the magnet can change the
direction of iron filings. This is called the magnetic field.

In a magnetic field there are magnetic lines of force.

Not every part of the magnetic field around a magnet is the same.

The earth has a magnetic field.

The concentration of the lines of force around any part of the magnet determines the strength of the field at that point.

Magnetism will pass through solid objects.

Procedure   I.   [K – 2]   The Magnetic Field

STEP 1. Take a paper clip and attach some string to one end of it. Secure the
other end of the string to the desk by either tieing it to something or
placing a heavy book over it. Hold the clip and string up and support
a magnet so that it is just above the clip. See Diagram 1. The magnet
may be secured by books or a clamp on a ring stand.

(1)

Magnetic field

Paper clip

String

Ask: Why does the paper clip stay suspended in mid-air?
Have we overcome the pull of gravity on the paper clip?
How have we done this?

STEP 2. Bring another magnet close to the clip.

Ask: Why does the clip fall?

Procedure   II.   [K – 2]   What Is the Magnetic Field?

STEP 1. Place a bar magnet under some cardboard or thick paper. Sprinkle
some iron filings on the cardboard. Have the students look at what
happens to the filings.

Ask: How are the filings scattered around the cardboard?
How far out were the filings affected by the magnet?

Did it look as though there might be lines of iron filings rather
than solid filings?

Where was the greatest concentration of iron filings?

Does anyone know what these lines of filings are called?

Have we made a map of the field of the magnet?

Do the lines of force cross each other?

Explanation: The iron filings have become magnetized by induction.
They organize themselves into little magnets which point north and
south and which are arranged in lines. These are called magnetic lines
of force. They run from the north to the south pole without crossing.
The more lines of force there are in an area, the greater the magnetic
field. The ends of the magnet, therefore, will have the greatest force.

STEP 2. Make a drawing of Diagram 2 on the board to show the magnetic
field and the magnetic lines of force.

(2)

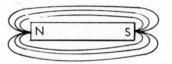

Procedure   III.   [K – 6]   The Earth's Magnetic Field

STEP 1. *Ask:* Why does a compass point north?

Draw on the board Diagram 3
of the earth's magnetic field.

Ask: What end of the compass needle
is really pointing north and why
is it attracted to the north?

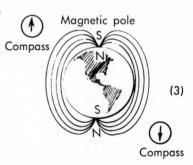

(3)

STUDENT ACTIVITIES

1. Make a diagram of the paper clip, books, and magnet. Explain your diagram.

2. Draw the magnetic field and label the magnetic lines of force.

3. If you were going to drop some iron filings on a magnet, where would they be
   pulled to the magnet the fastest and why?

4. From the demonstrations done in class, how do you know that magnetism will
   pass through solid substances?

5. What is a magnetic field?

6. Where is the magnetic field the strongest around a magnet?

7. Draw a diagram of the magnetic field of the earth.

8. Why does a compass point to the North Pole?

WHAT IS STATIC ELECTRICITY?
[4–6]

Concepts

All bodies are capable of producing electrical charges.
Conductors allow electrons to move, but insulators do not allow electrons to
   move on them easily.
Like charges repel; unlike charges attract.

Procedure

STEP 1. Obtain the following materials: lucite or resin rod, wool, flour, glass
   rod, small pieces of paper, balloon, tap water, piece of silk.

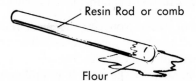

Resin Rod or comb

(1)

Flour

STEP 2. Take a resin rod (a hard rubber comb can be used to substitute for
   this), and rub it with the wool cloth.

   Ask: What do you think will happen when the rod is touched to the
      flour?

STEP 3. Touch the rod to some flour.

   Ask: Why do you think the flour sticks to the rod?

   Clean the same rod. Rub it again and touch it to small pieces of paper.

   Ask: Why does the rod pick up the paper?
      Why won't the rod pick up or attract a large piece of paper?

   Explanation: The electrical force or charge on the rod is not large
   enough to overcome the larger gravitational force the earth has for the
   paper; therefore, a small electrical force cannot pick up a large object.

STEP 4. Rub the rod briskly. Then turn on a water tap so that the water comes
   out in a very slow stream.

   Ask: What do you think will happen to the stream when the rod is
      moved close to it?

   Have the class note how close you have to bring the rod before it affects
   the stream. Develop the concept that there is an invisible field of

electrical force around the rod which either pushes or attracts the water. This force cannot be seen, but we know it is there because of what it does to the stream. Define force as a push or a pull. In this case you can push or pull the water without even touching it just by moving the rod toward and away from the water.

STEP 5. Repeat the experiment, but this time before you bring the rod close to the water, rub your hand over it.

(2)

Electric field

Ask: What do you think will happen now when the rod is placed close to the water?

How can you explain the difference this time?

Explanation: When you rub the resin rod with wool or fur, you rub electrons off the wool onto the rod. The rod, however, is an insulator, so the electrons don't move. The rod is negatively charged. When you rub your hand over the rod, it is discharged. The electrons leave the rod and enter your hand. The rod becomes neutral.

STEP 6. Write the following on the board:

Insulator: A substance that will not allow electrons to move easily.

Conductor: A substance that will allow electrons to move easily. Metals are good examples.

STEP 7. Inflate two balloons. (This experiment may also be done with pith balls.) Tie a string to each of them and suspend them from a bar, as shown in Diagram 3. Rub each of the balloons with wool.

(3)

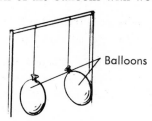

Balloons

Ask: Why do the balloons repel each other?

What do you think will happen if a charged resin rod is brought near the balloons?

STEP 8. Rub the resin rod with wool and place it near the balloons.

Ask: Why do you think the balloons are repulsed from the rod?

Explanation: These balloons were charged in the same way. Therefore, each must have the same charge. When they do have the same charge, they repel each other. Like charges repel.

Ask: What do you think will happen to the balloons if I touch them with a glass rod?

STEP 9. Rub a glass rod with a piece of silk and place it near the balloons.

Ask: What did the glass rod do to the balloon compared to the resin rod?

What can we conclude about the charge on a resin rod compared to a glass rod?

Explanation: The glass rod will have a positive charge, since electrons were rubbed off the rod onto the silk. It will attract the balloon, because the balloon was negatively charged by the resin rod and unlike charges attract.

STEP 10. Rub an inflated balloon against a piece of wool. Then place it next to a wall. If it has a large static charge, it will cling to the wall. See Diagram 4.

Ask: Why doesn't the balloon fall?

Is the force that pulls the balloon to the wall greater or less than the gravitational force pulling the balloon down to earth?

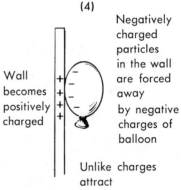

(4)

Wall becomes positively charged

Negatively charged particles in the wall are forced away by negative charges of balloon

Unlike charges attract

Explanation: When you rub the balloon, it becomes negatively charged. When it is placed next to the wall, its negative charge forces the electrons in the wall away from the surface, leaving the surface positively charged. The balloon sticks because the unlike charges attract. The balloon is negative and the wall surface is positive. See Diagram 4.

STUDENT ACTIVITIES

True or False

_____ 1. All matter can be charged electrically.

_____ 2. Electrons can move.

_____ 3. When you rub a lucite or resin rod on wool, the rod becomes negatively charged.

_____ 4. If something is negatively charged, that means that it usually has more electrons on it than it would have if it were neutral.

_____ 5. Like charges attract.

Short Answer

1. What is a conductor?

2. What is an insulator?

Exercises

1. Draw a charged rod and show how far out the electrical field might go.

2. Draw what will happen to two balloons when both of them have the same charge.

3. Draw what happened to the water when a charged rod was placed near it.

4. Draw what happened to the balloon when a charged lucite rod approached it.

HOW CAN YOU MAKE ELECTRICITY BY MAGNETISM?

Concepts

Around a magnet there are magnetic lines of force.
A magnet has force.
If you break the magnetic lines of force, you can make electricity.
A force is defined as a push or a pull.

Procedure

STEP 1. Take some wire and wrap 20 to 30 turns of it around the compass, as shown in Diagram 1. Loop the other end of the wire several times as shown in Diagram 1 and connect the ends.

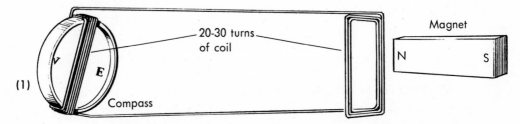

(1)

Ask: What happens when electricity goes through a wire?

Explanation: It makes a magnetic field around the wire.

Ask: If electricity makes magnetism, do you suppose that magnetism might make electricity?

STEP 2. Take a straight bar magnet and plunge it back and forth inside the loops. Have some of the students watch what happens to the compass when you do this.

Explanation: The compass needle will first move in one direction and then in the other.

Ask: Why do you think the compass needle was deflected? What attracts a compass needle?

Explanation: A compass is a magnet, and the needle can be deflected by another magnet.

STEP 3. *Ask:* If the compass needle is deflected, there must be some magnetism made near the compass. Where was the magnetism made?

Explanation: In the wire going around the compass a magnetic field was produced.

Ask: If there is magnetism in the wire going around the compass, then there must be what occurring in the wire?

STEP 4. This electricity in the wire was made only when I moved the magnet in and out of the loop.

Explanation: Around every magnet there are invisible magnetic lines of force. A force is defined as a push or a pull. Around every magnet there is an area which can push or pull things such as iron filings. This area is thought to consist of lines of force; when these lines of force are broken by plunging the magnet back and forth through a coil of wire, electricity is made in the wire. Electricity is defined as a flow of electrons. The magnetic force, a push or a pull, can move the electrons along the wire, thereby making electrical current. When an electrical current is produced, there will be a magnetic field around the wire. This magnetic field causes the magnet to move. This is the principle involved in making electricity in a dynamo.

STUDENT ACTIVITIES

1. What happened to the compass when the bar magnet was pushed back and forth inside the loop of wire?

2. What do you think would happen if you used a stronger magnet to push back and forth in the loop?

3. Why did the ends of the wires in the loop have to be connected?

4. What was made in the loop of wire when the magnet moved inside the loop?

5. What do you think would happen if you pushed the magnet back and forth faster and faster in the loop? Would more electricity be produced?

6. Why did we use the compass in the experiment?

7. This experiment shows the relationship between magnetism and _____.

8. What is a force?

9. What is a magnetic force?

10. What happens to the compass when you move it into the coil? When you pull it out of the coil?

11. How do you know from experiments that there is a magnetic force?

WHAT IS AN ELECTROMAGNET?

Concepts

When electricity passes through a wire, it produces a magnetic field around the wire which acts like a magnet.

A magnetic field can make iron temporarily magnetic.

The more current that flows through a wire in a unit of time, the more magnetism that will be made around the wire.

If a circuit is broken, electricity will not flow.

Procedure

STEP 1. Wrap some insulated copper wire around a nail several times as shown in the diagram. Scrape the insulation off two ends of the wire and connect one end to one terminal and the other end to the other terminal of a dry cell.

(1)

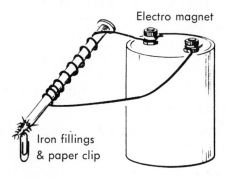

Electro magnet

Iron fillings & paper clip

Ask: What do you think will happen to some iron filings if I place them on the wire?

STEP 2. Place some filings or a paper clip on the wire.

> *Explanation:* They will stick to the nail because when electricity flows through a wire, a magnetic field is produced around it. This magnetic field induces magnetism in the nail.

> *Ask:* Why do the iron filings stay on the nail?
> What do you think will happen if I disconnect one of the terminals?

> Disconnect one of the terminals.

> *Ask:* Why do the iron filings fall when I disconnect the terminal?
> What happens to the flow of electricity when I disconnect it from one of the terminals?
> Can we say that it looks as though electricity will flow only when there is a complete circuit?

> *Explanation:* The circuit consists of one wire wrapped around the nail, the ends of which are connected to the terminals. In other words, there is a circle present from the battery back to the battery.

STEP 3. *Ask:* What can we say about the production of magnetism around the wire when electricity goes through it?
What do we call a magnet made by electricity passing through a conductor?

> *Explanation:* Electromagnet.

> *Ask:* If one piece of wire has a little magnetism around it, what will happen if the number of wrappings around the nail is increased?
> Do you think it will have more magnetism?
> When electricity flows through the wires around the nail, does it make the nail a permanent or temporary magnet?
> How do you know that the nail is magnetized only so long as current is passing through the wire?

STUDENT ACTIVITIES

1. How many terminals are there on a battery?

2. Draw an example of a complete circuit from a battery back to the battery.

3. What is the name of a magnet that is made by electricity passing through a conductor?

4. When electricity passes through a wire, will iron filings stick to the wire?

5. If you make more wrappings of wire around a nail and connect it to the terminals, will there be more or less magnetism?

6. If you increase the current going through a wire, do you think you would also increase the magnetism around the wire?

7. Was the nail used in the experiment temporarily or permanently magnetized by the current going through the wire?

WHAT IS A PARALLEL AND A SERIES CIRCUIT?

Concepts

In order for the electrons to move in a circuit, there must be a path that is unbroken to and from the source of electrical energy.

If one lamp burns out in a series circuit, the circuit is broken.

In a parallel circuit one lamp can burn out, but the rest of the circuit may still function.

Procedure

STEP 1. Assemble the apparatus in a series circuit as shown in Diagram 1. Keep the switch open.

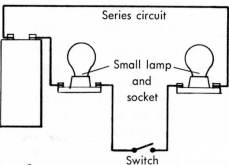

(1)

Ask: Why aren't the lights on?
What will I have to do to make the lights go on?

Close the switch.

Ask: When I put the switch down, why do the lights go on?
What do you think will happen if I unscrew one of the lights?

Unscrew one of the lights.

Ask: Why did the other light go out when I unscrewed one of the lights?

Explanation: Electricity will not flow unless there is a complete circuit. When you unscrew a bulb or open a switch, you break the circuit, so the current cannot flow.

STEP 2. Assemble the parallel circuit as shown in Diagram 2. Keep the switch open.

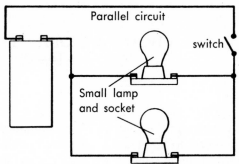

(2)

Ask: Why don't the lights burn?

Close the switch.

Ask: How many paths are there for the electrical current to take back to the battery in this circuit compared to the series circuit?
What do you think will happen if I unscrew one of these lights?

Unscrew one of the lights.

Ask: Why does the other light burn in this circuit, whereas it would not burn in a series circuit?

Explanation: In a parallel circuit there may be more than two paths by which the electrical current can complete its circuit. If one of the circuits is broken, the current can still use the other circuit.

STUDENT ACTIVITIES

1. Draw a circuit.

2. Draw a parallel circuit.

3. Draw a series circuit.

4. What kind of circuits do you think there are in your home? Why?

5. What kind of circuits are there in cheap Christmas tree light strings?

6. What kind of circuits are there in expensive Christmas tree light strings?

7. When you unscrew the light bulb in the series circuit, why does the other bulb stop burning?

8. When you unscrew the light bulb in the parallel circuit, why does the other light keep on burning?

9. Where does the electricity come from in this experiment?

10. What function does a switch have?

HOW ARE OBJECTS PLATED?
[4 – 6]

Concepts

Electricity can be used to plate substances.

The object to be plated is connected to the negative terminal of a battery.

A bar of pure metal of the type desired in plating an object is connected to the positive pole of the battery.

Both the bar and the object for plating must be immersed in a solution that has the same type of particles of metal, ions, as will be used in plating.

Procedure

STEP 1. Put one teaspoon of copper sulphate in a beaker of water and stir until the solution is dissolved. Connect the batteries as shown in the diagram. The positive pole is wired to the copper bar and the negative lead goes to the nail.

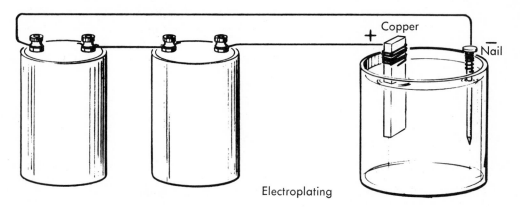

Electroplating

STEP 2. Place the copper strip and the nail in the copper sulphate solution.

Ask: What do you think I am going to do with this apparatus?
What do you think will happen to the nail?

Allow the current to flow for several minutes.

Explanation: The copper sulphate, which is a salt, will ionize and carry a current. The copper bar steadily releases positively charged copper ions, and these are attracted to the negative pole, the nail. The process continues until the copper is used.

STEP 3. After several minutes, when the nail is plated with the copper, take it out of the solution and show it to the class.

Ask: What happened to the nail?
Why do you think the nail was coated with the copper?
Why did we use the batteries in this experiment?
What is this process called by which a metal is plated with another metal by electricity?
Is there a circuit when the nail is being plated?
Where does the copper come from that plates the nail?
What do you think would happen if we replaced the nail with some other metal?
What would we have to do if we replaced the copper strip with some other metal?
Do you think this experiment would work if we used only one battery?

STEP 4. Connect only one battery to the two metal strips and nail. Observe whether the nail becomes plated.

Explanation: Copper sulfate, when dissolved in solution, breaks into copper ions and sulfate ions. The electrical current causes the copper ions to be attracted to the negative pole, the nail. The sulfate ions are attracted to the positive copper bar. They combine with the copper bar to make copper sulfate, which is then dissolved and replenishes the used copper and sulfate solution. In this way, the copper bar is slowly used, and the nail becomes plated. Many of our gold and silver objects are really plated over cheaper metal cores. A solution that conducts an electrical current is called an electrolyte.

STUDENT ACTIVITIES

1. Draw the apparatus used in the experiment.

2. Do the wires between the batteries go from one positive pole to the other positive pole, or do they go from the positive pole to the negative pole?

3. What was the name of the solution used in the experiment?

4. Would the solution work if it did not have copper in it?

5. From where did the nail get its copper plate?

6. Was there a complete electrical circuit in the experiment? Explain how the circuit was made.

7. What purpose did the dry cell have in this experiment?

8. What would have happened if you had put the nail where the copper strip was and the copper strip where the nail was located? (You may want to test this in class if you have time.)

SECTION THREE
COSMOLOGY: EARTH SCIENCE

Astronomy

1. What Is the Shape of the Earth? [K – 4]
2. Why Do We Have Day and Night? [K – 6]
3. Why Does the Moon Shine? [K – 6]
4. Why Do We Have Phases of the Moon? [1 – 6]
5. What Causes the Tides? [5 – 8]
6. What Is a Shadow? [1 – 6]
7. What Is an Eclipse? [4 – 6]
8. What Is the Shape of Our Sun? [K – 3]
9. What Size Is the Sun Compared to the Earth? [K – 2]
10. What Does the Sun Do for Us? [1 – 3]
11. How Long Is a Year? [3 – 6]
12. What Causes the Seasons? [6 – 8]
13. Why Do Stars Appear Close or Far Apart? [K – 4]
14. How Do the Planets Move? [5 – 8]
15. What Causes Some Stars to Be Different Colors? [5 – 8]
16. How Far Away Are the Planets from Each Other? [1 – 3, 4 – 6]

Geology

1. How Does Erosion Affect the Soil? [3 – 6]
2. How Can We Make a Fossil? [K – 6]
3. What Is a Fault? [K – 8]

ASTRONOMY

The first two lessons in this section "What Is the Shape of the Earth?" and
"Why Do We Have Day and Night?" should be given together, so that the children

417

can see that the shape and rotation of the earth explains why there is day and night. The emphasis should be on having the children discover the proof for these concepts.

The next section has five lessons concerning the moon and its characteristics and effects. As many of these as possible should be combined in one unit; these lessons generally present little difficulty to teachers or students.

The third series of lessons concern the role of the sun in the solar system. These should if possible be included in one unit. The teacher should emphasize to the children that they should never look directly at the sun except for a second or two and then only when using filters. Harmful ultraviolet rays will pass through smoked glass and film; but if a child looks for just a second, it will not be dangerous. The concepts involved in these lessons present little difficulty to children as a rule.

The lessons "How Long Is a Year?" and "What Causes the Seasons?" are interrelated and should be given together if the grade level will allow it.

The lesson "Why Do Stars Appear Close or Far Apart?" introduces students to some understanding of perception — specifically that things at great distances may look closer than they are. This lesson can be given at higher grade levels but the approach should be modified for the more mature student.

The last three lessons in the astronomy section "How Do the Planets Move?" "What Causes Some Stars to Be Different Colors" and "How Far Away Are the Planets from Each Other?" can be easily incorporated in one unit. The lesson "What Causes Some Stars to Be Different Colors" develops the fact that astronomers must rely mainly upon visible light and other electromagnetic waves as their source of information about the heavens. The lesson offers a wonderful opportunity to show the importance of laboratory research. The teacher can point out that laboratory research on the properties of light can have direct application to astronomy. For example, if a white flame is hotter than a red flame in the laboratory, it is reasonable to assume that a white star would probably be hotter than a red one. By research such as this, we can broaden our knowledge of astronomy.

WHAT IS THE SHAPE OF THE EARTH?
[K–4]

Concepts

The earth is round like a globe.
The earth is very large.

Procedure

STEP 1. Obtain several rubber or plastic balls of various sizes and, if possible, a globe of the earth. Display the balls to the class.

COSMOLOGY: EARTH SCIENCE

Ask: What do you notice about the different balls?
If the earth is round, do you think it would curve like these balls?

Show the class how each ball curves. Indicate by using the blackboard that a large ball would have a very slight curve.

STEP 2. *Ask:* Do you think our earth is curved?

Have the class look at the horizon.

Ask: Does anyone know what the horizon is?

Explanation: Tell the class that the horizon is where the earth curves out of sight so that you cannot see farther. Make a drawing on the board to show how the earth curves out of sight, as indicated in Diagram 1.

(1)

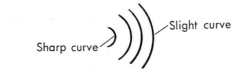

STEP 3. *Ask:* Do you know of anything we could do in order to see more of the earth's surface?
Do you think if I were flying in an airplane or rocket that I would be able to see more of the earth?
How do you think the earth would look to me?

Show them some pictures of the earth which have been taken from rockets circling the earth.

(2)

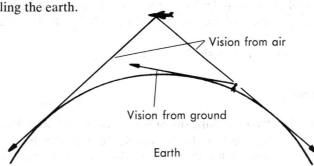

Ask: Why can the rocket take a picture of so much more of the earth?
What does the earth look like?
Does it look round?

If there is a second story in the building, have the class move upstairs to see if they can see things they could not see on the ground, such as distant smoke stacks, more houses, etc.

Ask: How does this prove that the earth is round?

STUDENT ACTIVITIES

1. What shape is the earth?

2. Draw the shape of the earth.

3. In the picture, mark the horizon.

(3)

4. Why can you see more of the earth when you are up high?

5. Draw why you think you could see more of the earth from the air.

WHY DO WE HAVE DAY AND NIGHT?
[K – 6]

Concepts

The earth rotates.
It turns from west to east.
It takes 24 hours for the earth to make one complete turn.
The rotation of the earth explains why part of the 24 hour period is night and part is day.
The sun is always shining.

Procedure

STEP 1. Obtain a filmstrip projector or strong flashlight, knitting needles, and clay. Push a knitting needle through a globe formed from clay, as indicated in the diagram. Darken the room as much as possible. Flash a light onto the globe so that half is in the light. Tell the class that the globe represents a model of the earth and that the strong light of the projector represents the sun.

Ask: Can any of you tell from this demonstration on which part of the globe it would be day and on which part it would be night?
How much of the earth is in sunlight and how much is in darkness?
Does the sun always shine somewhere on the earth?

COSMOLOGY: EARTH SCIENCE

STEP 2. Stick a pin or a small figure on a spot of the globe on the sunlight side which represents where you live.

Ask: How could I make night come to the point where I live?

Turn the globe slowly, indicating to the class where night would begin to fall, and where it would be midnight and sunrise. In order to show this, the globe must be turned counterclockwise, as indicated in the diagram.

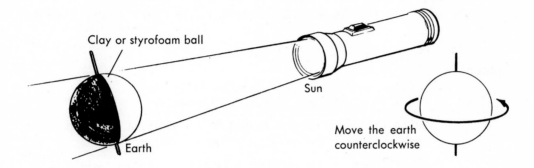

Clay or styrofoam ball

Sun

Earth

Move the earth counterclockwise

Ask: When my pin is on the same side as the sun, what time of day is it?
      When it is on the opposite side, what time of day is it?
      If the earth did not spin (rotate), what would happen?
      What side of the earth would you want to be on then? Why?

Explanation: Point out that when your needle moves away from the sun it would gradually become darker and when it moves toward the sun it would gradually receive more light.

STUDENT ACTIVITIES

1. True or False

____ a. The earth spins (rotates).

____ b. It turns from west to east.

____ c. The spinning gives us daytime on one side of the earth and nighttime on the other side.

____ d. It takes 36 hours for the earth to make one turn.

2. Have one or two students stand to represent the earth and shine a light on them. Have them turn. They will sense the change of light on their face as they move. Have them tell what time of day it is as they turn in front of the light.

3. Explain why there are day and night on the earth.

WHY DOES THE MOON SHINE?
[K – 6]

Concepts

We see things when they give off their own light or when they have light shine on them.

The moon does not give off its own light. It reflects light it receives from the sun.

Procedure

STEP 1. *Ask:* Does anyone know why the moon shines?

Darken the room. Have a student hide a globe in the room. Have another student try to find the globe with a flashlight.

Ask: Can you see the globe when light does not shine on it?
When you see the globe, is it because it is giving off its own light, or is it reflecting light?

STEP 2. Have the class look at the ceiling lights.

Ask: Can you see the lights in the dark?

Turn on the lights.

Ask: Now can you see the lights?
Can you see the globe?
What is different about the way the lights give you light and the globe gives you light?
Do you know how it is possible for the moon to shine?
Where does the light that the moon reflects come from?

Explanation: The sun gives off light, which is reflected by the moon.

STEP 3. Take a globe or a basketball, a flashlight, and a small ball. Arrange them as shown in the diagram.

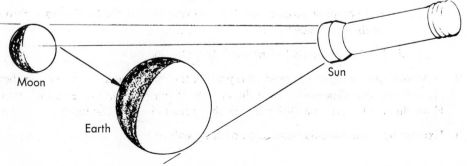

Ask: What is the flashlight supposed to represent?
Which side of the globe is day and which side is night?
How is it possible for you to see the moon when you are on the dark side of the earth?

STEP 4. Cover a softball with aluminum foil and shine a filmstrip projector light on it.

Ask: Why does the ball, which represents the moon, shine?

STUDENT ACTIVITIES

1. What does the sun give off?

2. Where does the moon get its light that we see?

3. Draw how you would place the earth, moon, and sun in order for you to see the moon at night.

4. What are the two ways in which we see something?

WHY DO WE HAVE PHASES OF THE MOON?
[1 – 6]

Concepts

Sometimes the moon appears fully round.
We see that the moon appears to change shape.
Sometimes the moon seems to get smaller and smaller. At other times it seems to get larger and larger.

Procedure

STEP 1. Obtain black construction paper, white soft chalk, globe, a flashlight or a projector, and a small ball. Take the children outside during the moon's last quarter, when it is visible during the daytime. Consult local newspapers for times. Do the same thing for several days and have the children observe the moon and draw the shape of the visible part of the moon. Emphasize that the entire moon is in the sky but that we see only part of it.

Ask: What did you learn from your drawings of the moon?
Did the moon's shape change from day to day?
Does anyone know why the moon's shape changed?

STEP 2. Arrange the apparatus as shown in Diagram 1. Place a pin on the night side of the earth as shown. Darken the room. Move the small globe around the earth.

(1)

Ask: How much of the globe would you see if you were where the pin is stuck on the globe?

Move it some more.

Ask: On which side of the earth is the moon when you can't see it? Where is the moon when it is full?

STEP 3. Draw Diagram 2 on the board and explain some of the phases of the moon.

(2)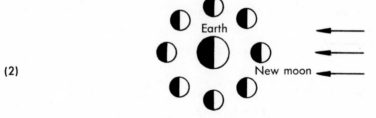

STEP 4. Have a child carry a basketball around the room to represent the phases of the moon, as shown in Diagram 3.

(3)

STEP 5. Have the children walk around each other and compare their faces with the "face" of the moon. [1 – 3]

STUDENT ACTIVITIES

1. If the moon isn't out at night, on what side of the earth must it be located?

2. Draw how the full moon would look from the earth.

3. What causes the phases of the moon?

4. If the moon could remain still in the sky, how would it look every night?

WHAT CAUSES THE TIDES?
[5 – 8]

Concepts

Gravitational attraction of the moon and the sun causes tides.

The moon is smaller than the sun, but because it is closer to the earth its tidal pull is greater than that of the sun.

Tide is highest when moon and sun are pulling on the earth in a straight line. This occurs twice a month.

Low tides occur when moon and sun are pulling at right angles to each other.

Gravity decreases with the distance between two objects.

Procedure

STEP 1. Blow up a balloon and tie it closed. The balloon is to represent the earth. Obtain two globes or balls to represent the moon and sun.

Ask: What do you think causes the tides of the earth?

STEP 2. Take a magnet and place it above a paper clip, as shown in Diagram 1.

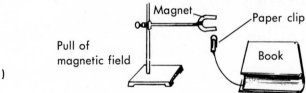

(1)

Ask: What holds up the paper clip?
Can you see this force?
How do you know it is there if you can't see it?
What is the name of this force?

Explanation: This is magnetic force. It is shown in this demonstration to illustrate what a force is and that a force may be invisible. Tides are not caused by magnetic force but gravitational force. See the Discovery Lesson on Gravity for further help.

STEP 3. Define force: force is either a push or a pull exerted on an object. Gravity is also a force that you can't see. The greater the mass of an object, the heavier it is, and the more gravitational force it has. The closer an object is to another, the greater the gravitational attraction there will be between them. Mass is defined as the amount of matter a body contains.

Ask: Now, knowing this, what effect do you think the moon will have on the water of the earth?

How will it pull the water?

STEP 4. Place the moon, sun, and earth (balloon) in a straight line as shown in Diagram 2. Demonstrate by having a student hold the balloon and the teacher pull it with one hand toward the moon and sun with the other hand.

(2)

Sun

Moon

Earth

Ask: If the balloon represents the earth, what would the pulling I am exerting on the balloon represent?

What do you think will happen if I place the sun and moon at right angles?

How will the gravitational forces vary?

Pull the balloon most in the moon's direction and exert much less force in the sun's direction.

Ask: From the way I am pulling the balloon, which has greater gravitational pull on the earth, the moon or the sun?

Why does the moon have greater pull on the earth when it is so much smaller than the sun?

Explanation: The moon has greater effect because it is so much closer to the earth than the sun.

STEP 5. Draw Diagrams 3 and 4 on the board to explain the tides and to summarize.

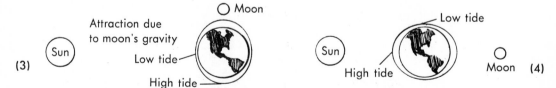

(3)

Attraction due to moon's gravity

Moon

Low tide

High tide

Sun

Low tide

High tide

Sun

Moon

(4)

STUDENT ACTIVITIES

1. Draw the positions of the moon, earth, and sun when there is a very high tide. Outline on your paper how the water around the earth would look.

2. Draw how the water would look over a part of the earth when there is a low tide.

3. Why does the moon have a greater effect on the tide than the sun?

4. How do you know there is a magnetic force when you cannot see it?

5. Can you see gravitational force?

6. Define the word "force."

7. What holds you down in your chair?

8. Do you think that the gravitational forces of the moon and sun might cause the continents of the world to expand and shrink at different times of the day? Explain your answer.

WHAT IS A SHADOW?
[1 – 6]

Concept

Shadows change in size and position during the day.

Procedure

STEP 1. *Ask:* How can I make a shadow?

Get a filmstrip projector and project the light on a screen or wall. Hold objects between the light and the screen.

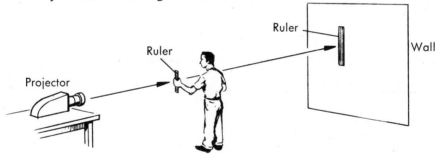

Ask: What do you see on the screen?
Why was the shadow produced?
How could I make the shadow bigger?

Explanation: Move the object closer to the projector.

Ask: What happens to the shadow when I move the object closer to the projector?
If the light changes, do you think the shadow will generally change?

STEP 2. Take the class outdoors on a sunny morning. Have the children measure their shadows with string or trace them on paper or with chalk on the concrete walk. Have them measure their shadows again at noon and at the end of school.

Ask: What happens to the shadows from morning to noon?
What happened to your shadow in the afternoon?

Explanation: The children's shadows will get shorter toward noon and then start to lengthen again after noon. There will be a shift in the position of the shadows.

Ask: Do shadows change during the day?

What time of day was your shadow the biggest?

When was your shadow the smallest?

Can you think of any way we could make a chart to show how shadows change during the day?

STEP 3. Discuss sundials and their limitations.

Ask: Why is a clock more accurate?

STUDENT ACTIVITIES

1. Draw how your shadows looked in the morning; at noon; in the afternoon.

2. If you were lost in the forest and wanted to know if it were noon, how could you tell this without a clock?

3. When we brought the object close to the projector, what happened to the shadow it made?

4. Why do you think your shadow changed during the day?

5. How could you tell time by using the three sticks pictured?

6. Using the above sticks as shown, where would we find that the shadows were in the morning?

WHAT IS AN ECLIPSE?
[4–6]

Concepts

The shadow of the moon on the earth causes a solar eclipse.

The shadow of the earth on the moon causes a lunar eclipse.

To see a solar eclipse, you have to be on the sunny side of the earth.

To see a lunar eclipse, you have to be on the night side of the earth.

The side of the earth facing the sun is day; the side facing the moon is night.

The earth is round.

Procedure

STEP 1. Obtain a film projector or flashlight, two globes (styrene plastic balls will do). Have one ball smaller than the other. Let it represent the moon.

Ask: Can any of you explain what causes an eclipse?

If I let the projector represent the sun and the large globe the earth, where will I have to place the moon in order to make a solar (sun) eclipse?

Explanation: "Eclipse" means to leave or block out. A solar eclipse means to block out the light from the sun. Draw Diagram 1 on the board, but leave out the information about the eclipse.

Ask: Can anyone tell why few people ever see a total eclipse?

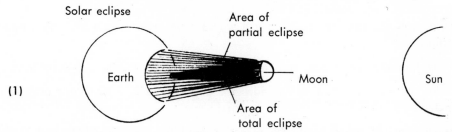

(1)

Explanation: A total solar eclipse covers a small area of the earth, whereas a partial eclipse may cover a much larger area. See Diagram 1.

STEP 2. Place the moon as shown in the diagram. Move the moon so that the shadow passes above or below the earth. Have the students note how the shadow of the moon varies.

Ask: From observing what happens to the moon as we vary its orbit, why don't you think we have a solar eclipse every month?

Explanation: The plane of the moon's orbit is inclined approximately five degrees to the plane of the earth's orbit. For this reason, an eclipse does not occur each time the moon is full.

Ask: From this demonstration, on what side of the earth would you have to be in order to see a solar eclipse?

Why doesn't a solar eclipse last all day?

Explanation: It doesn't last because the moon is moving in its orbit around the earth. A solar eclipse does not occur each new moon, because the inclination of the moon's orbit to the earth's orbit causes the moon's shadow during the new moon phase to sweep sometimes above and sometimes below the earth.

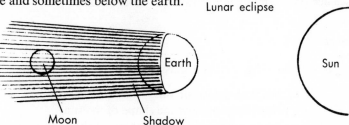

(2)

STEP 3. *Ask:* Where would I have to place the moon in order to make a lunar eclipse?

Move the moon behind the earth to show how the earth's shadow is cast on it. Draw on the board Diagram 2, showing a lunar eclipse.

Ask: From this demonstration, how do you know the earth is round? Why do you think there is not a lunar eclipse every month?

STUDENT ACTIVITIES

1. Draw how the sun, moon, and earth would have to be placed to form a lunar eclipse.

2. Draw how the sun, moon, and earth are placed when a solar eclipse occurs.

3. Color the earth to show which sides are day and night. Label your drawings, including the sun.

4. Show how the moon might be placed behind the earth so that there is no lunar eclipse.

5. Draw how the earth's shadow might look on the moon when there is a lunar eclipse.

6. Draw how the shadow of the moon might look as it hits the earth. Label the areas that would cause a total eclipse and a partial eclipse.

7. What causes night and day on the earth?

8. Draw how the moon would look when there is a partial eclipse.

WHAT IS THE SHAPE OF OUR SUN?
[K – 3]

Concepts

Our sun is a round ball of hot materials and is called a star.
The sun is the closest star to the earth.
Science proves many things through observation.

Procedure

STEP 1. Obtain some smoked glass or exposed X-ray films.

Ask: What shape is our sun?
How do you know the shape of the sun?
How could we prove the shape of the sun?

What color is the sun?

How do we know the color?

Take the class outside or near a window where they can look at the sun. Give them some smoked glass or exposed film. Have them look at the sun through the smoked glass. CAUTION: Have them look only a fraction of a minute because harmful radiation can damage the retina. Emphasize this danger so that children will not at a later time look at eclipses and hurt their eyes.

Exposed film or smoked glass

Sun

Ask: What shape is the sun?

How do we know from doing this the shape of the sun?

Did we prove its shape by observation?

Explanation: We proved the shape of the sun by observing it, or going out and seeing how it looked.

STEP 2. *Ask:* What color did the sun look to you?

How do you know that it is that color?

Would you say that the sun is giving off light?

How do you know this is true?

Explanation: We know that the sun is giving off light because we can see the light it sends us. We couldn't see it if it did not give off light. At night it is dark because the sun's light doesn't shine on our part of the earth. Objects in the heaven which are hot and gaseous, and which give off their own light are called stars. The sun is the closest star to the earth.

Ask: Why did we use the film or smoked glass to look at the sun?

Explanation: Since the film is black, it absorbs most of the light, but it does allow some light through. This helps to filter out light which might harm the eyes.

STUDENT ACTIVITIES

1. Draw and color the shape of the sun.

2. Why shouldn't you look directly into the sun?

3. How did we prove that the sun is yellow?

4. What proof do you have that the sun is round?

5. Why did we use the film to look at the sun?

WHAT SIZE IS THE SUN COMPARED TO THE EARTH?
[K – 2]

Concepts

The sun is many times larger than the earth.
Objects which are far away look smaller.
Stars are very big in size, but they look small.
Stars vary in size, brightness, and position.

Procedure

STEP 1. Obtain a basketball and some radish seeds.

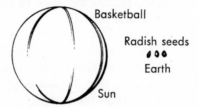

Ask: Which do you think should represent the sun and which should represent the earth?

Explanation: Over a million earths could be placed inside the sun.

STEP 2. Have the students, under the supervision of their parents, observe the sky on a clear night.

Ask: How are the stars different from each other?

STEP 3. Take children into a darkened gymnasium, auditorium, or hallway. Have one student hold a flashlight at the opposite end. Have him move toward the class.

Ask: How does the light change when it gets closer to us?
Do you see why some stars look different?

Explanation: As the light gets closer, it is brighter and larger. Stars vary in size, brightness, and position. Stars which are closer to the earth will generally appear brighter and larger, although in reality they may be smaller than distant stars.

STUDENT ACTIVITIES

1. Draw a picture of the sun and make a diagram of the earth next to it.

2. True or False

    _____ a. The sun is many times bigger than the earth.

    _____ b. Stars are smaller than the earth.

    _____ c. Objects which are far away look big.

    _____ d. All stars are the same size.

    _____ e. Some stars are bright.

    _____ f. Stars have certain positions in the heavens.

WHAT DOES THE SUN DO FOR US?
[1 – 3]

Concepts

The sun gives us energy in the form of heat and light.
The light of the sun can be brought to a point by using a lens.

Procedure

STEP 1. Hold up a small magnifying glass in front of the class (this experiment can best be done outside of the classroom).

Ask: What do I have in my hand?
What does it do?

Explanation: A magnifying glass can bend the light rays and bring them to a point.

STEP 2. Move the lens over a piece of paper in such a manner that it will focus the sunlight on a point on the paper. This can be achieved by moving the lens back and forth above the paper until you get a small point of light focused on it.

> *Ask:* What do you think will happen to the paper?
> Where does the light come from that is focused on the paper?

> *Explanation:* The lens focuses sunlight on the paper. This concentrated light warms the paper, causing it to smolder and burn.

> *Ask:* What does this demonstration show about the sun?
> Does the sun give us energy in the form of heat?
> What if there were no sun; do you think the earth would be very cold?

STEP 3. Have some students feel the warmth under the magnifying glass by placing their hands there for a few seconds.

> *Ask:* Can you feel the warmth of the sun's rays?
> Why do we need the warmth of the sun?

STUDENT ACTIVITIES

1. What do we get from the sun?

2. Make a diagram showing how the magnifying glass changed the direction of the rays coming through it.

3. Why did the paper burn, whereas the magnifying glass did not burn?

4. Why is the sun important to us?

5. Why did the teacher have to move the lens up and down before she was able to get the paper to burn?

7. What would happen to plants if there were no sunlight?

6. Why is it colder at night than during the day?

HOW LONG IS A YEAR?
[3 – 6]

Concepts

The earth moves around the sun (revolves).
It takes one year for the earth to make one trip around the sun.

The earth rotates as it revolves around the sun.
The earth moves around the sun in an elliptical path.
An earth year is 365¼ days.

Procedure

STEP 1. Draw an ellipse on the floor with chalk, as shown in the diagram. In the center of this ellipse place a light, a lamp, or a projector on the floor.

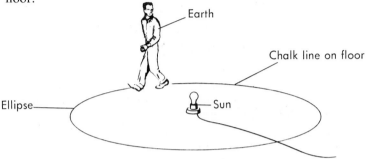

Ask: If the spinning of the earth makes night and day, what do you think determines how long a year is on the earth?
Why do you think I made the chalk line on the floor?
What do you notice about the way I made the line?

Explanation: Draw an ellipse on the blackboard and point out to the children that it is somewhat circular but not a perfect circle.

Ask: Can anyone tell me what the lamp is supposed to represent in the middle of the ellipse?
Can anyone show me how the earth might move around the sun?

STEP 2. Have a student walk on the chalk line around the lamp.

Explanation: If the student doesn't rotate while he is walking around the lamp, ask the class what is wrong with the way he moves around the sun. Point out that each spin (rotation) is equal to one day.

STEP 3. Have several students go around the sun and rotate while they go. Indicate to the students that they represent the earth and that the lamp indicates the sun.

Ask: Does anyone know how many days it takes to make a year?

Explanation: Explain to the class that it takes 365¼ days to make one year, or that it takes that long for the earth to complete one circle (orbit) around the sun.

Teacher's Note: The use of a planetarium as a visual aid is advised.

STUDENT ACTIVITIES

1. Draw and explain how the earth goes around the sun.

2. Why is a year 365¼ days long?

3. What is the shape of the path the earth takes around the sun called?

4. What does the earth do as it goes around the sun? Does the earth spin or go straight as it moves around the sun?

WHAT CAUSES THE SEASONS?
[6 – 8]

Concepts

The sun gives off light and heat.

The more sun rays that hit a section of the earth, the warmer that section will get.

When it is light on one side of the earth, it is dark on the other side of the earth.

The rotating of the earth causes night and day.

The earth makes one revolution around the sun in one year.

Procedure

STEP 1. Shine a flashlight as shown in Diagram 1.

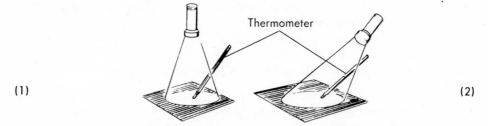

(1)   (2)

Ask: What do you notice about the way the light shines on the paper? Does the light seem to go in a straight line?

What do you suppose will happen if I turn the flashlight so that the light hits the paper on a slant? (See Diagram 2.)

In which way, the direct or slanted, do you think the temperature would be the greater?

How could we determine whether your answer is correct?

STEP 2. Take two thermometers and two flashlights and shine them as shown in Diagrams 1 and 2. Place a thermometer in the path of each of these rays to see whether you can detect a minor difference in temperature.

Explanation: From these experiments we can conclude that when light rays hit an object in a straight line compared to a slant, the object will be warmer.

STEP 3. Obtain two plastic or rubber balls. Place one of these on a nail as shown in Diagram 3 and the other as shown in Diagram 4. A globe of the earth may be substituted for the second globe. Take a flashlight and shine light directly on each of the globes.

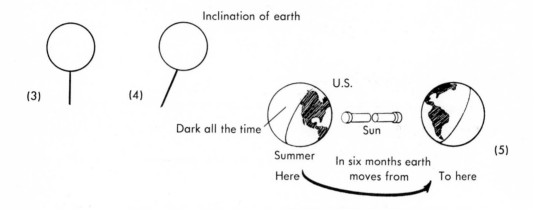

Inclination of earth

(3)

(4)

Dark all the time

U.S.

Sun

Summer Here

In six months earth moves from

To here

(5)

Ask: What do you notice about the way the light hits the two globes?
Can you figure out from this demonstration what causes days and nights?
If the earth were not inclined as is the first globe, do you think we would have any seasons?

Now point the flashlight at the second globe, and move the globe around the flashlight. See diagram on how you are to move the flashlight and globe.

Ask: What do you notice about the way the light strikes the globe as I move the globes, stopping at several places?
What do you think the season would be here?

STEP 4. Draw Diagram 5 on the board to demonstrate that the inclination of the earth causes the seasons.

Ask: How long does it take for the earth to make one trip around the sun?
What is the difference in the position of the earth in January compared to June?
When it is winter in New York, what season is it in Argentina?
What does the inclination of the earth have to do with making the seasons?

STUDENT ACTIVITIES

1. Draw how the earth would be inclined when it is January in the United States. Show how the sun's rays would hit the earth.

2. Look at the diagram below. From this drawing, why do you think it is warmer in the summer?

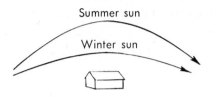

3. Why is direct sunlight warmer?

4. What causes the seasons?

5. Explain why the earth has a year.

WHY DO STARS APPEAR CLOSE OR FAR APART?
[K – 4]

Concepts

There are millions of stars, and they are tremendous distances from each other. Our great distances from the stars make them appear closer together.

Procedure

STEP 1. Place 50 bottle caps or marbles in a cluster so that no one marble or cap is less than one inch from its nearest neighbor. Have some students stand in front of these, facing them.

Ask: What do you think will happen to the way you see these objects as you move away from them?

Have them move slowly away from the objects. When they get to the back of the room,

Ask: How do the objects appear now?

Explanation: As the children move away from the objects, the marbles or caps will appear to move closer together.

STEP 2. *Ask:* Do you get any ideas from this demonstration which might explain why the stars look so close together?

Some stars look very close together in the sky, but we know that they are very far apart.

Ask: What do we know, then, about how far away these stars are?

Explanation: There are millions of stars, and they are tremendous distances from each other. Our great distance from the stars makes them appear to be much closer together.

STUDENT ACTIVITIES

1. Why do stars appear to be close together?

2. What happened to the way the bottle caps or marbles looked when you moved away from them?

3. Draw how the marbles looked when you saw them in front of you and then how they looked when you were in the back of the room.

4. If you fill a Chinese checker board with marbles, does it make the shape of a star, or does it represent many "little stars?"

5. If you look at cars at different distances, which are smaller, the near ones, or those far away?

HOW DO THE PLANETS MOVE?
[5 – 8]

Concepts

Planets move around the sun.
There are nine planets that move around the sun.
Planets vary in size and distance from the sun.
The planets farthest from the sun have the longest year and the longest path to follow.

Procedure

STEP 1. Obtain a lamp and clay that can be shaped into small balls or several small styrifoam balls from the local dime store. (Paper or papier-mâché which can be placed on a tack board or hung with wires from the ceiling can also serve for this purpose.) Shape the balls so that they vary in size as indicated by either scale below.

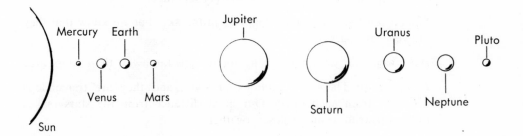

Teacher's Note: As an art project, make a mobile of the solar system.

	Small — Size in Diameter	Larger Scale
Mercury	$\frac{1}{16}$ in.	$\frac{1}{4}$
Venus	$\frac{2}{16}$ in.	$\frac{5}{8}$
Earth	$\frac{2}{16}$ in.	$\frac{5}{8}$
Mars	$\frac{3}{32}$ in.	$\frac{3}{8}$
Jupiter	$1\frac{5}{16}$ in.	$6\frac{3}{4}$
Saturn	$1\frac{1}{16}$ in.	$5\frac{1}{2}$
Uranus	$\frac{1}{2}$ in.	$2\frac{1}{4}$
Neptune	$\frac{9}{16}$ in.	$2\frac{1}{4}$
Pluto	$\frac{7}{16}$ in.	$\frac{1}{4}$
Sun		5 feet

The scales of $\frac{1}{16}$ or $\frac{1}{4}$ in. are equal to about 4000 miles. Make a ring to shape over Saturn.

Explanation: Planets are not on fire (burning gases) like the sun, but reflect their light from the sun.

Ask: Where should I place the sun?
What planets should I place next to the sun?

STEP 2. Attach the clay balls to paper clips and tape them to the sides of a shoebox or hang them from a tackboard. The names of the planets should be written below them. Each student could make a model of the solar system if they use a shoebox. Emphasize that there are nine planets and that their size varies. Also point out that it is impossible to have an accurate comparison of the planets with the sun, because the sun is so big compared to the planets.

Ask: Does anyone know what we call all the planets and the sun?

Explanation: Point out that this is called the solar system and that the word "solar" comes from the Latin word meaning sun.

STEP 3. Display the solar system for several days and go over the names of the different planets once each day.

> *Ask:* How do all planets move around the sun?
> Is the earth a planet?
> Does it move around the sun?

STUDENT ACTIVITIES

1. Make a diagram of the planets and the sun.

2. Show how the planets move around the sun.

3. Which planet is the largest planet?

4. Which planet has rings?

5. Which planet is the smallest planet?

6. Which planet is closest to the sun?

7. Which planet is farthest from the sun?

8. Which planet would take the longest to go around the sun?

9. Which planet would have the longest year?

10. Which planet do you think would be the coldest because it is so far from the sun?

11. Which planet do you think would be the warmest?

12. Do all the planets in our solar system move in the same direction?

WHAT CAUSES SOME STARS TO BE DIFFERENT COLORS?
[5 – 8]

Concepts

When objects are heated, they may change color.
White-hot objects are hotter than red-hot objects.
Stars which are white are believed to be hotter than yellow stars, and yellow stars are hotter than red stars.

Teacher's Note: Caution children in the lower grades against heating objects to show change of color.

Procedure

STEP 1. Obtain the following materials: pliers or tongs, a piece of nichrome or copper wire, propane gas torch.

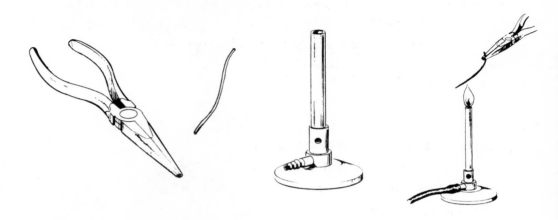

Ask: If you saw two pieces of iron, both of which had been in a furnace, and one piece was red and the other was white, which one would you think was the hotter?

With a pair of pliers hold a wire above a Bunsen burner.

Ask: What do you think will happen to the wire as I heat it?

Explanation: The wire will change color, becoming red, then yellow, and finally white as the temperature increases.

STEP 2. *Ask:* What did you notice about the way the wire changed color?
What made it change color?
What were the different colors that the wire gave off in the process of being heated?
What color do you think was the hottest? the coldest?
If you looked at a star in the heavens and you noticed that it was red, do you think it would be a very hot star compared to one you saw that was yellow?

Explanation: Red stars are believed to be cooler than yellow stars, and white stars are hotter than either red or yellow stars.

Ask: Do you see from this demonstration how it is possible for an astronomer (a scientist who studies the stars) to tell how hot a star is without ever going to it?

Explanation: The color of the stars cannot be detected with the naked eye. The astronomer must use astronomical instruments in order to do this.

STUDENT ACTIVITIES

1. If you were going to heat some charcoal, which of the following types of light do you think it would give off first: red, yellow, or white?

2. What happened to the wire in the above demonstration as it was heated?

3. Can you think of some things an astronomer might want to study in the laboratory that would help him better to understand the stars?

HOW FAR AWAY ARE THE PLANETS FROM EACH OTHER?
[1–3, 4–6]

Concepts

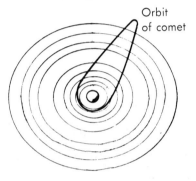

Orbit of comet

The distances between planets are enormous.
Comets are present in the solar system.
The closer a planet is to the sun, the warmer
   it will be.
Comets in their trip around the sun cross the
   orbits of planets.

Procedure

STEP 1. Give the children a planet chart or have them make one showing the distances between planets. Have them take their charts and yardsticks out to the playground. Let one or several children represent each of the nine known planets, and one the sun. Using one inch for one million miles, place the children in sequence to represent each planet in its orbit (see chart).

Explanation: Converting the chart of planets from millions of miles to inches would result in the planet Mercury being 36 inches (one yard) from the child representing the sun. The others would be proportionally placed until the planet Pluto would be over 3700 inches, or 102 yards, away. Stress should be made of the fact that the sizes of the planets vary and that this demonstration does not take this into account. It is impossible for students to understand the great distances involved in space, but this demonstration will stimulate them better to understand the enormity of it. Have the students move around the sun.

Ask: How should you move about the sun?

Explanation: They should move in elliptical orbits. Have one student run and cross all the orbits of the planet, circle the sun, and return to his original position.

STEP 2. *Ask:* What did the student who crossed the planet orbits represent?
What did we show by our demonstration on the playground?
What was wrong about our demonstration?
Were the planets all the proper relative size?
What did we leave out in our demonstration?

Explanation: We did not include the moons of Jupiter and Earth or planetoids. Planetoids are small planetlike objects found in orbits mainly between Mars and Jupiter. Draw on the board how comets would circle the sun (see diagram).

Ask: How does the orbit of a comet differ from those of a planet?
Which planet do you think would be the warmest planet?

Explanation: Mercury would be the warmest, because it is closest to the sun.

STUDENT ACTIVITIES

1. What did the demonstration that we did prove?

2. Which planet would you like to be and why?

3. Why didn't we have moons on the playground?

4. Draw a planet's orbit.

5. Draw how a comet path would cross the earth's orbit around the sun.

6. Which planet is farthest from the sun?

7. Which one is closest?

8. Expose children to references on planets for getting information about the solar system. Have the children meet together after researching for the purpose of preparing a chart of the vital information about the planets. One type of chart that could cooperatively be made is shown below.

Position from Sun	Name of Planet	Millions of Miles from Sun	Number of Known Moons
1	Mercury	36	0
2	Venus	67	0
3	Earth	93	1
4	Mars	142	2
5	Jupiter	484	12
6	Saturn	887	9
7	Uranus	1785	5
8	Neptune	2800	2
9	Pluto	3700	0

GEOLOGY

The discovery lessons on geology in this section are only examples. Teachers would need to devise far more lessons for any one unit.

Geology lends itself easily to student-performed experiments, and whenever possible, it is more desirable to have children do experiments than observe demonstrations. Refer to the student experiment section of this book. It contains several student experiments for geology.

HOW DOES EROSION AFFECT THE SOIL?
[3 – 6]

Concepts

Soil consists of several different layers.
Soil is made from rock.
There are many kinds of soil.
Erosion is the wasting away of soil.
Soil has organic material (material which is living or has been living) that enriches it.

Procedure

STEP 1. *Ask:* How could we make some soil here in our classroom?

Hit a rock with a hammer so that small pieces of the rock are chipped away.

Explanation: These chips will be incorporated with the soil and thereby become a part of it. Soil, then, can be made from rocks.

Ask: Is all soil the same?
How do you know soil changes from one place to another?
How does the soil on the desert or beach differ from soil in the mountains?

You know soil must vary, because it is composed of different-sized particles and has different color.

STEP 2. *Ask:* Does the soil seem to vary as you look at it from the surface down?

Fine particles

Layers of Soil

(1)

Heavy particles
are deep

Fill a quart jar three-fourths full with soil. Add water until the jar is full. Place a lid on it.

Ask: How do you think the soil will settle in the bottle?
What particles will settle to the bottom first?

Shake the jar vigorously. Attempt to get soil which has some decayed plant material, such as hay particles, in it.

Ask: What do you notice about the way the soil settles?
Can you see any little pieces of grass or wood in the soil?
In which layer does it seem mainly to be found?

Take two cans and fill them with soil. To one can mix a lot of dead grass, leaves, or peat moss with the soil. Water each can with the same amount of water. Have the students observe the cans for several days.

Ask: Which can seems to be able to retain moisture best?
Why is organic material good for the soil?

STEP 3. Have each student bring two milk cartons to class. Cut out one of the long sides of both of the cartons. Fill the cartons with dirt. In one plant grass seed just under the surface of the dirt. Water the seeded carton until the seeds have sprouted. At first it might be better to place a damp cloth over the seeded plot in order to retain moisture. When the grass is about an inch or more in length, tip both the seeded carton and the unseeded one, as shown in Diagram 2. Place aluminum pans as shown in the diagram. Sprinkle water on the cartons. Repeat this procedure for several days.

Grass   No grass

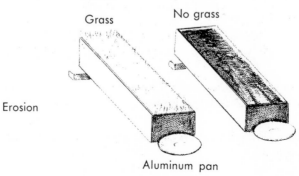

Erosion

(2)

Aluminum pan

Ask: Which carton loses the most soil?

Why does one carton lose less soil than the other?

How can we prevent erosion in our soils?

STUDENT ACTIVITIES

1. Draw a diagram of how the topsoil might look in a side view.

2. How do you know there are many kinds of soil?

3. What is erosion?

4. How may erosion be controlled?

5. Draw in the diagram what you would do to control erosion.

6. Where is the organic material mainly located in the soil?

7. In the experiment we did with the milk carton, why didn't we plant seeds in both cartons?

8. What do you call the carton that had no seeds in it?

9. How is soil made from rocks?

10. Make a "mountain" of foil, dirt, and sand. Pour water over it slowly and observe. Which eroded away first?

HOW CAN WE MAKE A FOSSIL?
[K – 6]

Concepts

A fossil is any remain, impression, or trace of an animal or plant of a former geological age.

Fossils can be found in sedimentary rock.

Sedimentary rock is formed from mud and silt.

Organisms whose fossils are uncovered lived and died in the period when the layers in which their remains are found were laid down.

Older layers of rocks have fossils which are unlike the animals and plants now living.

Procedure

STEP 1. If possible, hold up some examples of fossils, or show some pictures of fossils.

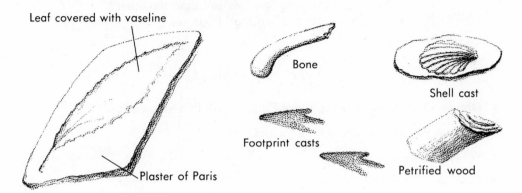

Types of Fossils

Ask: Do any of you know what a fossil is?
Have you ever seen a rock that had the imprint of a leaf on it?

Dip your thumb in some ink and make an imprint of it on a piece of paper.

Ask: Do you understand how imprints are made?
How do you think we could make an imprint of a leaf?

STEP 2. Give each student a small piece of cardboard, a leaf, some vaseline, and some prepared plaster of paris.

    Ask: Do you have any idea of how you might make an imprint of a leaf?

    Have them coat the leaf with vaseline. Place the leaf on about one-eighth inch of plaster of paris, cover the leaf with some more plaster of paris, and allow to dry on the window sill. After the plaster of paris has dried, have the students lift up their leaves. Point out that the plaster would be like small particles of dirt (sediment) dropped by a river and that it takes millions of years to make hard rock out of sediment.

STEP 3. *Ask:* What have you discovered about your plaster of paris?
Did it make an imprint?
Do you think a similar imprint could be made in nature, mud being used instead of plaster of paris?

Show them some pictures of some actual fossils of leaves. If possible, show them fossils of some forms of extinct life. Have them make some imprints from mud.

    Ask: From the fossils you see, do you think that there might have been some animals and plants on earth that are no longer living?

STUDENT ACTIVITIES

1. Have the class make diagrams of their fossils.

2. Discuss how fossils were made in nature.

3. Have them make some sedimentary soil (see section, "How Is Sedimentary Rock Formed?"). This section can be adapted easily for the K – 3 grade level.

4. Have the students bring in any fossils they might have at home and discuss where they or their family found them.

WHAT IS A FAULT?
[5 – 8]

Concepts

Some land has been formed by sedimentation, causing layering.
When too much force is applied to the earth's structure, the earth cracks.
The point where the earth's crust cracks is called a fault.
A normal fault is where the earth's crust drops or rises.
A thrust fault is where the earth's crust rises over an adjacent part of the earth.
Earthquakes may be caused by the earth's crust sliding along a fault.

Procedure

STEP 1. *Ask:* What is an earthquake?
               What do you think causes an earthquake?

Take a balance and on one side place some sand and on the other side a dish of water so that both sides are in balance. See Diagram 1.

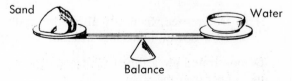

Sand   Water

(1)

Balance

Ask: What do you suppose will happen if I take some sand from the one side of the balance and place it on the other side? Do this.
      If the balance represents the earth's crust, how might this demonstration be similar to what happens in nature?
      Do you think material is being worn down from mountains and being carried to the sea?

Explanation: Erosion is always taking place, wearing down land. This debris is often carried to the sea. When material gets to the ocean floor, it causes the floor to get heavier, which may cause the crust of the earth in that area to move.

STEP 2. Take some foam rubber and paint broad lines on it to represent strata. See Diagram 2. Cut the rubber as shown in the diagram.

(2)

STEP 3. Place two of the pieces as indicated in Diagram 3 in front of the class, and tell them that these are to represent rock.

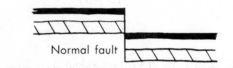

(3)

Ask: How do you think this rock structure could have reached this condition in nature?

Explanation: The rock structure could have formed a fault owing to stresses within the earth, and the stress in the earth could have then caused it to rise or fall. Tell the class that this kind of a fault is called a normal fault.

STEP 4. Place a rock structure as shown in Diagram 4. This is what a geologist might see in nature, and he must interpret what occurred.

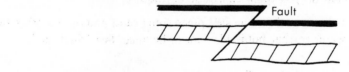

(4)

Ask: Do you see where a fault might exist?
How do you think this structure was formed?

Demonstrate how a thrust fault could occur by pushing one section of the rubber over the other.

STUDENT ACTIVITIES

1. What causes earthquakes?

2. Draw a diagram of a normal fault.

3. Draw a diagram of a thrust fault.

4. In the diagram below, the black represents a coal seam. Layer 1 has been all mined. How could a geologist aid the coal company in locating where the rest of the coal might be located?

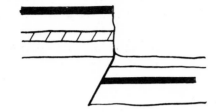

(5)

SECTION FOUR
STUDENT EXPERIMENTS

Geology

1. How Do We Make Crystals? [1 – 6]
2. How Does a Geyser Work? [2 – 6]
3. How Can We Make a Volcano? [3 – 6]
4. What Are a Fossil and a Fossil Bed? [3 – 6]

Meteorology — Weather

1. What Good Is Solar Energy? [2 – 4]
2. How Can You Make a Barometer? [5 – 6]
3. How Can We Make a Cloud? [3 – 6]
4. How Big Should You Make a Parachute? [K – 6]

Physical and Chemical Changes

1. What Do You Need in Order to Have Burning? [3 – 6]
2. How to Make Oxygen in Class [3 – 8]
3. What Will Happen to an Ice Cube? [K – 6]
4. How Much Water Will Snow Make? [2 – 5]

Miscellaneous

1. How Can You Make a Fleet Move Without Touching Them? [K – 6]
2. What Causes Sound? [2 – 6]

STUDENT
EXPERIMENT SECTION

It is more desirable to have students do experiments themselves than to have them watch demonstrations. The following section contains examples of student experiment work sheets which may be used as guides by teachers who are writing their own lessons. No effort has been made to include all science subject areas because it is thought that with a little practice teachers can easily devise their own experiments.

The following lessons have all been tested by elementary teachers and have been used by students with little or no difficulty.

A teacher in making student lessons should first decide what concepts she wants to teach, then think of or look for ways in which experiments can be performed to develop these concepts in the minds of the children. The "Sourcebook for Elementary Science," published by Harcourt, Brace & World, Inc., can be helpful in suggesting experiments.

HOW DO WE MAKE CRYSTALS?
[1 – 6]

Materials: small piece of coal, salt, copper sulfate, alum, potassium permanganate, sugar, pencil, jars.

Procedure

STEP 1. Mix a spoonful of salt in a glass of water.

Stir the water well. Let the water stand for several minutes until it becomes clear. Then very gently pour some of the water in a jar lid and let it stand for several days.

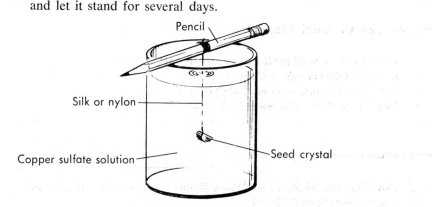

Pencil

Silk or nylon

Copper sulfate solution

Seed crystal

Ask: What do you think will happen to your salt solution?

STEP 2. Repeat the above experiment, but this time use copper sulfate or sugar instead of table salt (copper sulfate can usually be obtained from your high school chemistry stock room or from a local drug store).

Ask: What do you think will happen to this solution?

STEP 3. After the water evaporates from the copper sulfate or sugar solution, take one of the crystals and tie it with a clear piece of silk thread.

Caution: Be certain to have your hands very clean. Wash them thoroughly before doing this. Oil from your hands on the string will cause the experiment to fail. Get a jar and fill it three-quarters full of hot water. Add copper sulfate to it and stir until it will dissolve no more copper sulfate. Hang your seed crystal in the copper sulfate solution and watch it grow.

STEP 4. Have some students repeat the above and disturb their jars during the period of crystallization by shaking the jars.

Explanation: The slower the crystals grow, the larger they will become. If they seem to be growing irregularly, try to slow down the evaporation process by placing a lid on top of the jar with just a few holes in it. It is important that no one touch or disturb the crystals while they are growing. If they are disturbed in the growing process, they will break apart into hundreds of microscopic crystals.

Teacher's Note: Explain that most solids are crystalline in form, and that crystalline form is important in determining some of the properties of the substance. Some rocks have large crystals in them, and some rocks have small crystals because of differences in the rate of crystallization.

STEP 5. *Ask:* What happened to your water and salt?

STUDENT ACTIVITIES

1. Draw below how big your salt crystals are.

2. What happened to your seed crystals?

3. What made the difference in the size of the crystals in the two jars of copper sulfate?

4. Why do you think it is important to study crystals?

5. John found two rocks containing the same type of material. One had large crystals, but the other had small crystals. Why?

Teacher's Note: You can also use a piece of coal in a dish to which saturated salt solution has been added for several days. Dyes added to the solution make colorful crystals.

HOW DOES A GEYSER WORK?
[2 – 6]

Materials: pyrex funnel and saucepan.

Teacher's Note: Show some pictures of Old Faithful first to arouse curiosity.

Procedure

STEP 1. Fill the saucepan half full with water. Set the funnel in the pan as shown in the diagram. Heat the water with a burner. It is important that the water can get under the lip of the funnel. To insure this you can rest one edge on a nail or bottle cap.

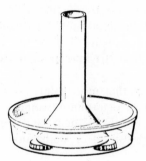

STEP 2. *Ask:* What do you think will happen to the water as you heat it?
Record what happened to the water.
Why do you think the water spurted out of the funnel?
What happens to water when you heat it?
Do you think water in a geyser would have to be heated before it would shoot up out of the earth?
Why aren't there geysers everywhere?

Teacher's Note: Geysers are only found in volcanic regions, or areas where there used to be volcanoes. Ground water beneath the ground is heated by hot rocks or gases. When the water gets hot enough, it expands and releases dissolved gases in the water which exert pressure. The gases plus the expansion of water force the water to the surface through partially obstructed cracks in the earth. It thereby forms a geyser.

HOW CAN WE MAKE A VOLCANO?
[3 – 6]

Materials: ammonium dichromate, magnesium powder,* clay, and magnesium ribbon. These chemicals may be obtained from a chemistry teacher or from a scientific supply house.

Procedure

STEP 1. Make a cone from some clay you obtained from around your school. Construct a volcano as shown in the diagram, on a board or Masonite. Place the ammonium dichromate in a dish and mix a couple of pinches of magnesium powder with it. Place this mixture in the cone. Stick a piece of magnesium ribbon in the middle of the dichromate.

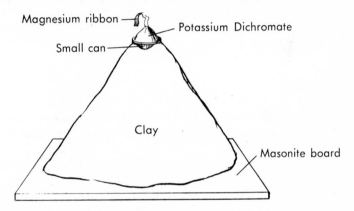

Caution: Do not light the volcano until the teacher tells you to do so. Turn out the lights in the room.

STEP 2. After the teacher has inspected everything, light the magnesium ribbon.

Caution: Bend the ribbon as shown in the diagram so that it is easy to light. Get your hand away from the ribbon, because it burns with a very hot flame.

STEP 3. Write down everything you observed about the way the volcano erupted.

STEP 4. *Ask:* What did you notice about the shape of the volcano after it stopped working?
What caused it to take that shape?

*The magnesium powder is not necessary, but it helps to make the material burn better.

Where did most of the ash from the volcano fall?
Can you now explain why a volcano has its shape?
Why don't volcanoes erupt all the time?

Teacher's Note: The volcanic cone above is typical of a cinder cone, but is not typical of a shield-type volcano, which is mainly formed by flows of lava. Most of the cinders fall next to the crater with fewer and fewer cinders falling away from the cone. The distribution of the cinders is similar to the way water spreads out when the nozzle of a hose is held straight up.

WHAT ARE A FOSSIL AND A FOSSIL BED?
[3 – 6]

Teacher's Note: To follow "How Can We Make a Fossil?" Discuss geology, mammoth, Arctic, Alaska, Siberia.

Materials: ice tray, fruit, water, and soil.

Procedure

STEP 1. Place some small pieces of fruit such as cherries and grapes in an ice tray and place the ice tray in a refrigerator.

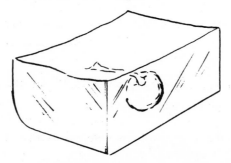

Ask: What do you think will happen to the fruit in the refrigerator?
How long do you think it will last in the refrigerator?

STEP 2. Place some soil and water in another ice tray and add some fruit to it. Place it in a refrigerator.

Ask: What do you think will happen to this fruit?
How long do you thing the fruit will last (be preserved)?
If an animal were to die in Alaska or in the Arctic and was covered by snow and ice, do you think it would last a long time in the ice?

Some years ago part of a mammoth (an animal which looks like an elephant) was found buried in the ice in Siberia. Does this prove that these animals used to live in Siberia?

STEP 3. Take your ice trays out each day and record what you see in them.

Ask: What do we call the remains of an animal or plant which has been found from previous geological times?

STEP 4. Make some mud so that it is fairly thick. Place it in the bottom of a small cardboard box. Smooth it out; press your hand in the mud so that you get a good impression. Cover the mud with a layer of sand several inches thick.

Ask: What do you think will happen to the impression of your hand?

After two or three days remove the sand carefully.

Ask: What has happened to your impression of your hand?
Is it still there?
What would you call this impression?
Do you think it is possible to find impressions of dinosaur foot imprints?

STEP 5. Take a model of an animal or a cutout of an animal and cover it with several sheets of paper.

Ask: What have you made?
What would each layer of paper be in nature?
What do you think a fossil bed is?
Why do you think a fossil bed usually must have layers of soil in it?

Teacher's Note: A fossil is any remains or evidence of previous life. It may have been buried in mud, covered by sand, volcanic ash, or other material, or frozen in ice or the ground. Some types of fossils are actual remains found in ice, amber, asphalt pits, oil shale, coal, and other carbonaceous remains. Others are petrified wood, and casts, including tracks, molds, and coprolites (hardened feces). Fossil beds occur only in areas containing sedimentary deposits. These are areas where soil has been washed or blown in and has covered the fossils.

WHAT GOOD IS SOLAR ENERGY?
[2 – 4]

Procedure

STEP 1. *Ask:* Do you know of any ways we can make the sun do work for us?

Take some salt and pour a lot of it in a small dish. Add water. Cover the salt water with a plastic bag and place your equipment in sunlight (see diagram).

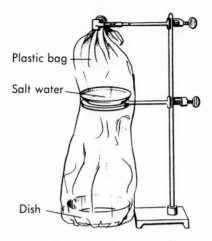

Plastic bag

Salt water

Dish

Ask: What do you think is going to happen to your salt water?

Why do you think we told you to cover the salt water with a plastic bag?

Record what happens to your experiment each day. Write down everything you see about it.

STEP 2.　Taste the water in the bottom dish.

Ask: Where did the water come from?

What happened to your salt solution?

Where did the water go?

What made the water disappear?

How does the sun's energy (solar energy) benefit man?

How could this method be beneficial to people who live near the ocean but don't have enough drinking water?

Teacher's Note: The water in the salt solution absorbs the sun's energy and evaporates, leaving behind the salt. The water later condenses on the plastic bag and runs down the side and is collected in the dish below.

HOW CAN YOU MAKE A BAROMETER?
[5–6]

Teacher's Note: Air pressure demonstrations should be done with this.

Materials: coffee can, a large balloon or a rubber drum, straw, glue, pin, and card.

Procedure

STEP 1. Cover a coffee can with a piece of rubber to make a drum. Slip a rubber band around the rubber to keep it on the can. See the diagram.

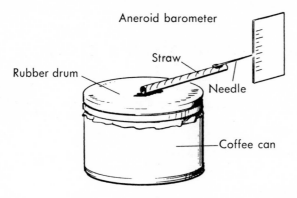

Aneroid barometer

Straw

Rubber drum

Needle

Coffee can

STEP 2. Place a small amount of glue in the center of the drum and attach a straw as shown in the diagram. Place another drop of glue on the end of the straw and attach a pin. Glue a pin to the other end of the straw.

STEP 3. Mark a card with some lines which are the same distance apart. Tack it on the wall as shown in the diagram.

STEP 4. What do you think will happen to your needle if there is a lot of air pressure?

Read your barometer for several days and record what happens.

	Barometer	*Kind of Weather That Day*
1.		
2.		
3.		
4.		
5.		
6.		
7.		

Ask: From your records, what can you say about the weather when your barometer reads high?

From your records, what can you say about the weather when the barometer reads low?

Can you think of any ways you might improve your barometer?

Explain why you think a barometer is a help to a weatherman (meteorologist) in predicting the weather.

Teacher's Note: The room temperature will affect this barometer so that it is not only measuring air pressure differences. It might be desirable to have some students keep their barometers outside class and compare their readings with those in class. When the air pressure increases, it pushes down on the rubber drum, causing the straw to give a high reading. When the air pressure is low, the opposite will happen. A falling barometer may indicate that a storm is approaching.

HOW CAN WE MAKE A CLOUD?
[3 – 6]

Teacher's Note: Discuss molecules first. Caution students about the dangers of boiling water.

Materials: gallon jug, matches, ice, and two flasks.

Procedure: Experiment I

STEP 1. *Ask:* Do you know any ways that you can make a cloud in the classroom?

Take a gallon jug, light a match, and drop it in the jug. Let it burn. As soon as it goes out, blow hard into the jug and then pull it away from your mouth quickly.

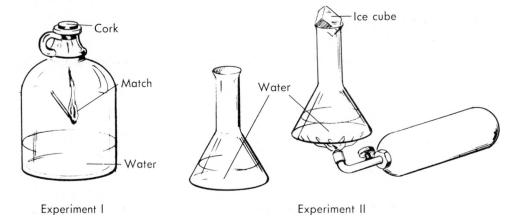

Experiment I · Experiment II

STEP 2. *Ask:* What did you notice about what happened in the jug?
Where did the water come from that made the cloud in the jug?

Try the experiment again, but this time don't use the match.

Ask: Why did you use the match?

Procedure: Experiment II

STEP 1. Take two flasks as shown in the diagram. Fill about one-quarter full with water. Heat one of the flasks. After it is fairly warm, remove the burner and place an ice cube in the top of the flask. See the diagram.

STEP 2. Record what happens.

> *Ask:* Why did a cloud form in one flask and not in the other?
> What did the ice do to the water in the air?
> When air rises it cools. From what you have learned in this experiment, can you explain why there is more rain and snow in the mountains?
> What do we have to do to air so that we can see water in it?
> Why does the air over heated water have more moisture?
> What happens to the moisture in the air when it cools?

Teacher's Note: In the jug experiment the match was necessary because it gave off tiny smoke particles which the water needs to have as a nucleus in order to condense easily. The sudden release of pressure in the moist air in the jug causes the temperature in the jug to drop, and the water then condenses. In the second experiment, the water in the flask is saturated with moisture. The ice cube cools the air and causes the water to condense. Emphasize to the class that the higher you go in the lower atmosphere, the more the temperature drops. This causes condensation and helps to explain why there is more rain and snow in mountain regions.

Clouds can also be made with alcohol and an air pump. This can be done to show that many fluids vaporize.

HOW BIG SHOULD YOU MAKE A PARACHUTE?
[K–6]

Teacher's Note: Demonstrations on air pressure should be used with this.

Materials: three pieces of cloth — square in shape and various sizes, and three objects which weigh the same (nuts and bolts will do).

Procedure

STEP 1. Make three parachutes of different sizes but attach equal weights to each parachute.

Ask: Which of these parachutes do you think will be the best? Explain why you chose that parachute.

STEP 2. Throw the parachutes into the air and let them fall. Record what happened.

Ask: Why do you think one parachute works better than another?
What are the parachutes catching as they fall?
If the parachute has a bigger surface, do you think it will be able to catch more air?
From this experiment what can you tell us about the air?
What do you think would happen if you used lighter weights on your parachutes?

Teacher's Note: The parachute demonstrates that there is air pressure. The larger the surface area of the parachute, the more air will collect beneath it, causing it to fall more slowly to the earth. Large weights such as are sometimes dropped from military planes require very large parachutes and may use more than one parachute.

WHAT DO YOU NEED IN ORDER TO HAVE BURNING?
[3 – 6]

Materials: glass pan or small aquarium or pan, glass jar, candle, and water.

Procedure

STEP 1. Take a candle and attach it to the bottom of a pan as shown in the diagram. Cover the pan with a little water. Light the candle. Cover the candle with a glass as indicated. Write down what happens after the candle burns.

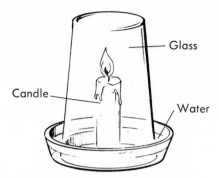

STEP 2. *Ask:* Why did the candle go out?
        What happened to the water in the jar?

Look at the information you collected and wrote down.

Ask: How far did the water move up the jar?

(Note: If you didn't measure how far the water moved, you should have done this. Accurate observation and measurement of what happens is important in doing an experiment. After this be very careful in measuring and writing down what happens in an experiment.

STEP 3. *Ask:* Why did the water move up only so far in the jar and then stop?

Teacher's Note: The oxygen is burned up in the air and changed to carbon dioxide gas. The water is pushed up the jar by atmospheric pressure. Oxygen is almost 20 per cent of the air, so about 20 per cent of the volume in the jar should be replaced by water. This amount is never reached because all of the oxygen is not burned, and because a number of other factors are also involved. For example, when you light the candle, the air is heated and expands forcing some air out of the bottle. Carbon dioxide gas is also produced which replaces some of the space occupied by oxygen. Students, however, can gain a fairly good understanding of the amount of oxygen that is in the air and of the fact that oxygen is usually necessary for burning. The experiment also stresses the importance of observation, accurate recording, and measuring of what takes place in the experiment.

HOW TO MAKE OXYGEN IN CLASS
[3 – 8]

Caution: The teacher should check the equipment before the student adds the chemicals in this experiment.

Materials: yeast, two jars, aquarium, cork, rubber tubing, and hydrogen peroxide. (The hydrogen peroxide can be obtained from the local drug store.)

Procedure

STEP 1. Fill the aquarium and jar with water as shown in the diagram. The jar can be filled with water and a lid or cap held over it while it is placed under the water. Then slide the lid off the jar under water. Pour some hydrogen peroxide in the bottom of the bottle as shown. Add water to dilute it. Add a small piece of yeast cake or some dry yeast to the hydrogen peroxide. Stopper the bottle with a one-hole rubber or cork stopper as shown in the diagram.

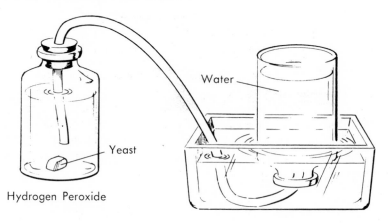

Water

Yeast

Hydrogen Peroxide

STEP 2. Write down what happens in the experiment.

Ask: What do you think has been collected in the bottle in the aquarium?

Why was the water forced out of the bottle?

Take the bottle out of the aquarium. Light a splintered piece of wood or a wood splint and blow it out, but leave a part of the splint glowing. Then insert it in the jar. If you don't want to use wood, you can use steel wool which you have heated to burning in a flame and then thrust it into the jar.

Caution: You should hold the heated steel wool with fairly long forceps or tweezers.

STEP 3. *Ask:* What happened?

Why did the wood or steel burn easily?

Teacher Explanation: Oxygen is produced by the action of the yeast and the hydrogen peroxide. This oxygen leaves the tube and bubbles through the water into the jar. Oxygen is lighter than water, so it bubbles to the top of the jar in the aquarium. The gas then forces the water down and out of the jar. Heated steel wool or a glowing splinter of wood will burn very easily in oxygen because the oxygen can combine with these substances so much more easily, since there is so much more of it available than is found in air.

WHAT WILL HAPPEN TO AN ICE CUBE?
[K–6]

Procedure

STEP 1. Get an ice cube; place it in a spoon.

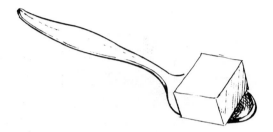

   Ask: What will happen to the ice cube?
   Do you know how we can make the ice cube melt faster?

STEP 2. Heat the spoon with a candle. After the ice cube melts enough to wet the spoon, take the ice out of the spoon. Heat the spoon some more with a candle.

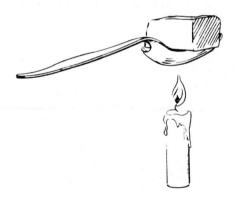

   Ask: What happened to the water?
   Did it turn back to ice?
   Did it leave?
   Why didn't you see it leave?
   What do you think the water changed to?

Teacher's Note: Explain that ice is a solid. When ice absorbs heat it changes to a liquid, water. Water, a liquid, when heated may change to water vapor or steam, a gas.

HOW MUCH WATER WILL SNOW MAKE?
[2 – 5]

Procedure

STEP 1. Fill a jar with snow. Mark the level of the snow. Let the snow melt.

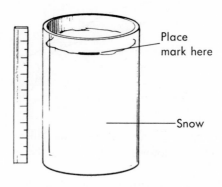

Place
mark here

Snow

STEP 2. After it has melted, mark the level of the water in the jar.

Ask: What do you conclude about how much snow it takes to make one inch of water?

Teacher's Note: Snow falls lightly on the earth, and its crystals leave air spaces between them. When the snow melts, the water takes up the spaces between the crystals, occupying much less space.

HOW CAN YOU MAKE A FLEET MOVE
WITHOUT TOUCHING THEM?
[2 – 6]

Materials: corks, needles, paper, magnets.

Procedure

STEP 1. Stick some needles through the corks and make some little paper sails like those shown in the diagram. Place corks in shallow water. Bring the magnets close to the boats.

STUDENT EXPERIMENTS

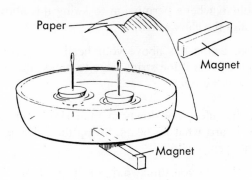

Ask: What causes the boats to move?

STEP 2. Place the magnets under the water near the boats.

> *Ask:* Are the boats still pulled?
> Will magnetism go through water?
> Will magnetism go through air?

STEP 3. Use your magnets to test if magnetism will go through other things. Hold a piece of paper between the magnets and the little boats.

WHAT CAUSES SOUND?
[K – 6]

Procedure

STEP 1. Obtain the following: wooden ruler, strong twine, staple.

STEP 2. Place a staple on the end of a ruler as shown in the diagram. Tie a piece of string securely to the end of the staple.

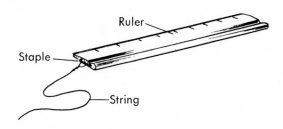

Caution: Be certain to see that the staple and string are securely tied.

STEP 3. Get your teacher's permission to swing this above your head and have the rest of the class watch.

Caution: Swing this above your head at least ten feet in front of any students so that if the string were to break, the students could get out of the way of the ruler.

STEP 4. Swing the ruler very slowly at first. Have someone in the class record on the board what he hears. Swing the ruler again, but faster. Record what happens again.

Ask: Why, do you think, did you hear a noise the second time?
What made the noise?
Why didn't you hear it when you swung the ruler the first time?

Teacher's Note: In order for a sound to be heard, an object must vibrate at least 16 vibrations per second. As the ruler spins rapidly overhead, it vibrates the air fast enough to produce a noise. There may be a period in which there is no sound; this is due to the fact that the ruler is not vibrating or is changing the way it is vibrating owing to the way the string winds up or unwinds as the ruler is spun.

SECTION FIVE
PICTORIAL RIDDLES
OF SCIENCE

1. What Does a Thermometer Do? [2 – 5]
2. How Can We Pour Pop Easily Out of a Can? [4 – 6]
3. Why Does a Candle Go Out in a Jar? [1 – 3]
4. What Is a Scale? [2 – 5]
5. What Is Wrong with the Way the Flower Is Growing? [2 – 4]
6. Why Do the Two Hills Look Different? [4 – 6]
7. How Is a Dam Built? [3 – 6]
8. What Is Wrong with the Diagram of the Solar System? [4 – 6]
9. Can You Stay Under Water? [1 – 3]
10. How Does a Ball Bounce? [4 – 6]
11. What Will a Magnet Attract (Pull)? [2 – 4]
12. What Is in an "Empty" Jar? [3 – 5]
13. What Happens When You Heat Water? [1 – 3]
14. What Caused the Sidewalk to Move Up and Down? [4 – 6]
15. How Does a Lever Work? [4 – 6]
16. How Does a Compass Point? [2 – 4]
17. Can You See Air? [K – 6]
18. Where Does Smoke Go? [3 – 4]
19. What Happens to a Scale When You Put Something on It? [2 – 4]
20. How Should You Pour Water Out of a Can? [4 – 6]
21. What Happens to a Scale with Weight on It? [2 – 4]
22. What Happens to a Rock and a Cork in Water? [2 – 5]

PICTORIAL RIDDLES

This section contains diagrams which are to be drawn on poster board and shown to the class. Each diagram illustrates a riddle presenting a simple scientific principle which the children are to answer. No attempt has been made to include all subject areas.

Teachers can easily make similar riddles. Primarily one must think of a scientific concept or principle, make a diagram or show some pictures related to the principle, and have the children discover what principle is involved.

An example of how to make a riddle on the primary level may be done as follows: A teacher has decided she wants to make children aware of the seasons. She decides to cut out pictures showing the various seasons and pastes them on a piece of poster board. She then cuts out a snowman and pastes it in a scene showing spring vegetation. When the board is held up to the class, she asks: "What is wrong with my poster?" The class responds. A child soon recognizes that a snowman would not be found in a picture having green vegetation and states this fact. The teacher then leads a discussion concerning the different pictures, the seasons they represent, and how environment and the type of life seen change with the seasons.

Riddles are good activities to introduce or conclude a unit. The answer to a riddle may take several class sessions. Children should also be encouraged to make science riddles. In those instances where feasible, the teacher should attempt to use equipment to test the students' hypotheses about riddles.

WHAT DOES A THERMOMETER DO?
[2–5]

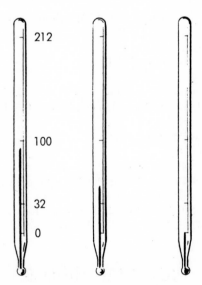

Teacher's Note: This should be done when the weather is very cold outside. Draw the three charts of thermometers, using large numbers. If possible, have the children look at a thermometer that has been placed outside. Later bring it in the room and have them look at it again.

Ask: Which of the thermometers on the chart shows it is hot?
Which thermometer shows it is cold?
What do you think the thermometer would do if it got colder?

HOW CAN WE POUR POP EASILY OUT OF A CAN?
[4 – 6]

(1)   (2)

Teacher's Note: Number 2 can has a top opening and a bottom opening. The top opening allows air to enter the can and force out the liquid. Number 1 can will not allow a continuous flow, because air must enter the can every so often. This should be demonstrated in front of the class so that the children can see it in operation.

Ask: Why does the water in Can 1 pour out in a different way from the water in Can 2?

WHY DOES A CANDLE GO OUT IN A JAR?
[1 – 3]

Teacher's Note: A bottle turned upside down may be used instead of the candle holder and the cork. The candle will go out because the oxygen will soon be used. Oxygen is necessary for burning.

WHAT IS A SCALE?
[2 – 5]

Teacher's Note: It might be well to have actual pop bottles and other bottles filled as indicated below and displayed on the teacher's desk.

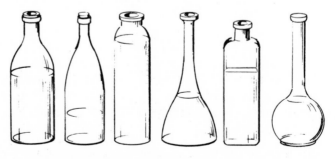

Ask: How would you make a scale out of these bottles?

Ask: Is the following a scale and why?

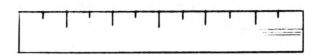

Ask: How would you make a scale out of the following?

WHAT IS WRONG WITH THE WAY THE FLOWER IS GROWING?
[2 – 4]

Teacher's Note: A plant will bend toward the light. A potted plant could be placed in a window and watched for several days to demonstrate that this is true.

WHY DO THE TWO HILLS LOOK DIFFERENT?
[4 – 6]

(1)

(2)

Teacher's Note: Do not write the words "eroded" or "noneroded" on the board next to the drawings until the students have discussed the question. Erosion does not occur in Drawing 2 because the trees, grass, and shrubs help to prevent water runoff. The soil then absorbs the water. In Drawing 1 there is nothing to prevent the water from flowing down the hill.

HOW IS A DAM BUILT?
[3 – 6]

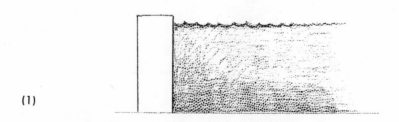

(1)

Ask: What is wrong with the dam in Drawing 1?

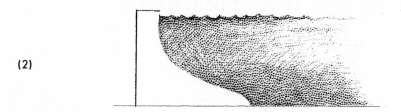

(2)

Ask: Why is the dam in Drawing 2 a better one?

Teacher's Note: The dam should be constructed like dam 2. The base of the dam should be thicker than the top, because pressure of water increases with depth. The deeper the water, the greater the pressure against the side of the dam, and the thicker it must be constructed to resist this force. After they know this, ask: Which is cheaper to build, a shallow swimming pool or a deep swimming pool? Why?

WHAT IS WRONG WITH THE DIAGRAM OF THE SOLAR SYSTEM?
[4–6]

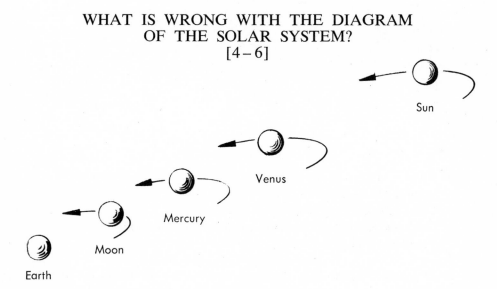

Teacher's Note: The earth is not the center of the solar system. The sun is at the center. The planets move around the sun in elliptical paths. Mercury, Venus, and the earth move around the sun in that order from the sun outward.

CAN YOU STAY UNDER WATER?
[1 – 3]

    Ask: What is wrong with the picture?
          What do we breathe?
          Can we breathe in water?
          Can some animals live in water, whereas others cannot?
          Could you walk under water?

    Teacher's Note: Explain that we must have oxygen from the air in order to breathe. The boy would soon die if he didn't come to the surface for air. Some animals, such as fish and the octopus, can obtain the oxygen they need from the oxygen dissolved in the water. The boy would not walk because of buoyancy. An immersed body is buoyed up by a force equal to the weight of the fluid it displaces. Emphasize the danger of going near ponds and water holes if a person can't swim.

HOW DOES A BALL BOUNCE?
[4 – 6]

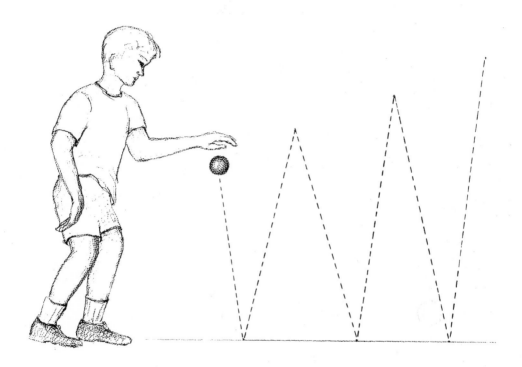

Ask: What is wrong with the drawing?

Teacher's Note: A bouncing ball must resist the pull of gravity. Since gravity is pulling on it at points 1 and 2, and the pull is applied all the time, the ball cannot bounce higher than point 1. It would have to be accelerating (speeding up) to go that high. It is slowing down because gravity is pulling on it. Each bounce after point 1 will, therefore, be lower. Some children might bounce a ball and measure the height to see what happens.

WHAT WILL A MAGNET ATTRACT (PULL)?
[2 – 4]

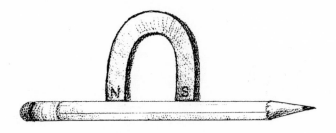

Ask: What is wrong with the diagram?

Teacher's Note: A magnet will not attract wood. The teacher might take a magnet and try to attract a pencil.

Ask: What will a magnet do?

WHAT IS IN AN "EMPTY" JAR?
[3 – 5]

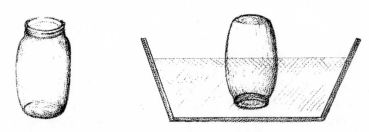

Ask: How can we prove that there is something in this jar?
Why does this diagram show that there is something in the jar?
What will happen to the jar if I hold it on its side for a time and then let go?

Teacher's Note: When the jar is held on its side, air bubbles will go to the surface, and the jar will be filled with water. When it is filled with water, it will sink.

WHAT HAPPENS WHEN YOU HEAT WATER?
[1 – 3]

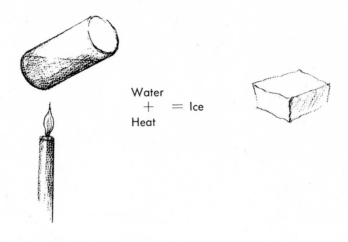

Water
+   = Ice
Heat

Ask: What is wrong with the diagram?

Ask: What must we do in order to change water to ice?

WHAT CAUSED THE SIDEWALK TO MOVE
UP AND DOWN?

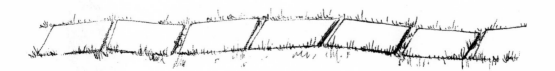

Teacher's Note: When most objects are heated, they expand. When the weather is hot the sidewalk expands. When the walk was made, no joints allowing for expansion were constructed. Bridges and highways often have expansion joints in them to allow for expansion owing to heating.

HOW DOES A LEVER WORK?
[4 – 6]

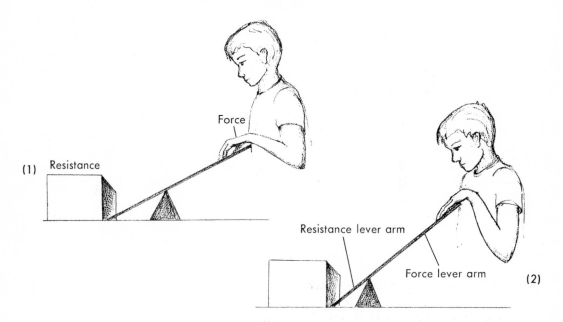

(1) Resistance

Force

Resistance lever arm

Force lever arm

(2)

Ask: Which box would be easier to lift?

Teacher's Note: Box 2 would be easier to lift, because its lever arm is much longer than that of box 1. The longer the force lever arm compared to the resistance lever arm, the easier it is to lift objects.

Ask: What is wrong with Diagram 3?

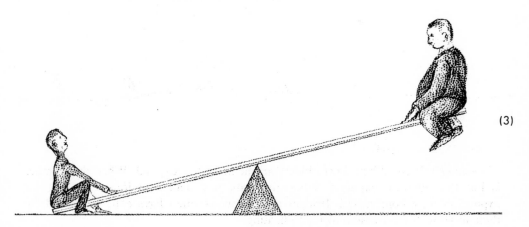

(3)

WHERE DOES SMOKE GO?
[3 – 4]

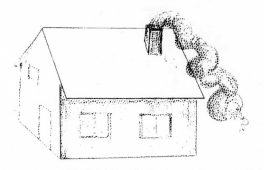

Ask: What is wrong with the picture?

     What do you notice about the smoke? Is smoke hot or cold?

Teacher's Note: The smoke would not fall, because it is made of hot gases. Hot gases such as air and smoke rise, whereas cold gases fall.

Ask: In our classroom, where is it the hottest?

Take a thermometer and place it near the ceiling and read it. Place it near the floor and read it again.

Ask: Which one was hotter and why?

WHAT HAPPENS TO A SCALE WHEN YOU
PUT SOMETHING ON IT?
[2 – 4]

Ask: What is wrong with the diagram?
Notice the needle.

Teacher's Note: Explain that the bottle plus its contents would weigh something. It would press downward, causing the needle to move on the scale.

HOW SHOULD YOU POUR WATER OUT OF A CAN?
[4 – 6]

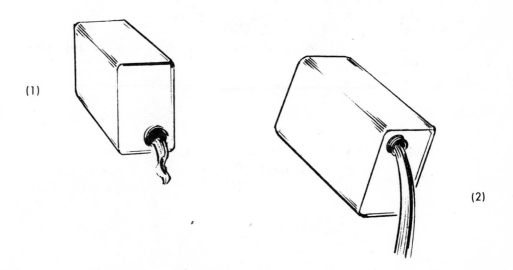

(1)

(2)

Ask: Which of the two ways above would be the best to pour liquid?

Teacher's Note: The method in Diagram 2 would be best, because it would allow air to enter the top of the can and push the liquid out. Can 1 would not pour water out in a steady stream. Some water would come out, then air would have to enter in order to allow more water to leave the can. The liquid would gurgle out.

WHAT HAPPENS TO A SCALE WITH WEIGHT ON IT?
[2 – 4]

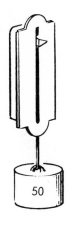  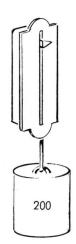

Ask: What is wrong with the diagram?
What must be done to correct the above diagram?
Which is pulling the hardest on the scale?

WHAT HAPPENS TO A ROCK AND A CORK IN WATER?
[2 – 5]

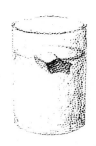 

Ask: What is wrong with the diagram?

Teacher's Note: Explain that some things float and some things sink. Rocks generally do not float, whereas a cork can float.

Appendix

COMMERCIAL SUPPLIERS OF SCIENCE KITS

American Basic Science Club, Inc.
501 East Crockett St.
San Antonio 5, Texas

Atomic Accessories, Inc.
811 West Merrick Rd.
Valley Stream, N.Y.

Atomic Corp. of America
14725 Arminta St.
Panorama City, Calif.

Baird-Atomic, Inc.
33 University Rd.
Cambridge 38, Mass.

Barnett Instrument Co.
Kraft St.
Clarksville, Tenn.

Cambosco Scientific Co.
37 Antwerp St.
Boston 35, Mass.

Carolina Biological Supply Co.
Burlington, N.C.

Creative Playthings, Inc.
P.O. Box 1100
Princeton, N.J.

W. H. Curtin & Co.
Box 14, New Orleans, La.

Dumville Manufacturing Co.
Box 5595
Washington, D.C.

Eckert Mineral Research, Inc.
110 East Main St.
Florence, Colo.

Fisher Scientific Co.
620 Fisher Building
Pittsburgh 19, Pa.

General Electric Co.
1001 Broad St.
Utica, N.Y.

A. C. Gilbert Co.
Erector Square
New Haven, Conn.

Irving Science Labs
2052 Hillside Ave.
New Hyde Park, N.Y.

J. Klinger Scientific Apparatus
82-87 160th St.
Jamaica 32, N.Y.

Laboratory Furniture Co.
Old Country Rd.
Mineola, N.Y.

Labosco, Inc.
Lombard, Ill.

Lafayette Radio
165-08 Liberty Ave.
Jamaica 33, N.Y.

Living Science Labs
1605 Jericho Tpke.
New Hyde Park, N.Y.

F. A. Owens Publishing Co.
Dansville, N.Y.

Paco Electronic Co.
70-31 84th St.
Glendale 27, N.Y.

Philco TechRep Division
P.O. Box 4730
Philadelphia, Pa.

Product Design Co.
2796 Middlefield Rd.
Redwood City, Calif.

Research Scientific Supplies, Inc.
Dept. ST8
126 West 23rd St.
New York 11, N.Y.

Science Education Products
2796 Middlefield Rd.
Redwood City, Calif.

Science Electronics, Inc.
195 Massachusetts Ave.
Cambridge 29, Mass.

Science Research Associates, Inc.
259 Erie St.
Chicago 11, Ill.

Science Service
1719 U St., NW
Washington 6, D.C.

Sesco, Inc.
1312 South 13th St.
Vincennes, Ind.

SUPPLIES AND EQUIPMENT AND MATERIALS FROM LOCAL SOURCES

Dime Stores

balloons
balls
candles
compasses (magnetic)
cotton (absorbent)
dyes
flashlights
glues and paste
inks

magnifying glasses
marbles
matches
mechanical toys
mirrors
mouse traps
scissors
sponges
thermometers

Drugstores

acids (HCL, etc.)
adhesive tape
alcohol (rubbing)
bottles
canned heat
carbon tetrachloride
castor oil
cigar boxes
cold cream
corks
cotton
forceps
heat-resistant nursing bottles
hydrogen peroxide
iodine
limewater
medicine droppers
mercury
pipe cleaners
rubber stoppers
soda bicarbonate
spatulas
straws
sulfur

Electrical Appliance Shops

bell wire
burned-out fuses and light bulbs
dry cells
electric fans
electric hotplates
flashlights
flashlight bulbs
friction tape
magnets (from old appliances)
old radios
soldering iron
sun lamp
worn-out extension cords, electrical
   appliances

Fabric Shops

cardboard tubes
cheesecloth

flannel
knitting needles
leather
needles
netting
silk thread
spools
scraps of different kinds of materials

Farm or Dairy

birds' nests
bottles
clay
containers
dry ice
gravel
hay or straw
humus
insects
leaves
lodestone
loam
rocks
sand
seeds

Fire Department

samples of material used to extinguish
   various types of fire
water pumping equipment

Garden Supply Stores

bulbs (crocus, tulip, etc.)
fertilizers
flower pots
garden hose
garden twine
growing plants
labels
lime
seed catalogs
seeds
sprinkling cans
spray guns
trowels and other garden tools

Gas Stations

- batteries
- ball bearings
- cans
- copper tubing
- gasoline
- gears
- gear transmission
- grease
- inner tubes
- jacks
- maps
- old wet-cell batteries
- pulleys
- tools
- valves from tires
- wheels

Grocery Stores

- ammonia
- baking soda
- borax
- candles
- carbon tetrachloride (carbona)
- cellophane
- clothespins
- cornstarch
- corrugated cardboard boxes
- fruits
- matches
- paper bags
- paper towelling
- paraffin
- plastic wrapping
- salt
- sponges
- sugar
- tinfoil
- vegetables
- vinegar
- wax
- waxed paper

Hardware Stores

- brace and bits
- cement
- chisels
- clocks

- dry-cell batteries
- electric push buttons, lamps, and sockets
- extension cords
- files
- flashlights
- fruit jars
- glass cutters
- glass funnels
- glass friction rods
- glass tubing
- hammers
- hard rubber rods
- insulated copper wire
- lamp chimneys
- metal and metal scraps
- nails
- nuts and bolts
- paints and varnishes
- plaster of Paris
- pulleys
- sandpaper
- saws
- scales
- scrap lumber
- screening
- screwdrivers
- screws
- steel wool
- thermometers (indoor and outdoor)
- tin snips
- toy electric motors
- turpentine
- wheelbarrow
- window glass (broken pieces will do)
- wire
- yardsticks

Machine Shops

- ball bearings
- iron filings
- iron rods
- magnets
- nuts and bolts
- screws
- scrap metals
- wire

Medical and Dental Offices and Hospitals

- all kinds of chemicals
- corks

flasks
funnels
glass tubing
hand lenses
litmus paper
microscopes
models, such as teeth
rubber sheeting
rubber tubing
rubber stoppers
test tubes
test tube holders
thermometers
tongue depressors

animal cages
aquariums
ant houses
birds
cages
fish
insects
nets (butterfly, fish, etc.)
plastic tubing
strainers
terrariums

Music Shops

broken string and drum heads
musical instruments
pitch pipes
tuning forks

Restaurants and Diners

bones (chicken, etc.)
bottles
cans (coffee, 5 gallon)
drums (ice cream)
dry ice
five gallon cans (oil)
food coloring
gallon jars (wide-mouthed, pickles,
    mayonnaise, etc.)
gallon jugs (vinegar)
pie tins

Pet Shops

air pumps
animals

This is only a partial list of the places in the immediate community that are possible sources of items for inclusion in a program of science in the elementary school. Other sources that should not be overlooked are local factories, the janitor of the school, the school cafeteria, radio and television repair shops, florists' shops, the other teachers in the school, the junior and senior high school science teachers, ad infinitum. The materials are there; it just takes a little looking.

There are times, though, when, in spite of the most careful searching, certain pieces of equipment or supplies are just not obtainable from local sources; also, there are many things that schools should buy from scientific supply houses. A partial list follows of some of the selected, reliable, scientific supply houses serving elementary schools.

SELECTED SOURCES OF SCIENTIFIC EQUIPMENT, SUPPLIES, MODELS, LIVING THINGS, COLLECTIONS, ETC.

Central Scientific Co.
1700 Irving Park Blvd.
Chicago 13, Ill.

Clay-Adams Co.
141 E. 25th St.
New York 10, N.Y.

Denoyer-Geppert Co.
5235 Ravenswood Ave.
Chicago 40, Ill.

Edmond Scientific Co.
Barrington, N.J.

Educational Services, Inc.
108 Water St.
Watertown, Mass.

Models of Industry
2804 Tenth St.
Berkeley, Calif.

New York Scientific Supply Co.
28 W. 30th St.
New York, N.Y.

A. J. Nystrom and Co.
3333 Elston Ave.
Chicago 17, Ill.

Science Associates
401 N. Broad St.
Philadelphia 8, Pa.

Science Kit
2299 Military Rd.
Tonawanda, N.Y.

C. H. Stoelting Co.
425 N. Homan Ave.
Philadelphia, Pa.

Standard Science Supply Co.
1232 N. Paulina St.
Chicago 22, Ill.

Science Materials Center
59 Fourth Ave.
New York 3, N.Y.

Turtox Service Dept.
General Supply House
8200 South Hoyne Avenue
Chicago 20, Ill.

Viking Importers
113 S. Edgemont St.
Los Angeles, Calif.

Ward's Natural Science Establishment, Inc.
3000 E. Ridge Rd.
Rochester, N.Y.

W. M. Welch Scientific Co.
1515 Sedgwick St.
Chicago, Ill.

SOURCES FOR SCIENCE CONTENT RESOURCE UNITS

Air Age Education, 100 E. 42 St., New York 17, N.Y.
Aluminum Co. of America, 818 Gulf Bldg., Pittsburgh, Pa.
American Can Co., 100 Park Ave., New York, N.Y.
American Cancer Society, 521 W. 57 St., New York 19, N.Y.
American Corp. (*Americana Encyclopedia*), 4606 East-West Hwy., Washington 14, D.C.

American Dental Association, 222 E. Superior St., Chicago 11, Ill.

American Forest Products Industries, Inc., 1816 North St. N.W., Washington 6, D.C.

American Gas Ass'n. Educational Services Bureau, 429 Lexington Ave., New York 17, N.Y.

American Geological Inst., 2101 Constitution Ave., Washington 25, D.C.

American Heart Ass'n., 44 E. 23 St., New York 10, N.Y.

American Iron & Steel Inst., 150 E. 42 St., New York 17, N.Y.

American Medical Association, 535 Dearborn St., Chicago 10, Ill.

American National Red Cross National Hq., Washington 13, D.C.

American Petroleum Institute, 50 W. 50 St., New York 20, N.Y.

American Telephone & Telegraph, 195 Broadway, New York, N.Y.

Animal Welfare Institute, 270 Park Ave., New York 17, N.Y.

Association of American Railroads, Transportation Bldg., Washington 16, D.C.

Automobile Manufacturer's Association, New Center Bldg., Detroit 2, Mich.

Boyd, Anne Morris and Rae E. Rips, United States Government Publications, N.Y.: H. W. Wilson, 1949.

Briggs, Thomas, "Commercial Supplementary Teaching Materials," *School and Society*, 64 (December 7, 1946), 402.

Bristol-Myers Prod. Division, 45 Rockefeller Plaza, New York, N.Y.

California State Dept. of Education, *Science in the Elementary School*, Sacramento, Calif., 1945.

Chrysler Corp. Educational Services, P.O. Box 1919, Detroit, Mich.

Collier and Son *(Collier's Encyclopedia)*, 640 Fifth Ave., New York 18, N.Y.

Columbia University Press *(Columbia Encyclopedia)*, 2960 Broadway, New York 27, N.Y.

Compton and Co. *(Compton Pictured Encyclopedia)*, 1000 N. Dearborn St., Chicago 10, Ill.

Consolidated Edison Co., 4 Irving Place, New York 3, N.Y.

Denoyer Geppert Co., 5235 Ravenswood Ave., Chicago 40, Ill.

DuPont de Nemours Information Division, Wilmington, Delaware.

Educational Research Bureau, 1129 Vermont Ave. N.W., Washington, D.C.

E.S.I. (Educational Services, Inc.), 108 Water St., Watertown, Mass.

Educators Association Inc. *(Volume Library)*, 307 Fifth Ave., New York, N.Y.

Educator's Mutual Insurance Co., Lancaster, Pa.

Encyclopaedia Britannica, Inc., 425 N. Michigan Ave., Chicago 11, Ill.

Field Enterprises *(World Book and Childcraft Encyclopedia)*, 510 Merchandise Mart Plaza, Chicago, Ill.

Ford Motor Co., Public Relations Office, 3000 Schaefer Rd., Dearborn, Mich.

Frontier Press *(Lincoln Library)*, Lafayette Bldg., Buffalo 3, N.Y.

General Electric Co., 1 River Rd., Schenectady, N.Y.

General Motors Corp., General Motors Bldg., Detroit, Mich.

Grolier Society Co. *(Grolier Encyclopedia, Book of Knowledge, Programmed Learning)*, 2 W. 45 St., New York 36, N.Y.

Hanna, Lavone A., Gladys Potter, and Neva Hagaman, *Unit Teaching in the Elementary School*, New York: Holt, Rinehart & Winston, Inc., 1956.

Horrall, Albion H., and others, *Let's Go to School,* New York: McGraw-Hill Book Co., Inc., 1938.

Illinois State Natural History Dept. of Registration and Education, Urbana, Ill.

Jones, Stacey V., *How to Get It From the Government,* New York: E. P. Dutton & Co., Inc., 1951.

Lincoln School Units of Work, New York: Bureau of Publications, Teachers' College, Columbia University, various dates.

Macomber, F. G., *Guiding Child Development in the Elementary School,* New York: American Book Company, 1941.
McCall, William A., ed., *Teachers Lesson Unit Series,* New York: Bureau of Publications, Teachers' College, Columbia University, 1941.
Miller, Bruce, *Sources of Free and Inexpensive Teaching Aids,* Bruce Miller, Riverside, Calif., 1954.
Murphy, Robert W., *How and Where to Look It Up,* New York: McGraw-Hill Book Co., Inc., 1958.

National Association of Audubon Societies, 1775 Broadway, New York, N.Y.
National Association of Manufacturers, 2 E. 48 St., New York 17, N.Y.
National Aviation Education Council, 1025 Connecticut Ave. N.W., Washington 6, D.C.
National Aeronautics & Space Administration, Washington, D.C.
National Coal Association, 15 & H Sts. N.W., Washington 5, D.C.
National College of Education, *(Records of the Children's School),* Evanston, Ill.: National College of Education, 1940.
National Canners Association, 1133 20 St. N.W., Washington 6, D.C.
National Dairy Council, 111 N. Canal St., Chicago, Ill.
National Foundation, Inc., 301 E. 42 St., New York, N.Y.
National Geographic Society, 16 & M Sts., Washington, D.C.
National Wildlife Federation, 232 Carroll St. N.W., Washington, D.C.

Pan American World Airways, 28-81 Bridge Plaza North, Long Island City, N.Y.
Proctor and Gamble, Education Dept., Cincinnati, Ohio

Salisbury, Gordon and Robert Sheridan, *Catalog of Free Teaching Aids,* Gordon Salisbury, Riverside, Calif., 1955
Science Service, 1719 N St. N.W., Washington 6, D.C.
Sears, Roebuck and Co., *(Our Wonderful World Encyclopedia),* 925 S. Homan St., Chicago, Ill.
Sources of Free and Inexpensive Educational Materials, Field Enterprises, Inc., 1955.
Standard Oil Co., Education Dept., 30 Rockefeller Plaza, New York 20, N.Y.
Standard Oil Co. of California, Education Dept., 225 Bush St., San Francisco, Calif.
Swift & Co., Agricultural Research Dept., Chicago, Ill.

United Carbide & Carbon Corp., 30 E. 42 St., New York 17, N.Y.
United Fruit Corp., Pier 3, North River, New York, N.Y.
United States Atomic Energy Comm., Public Information Service, 1901 Constitution Ave., Washington, D.C.
United States Dept. of Commerce, Weather Bureau Publ. Sect., Washington 25, D.C.

United States Dept. of Health, Education, & Welfare Printing Office, Washington 25, D.C.

United States Steel Corp., 71 Broadway, New York, N.Y.

University of California Elementary School Science Project, 2232 Piedmont Ave., Berkeley 4, Calif.

University of Illinois Elementary School Science Project, Urbana, Ill.

Utah State Dept. of Education, *Science Supplement to a Teachers Guide for the Elementary Schools of Utah,* Salt Lake City, Utah, 1946.

Westinghouse Electric Corp., Gateway Center, 401 Liberty Ave., Pittsburgh 30, Pa.

Williams, Catherine M., "Sources of Teaching Materials," *Educational Research Bulletin,* 34 (May 1955), 113-140.

SELECTED REFERENCES FOR THE TEACHER OR SCHOOL PROFESSIONAL LIBRARY

A. General Teacher Reference Books

Beauchamp, Wilbur L. and Helen J. Challand. *Basic Science Hand Book, K-3.* Chicago: Scott, Foresman & Co., 1961. 352 Pp.

Blough, Glenn O. and Julius Schwartz. *Elementary School Science and How to Teach It,* Third Edition. New York: Holt, Rinehart and Winston, 1964.

Burnett, R. Will. *Teaching Science in the Elementary School.* New York: Holt, Rinehart & Winston, Inc., 1957. 540 Pp.

Commission on Teacher Education, *Helping Teachers Understand Children.* Washington, D.C.: American Council on Education, 1945.

Craig, Gerald D. *Science for the Elementary-School Teacher.* New York: Ginn & Company, 1958. 894 Pp.

Crouse, William Harry. *Understanding Science,* revised edition. New York: McGraw-Hill Book Co., Inc., 1956.

Croxton, W. C. *Science in the Elementary School.* New York: McGraw-Hill Book Co., Inc., 1937. 454 Pp.

Cummings, Howard H., ed. *Science and Social Studies.* National Council for the Social Studies, National Education Association, Washington, D.C., 1957. 271 Pp.

Freeman, Kenneth, Thomas I. Dowling, Nan Lacy and James S. Tippett. *Helping Children Understand Science.* Atlanta, Ga.: Holt, Rinehart & Winston, Inc., 1958. 314 Pp.

Greenlee, Julian. *Better Teaching Through Elementary Science.* Dubuque, Iowa: William Brown Company, Publishers, 1954. 204 Pp.

————. *Teaching Science to Children,* revised edition. Dubuque, Iowa: William C. Brown Company, Publishers, 1955. 195 Pp.

Hubler, Clark. *Working with Children in Science.* Boston: Houghton Mifflin Company, 1957. 425 Pp.

Kambly, Paul E. and John E. Suttle. *Teaching Elementary School Science.* New York: The Ronald Press Company, 1963.

Lewis, June E., and Irene C. Potter. *The Teaching of Science in the Elementary School.* Englewood Cliffs, N.J.: Prentice-Hall, Inc., 1961.

Navarra, John G. *The Development of Scientific Concepts in a Young Child.* New York: Teachers College, Columbia University, 1955. 147 Pp.

———— and Joseph Zaffarone. *Science Today for the Elementary School Teacher.* Evanston, Ill.: Harper & Row, Publishers, 1959. 470 Pp.

Pitluga, George E. *Science Excursions in the Community.* New York: Teachers College, Columbia University, 1943. 194 Pp.

Tannenbaum, Harold and Nathan Stillman. *Science Education for Elementary School Teachers.* Boston: Allyn and Bacon, Inc., 1960. 339 Pp.

Wells, Harrington. *Elementary Science Education.* New York: McGraw-Hill Book Co., Inc., 1951. 333 Pp.

B. Suggestions for Organizing Science Programs (Pamphlets)

Ashley, Tracy H., et al. *An Administrator's Guide to Elementary School Science Program.* Association of Public School Systems, 525 W. 120 St., New York 27, N.Y., 1960.

Ashley, Tracy H. and Paul Blackwood. *Teaching Elementary School Science (Suggestions for Classroom Teachers).* U.S. Office of Education, Bulletin No. 4, 1948.

Blackwood, Paul E. *How Children Learn to Think.* U.S. Office of Education, Bulletin No. 10, 1951.

Blough, Glenn O. *It's Time for Better Elementary School Science.* Washington, D.C.: National Science Teachers Association, 1958.

Blough, Glenn O. and Paul Blackwood. *Science Teaching in Rural Small Town Schools.* U.S. Office of Education, Bulletin No. 5, 1949.

California Association for Supervision and Curriculum Development, *Leadership for Science in the Elementary Schools,* 1960, 88 Pp.

California State Dept. of Education, *Looking Ahead in Science,* 1960, 88 Pp.

Cornell Rural School Leaflets, Teachers Issues. Cornell Rural School Leaflet Office, Cornell University, Ithaca, New York.

Craig, Gerald C. *Science in Childhood Education.* New York: Teachers College, Columbia University, 1944.

———— "What Research Says to the Teacher," *Science in the Elementary School.* Department of Classroom Teacher, National Education Association, 1201 16th St. N.W., Washington, D.C., 1957.

Dunfee, Maxine and Julius Greenlee. *Elementary School Science: Research, Theory & Practice.* Association for Supervision and Curriculum Devleopment, Washington, D.C., 1957.

Fitzpatrick, F. L. *Policies for Science Education.* New York: Teachers College, Columbia University, 1960.

Gordon, Eva. *The School Science Center.* Cornell Rural School Leaflet, Vol. 49, No. 1 (1955).

Hefferman, Helen and O. E. Todd. *The Kindergarten Teacher.* Boston: D. C. Heath & Company, 1960.

Hochman, Vivienne and Mildred Greenwald. *Science Experiences in Early Childhood Education.* New York: Bank St. Publication, 1953.

Laboratories in the Classroom; New Horizon in Science Education. Science Materials Center, New York, 1960.

Merritt, Eleanor. *Instructional Materials Bulletin: Sources of Elementary School Science.* Curriculum Lab., Iowa State Teachers College, Cedar Falls, Iowa, 1959.

Science Education in American Schools. Forty-sixth Yearbook, N.N.N.E., Part 1. Chicago: University of Chicago Press, 1947.

Science for Today's Children. Thirty-second Yearbook, Bulletin of the Department of Elementary School Principals, Washington, D.C.: National Education Association, 1953.

"Science in the Elementary School," *National Elementary Principal,* Vol. 29, No. 4. Dept. of Elementary School Principal, National Education Association, 1950.

Shapp, Martha. *Planning and Organizing Science Program for Elementary Schools.* New York: The Grolier Society Incorporated, 1959.

Strickland, Ruth. *How to Build a Unit of Work.* U.S. Office of Education, Bulletin No. 5, 1940.

"Your School's Science Program," *School Management,* May, 1959.

Zim, Herbert S. *Science for Children and Teachers.* Association for Childhood Education International, National Education Association, 1953.

C. *Sources of Science Textbooks and Concept Charts*
(Publishers also supply excellent free teaching materials)

Abelard-Schuman Limited
6 W. 57 St.
New York 19, N.Y.

Allyn and Bacon, Inc.
150 Tremont St.
Boston 11, Mass.
(Exploring Science Series — Walter Thurber)

American Book Company
55 Fifth Ave.
New York 3, N.Y.
(ABC Science Series — Willard Jacobson)

William C. Brown Company, Publishers
135 S. Locust St.
Dubuque, Iowa

Childrens Press, Inc.
Jackson Blvd. & Racine Ave.
Chicago 7, Ill.

Doubleday & Company, Inc.
Garden City
New York

Ginn & Company
Statler Bldg.
Back Bay P.O. 191
Boston 17, Mass.
(Science Today & Tomorrow — Gerald Craig)

The Grolier Society Incorporated
575 Lexington Ave.
New York 22, N.Y.

Harcourt, Brace & World, Inc.
757 Third Ave.
New York 17, New York

D. C. Heath & Company
285 Columbus Ave.
Boston 16, Mass.
(Heath Science Series —
Herman and Nina Schneider)

Holt, Rinehart & Winston, Inc.
383 Madison Ave.
New York 17, N.Y.
(New Understanding Science —
Thomas Dowling)

Houghton Mifflin Company
2 Park St.
Boston 7, Mass.

J. B. Lippincott Co.
E. Washington Sq.
Philadelphia 5, Pa.
(Science — Victor Smith)

Lothrop, Lee & Shepard Co., Inc.
419 Fourth Ave.
New York 11, N.Y.

The Macmillan Co.
60 Fifth Ave.
New York 11, N.Y.
(Science-Life Series — J. Darrell Barnard)

McGraw-Hill Book Co., Inc.
330 W. 42 St.
New York 36, N.Y.

Prentice-Hall, Inc.
Englewood Cliffs, N.J.

Rand McNally & Co.
Box 7600
Chicago 80, Ill.
(Junior Scientist — Arthur Baker)

Harper & Row, Publishers
49 E. 33 St.
New York 16, N.Y.

Scott, Foresman & Company
433 E. Erie St.
Chicago 11, Ill.
(Basic Studies in Science Programs —
    Wilbur Beauchamp)

Charles Scribner's Sons
597 Fifth Ave.
New York 17, N.Y.
(Wonderworld of Science — Warren Knox)

The L. W. Singer Company, Inc.
249-259 W. Erie Blvd.
Syracuse 2, N.Y.
(Singer Science — George Frasier)

The Steck Company
Box 16
Austin 61, Tex.

Franklin Watts, Inc.
699 Madison Ave.
New York 21, N.Y.

Webster Publishing
Division of the McGraw-Hill Book Co.
1154 Reco Ave.,
St. Louis 26, Mo.

Whittlesey House
330 W. 42nd St.
New York 36, N.Y.

SCIENCE CONTENT PERIODICALS FOR TEACHERS AND CHILDREN

American Biology Teacher. The National Association of Biology Teachers, 19 S. Jackson St., Danville, Ill. Monthly.

American Forests. The American Forestry Association, 919 17th St. N. W., Washington, D.C. Monthly.

The American Journal of Physics. American Association of Physics Teachers, 57 E. 55th St., New York, N.Y. Monthly.

The Aquarium. Innes Publishing Co., Philadelphia 7, Pa. Monthly.

Audubon Magazine. The National Audubon Society, 1130 Fifth Ave., New York 28, N.Y. Bimonthly.

Biology & General Science Digest. W. M. Welch Co., 1515 Sedgwick St., Chicago 10, Ill. FREE.

Chemistry. Science Service, 1719 16 St. N.W., Washington 6, D.C. Monthly.

Cornell Rural School Leaflets. New York State College of Agriculture, Ithaca, N.Y. Quarterly.

Current Science and Aviation. American Education Publications, Education Center, Columbus 16, Ohio. Weekly during the school year.

Science and Children. National Science Teachers Association, Washington 6, D.C. Monthly (8 times a year).

Geotimes. American Geological Institute, 1515 Massachusetts Ave. N.W., Washington 5, D.C. Monthly.

Journal of Chemical Education. Business and Publication Office, 20th & Northampton Sts., Easton, Pa. Monthly.

Junior Astronomer. Benjamin Adelman, 4211 Colie Dr., Silver Springs, Md.

Junior Natural History. American Museum of Natural History, New York, N.Y. Monthly.

Monthly Evening Sky Map. Box 213, Clayton, Mo. Monthly.

My Weekly Reader. American Education Publications, Education Center, Columbus 16, Ohio.

Nature Magazine. American Nature Association, 1214 15th St. N.W., Washington 6, D.C. Monthly Oct. to May and bimonthly June to Sept.

Our Dumb Animals. Massachusetts Society for the Prevention of Cruelty to Animals, Boston 15, Mass. Monthly.

Outdoors Illustrated. National Audubon Society, 1000 Fifth Ave., New York, N.Y. Monthly.

Physics and Chemistry Digest. W. M. Welch Co., 1515 Sedgwick St., Chicago 10, Ill. FREE.

Physics Today. American Institute of Physics, 335 E. 45 St., New York 17, N.Y. Monthly.

Popular Science Monthly. Popular Science Publishing Co., 355 Lexington Ave., New York 17, N.Y. Monthly.

School Science and Mathematics. Central Association Science and Mathematics Teachers, P.O. Box 48, Oak Park, Ill. Monthly (9 times a year).

Readers Guide to Oceanography. Woods Hole Oceanographic Institute, Woods Hole, Mass. Monthly.

Science. American Association for the Advancement of Science, 1515 Massachusetts Ave. N.W., Washington 5, D.C.

Science Digest. 959 8th Ave., New York 19, N.Y. Monthly.

Science Education. Science Education Inc., C. M. Pruitt, University of Tampa, Tampa, Florida. Published 5 times yearly.

Science Newsletter. Science Service, Inc., 1719 N. Street N.W., Washington 6, D.C. Weekly.

Scientific American. 415 Madison Ave., New York 17, N.Y. Monthly.

Scientific Monthly. The American Association for the Advancement of Science, 1515 Massachusetts Ave., Washington 5, D.C.

Space Science. Benjamin Adelman, 4211 Colie Dr., Silver Springs, Md. Monthly during school year (formerly *Junior Astronomer*).

Science Teacher. National Science Teachers' Association, National Education Association, 1201 16 St. N.W., Washington 6, D.C. Monthly, except June, July, August.

Science World. Scholastic Magazines, Inc. 50 W. 44 St., New York 36, N.Y.

Sky and Telescope. Sky Publishing Corp., Harvard College Observatory, Cambridge 38, Mass. Monthly.

Tomorrow's Scientists. National Science Teachers Association, Washington, D.C. 8 issues per year.

UNESCO Courier. The UNESCO Publications Center, 801 3rd Ave., New York 22, N.Y. Monthly.

Weatherwise. American Meteorological Society, 3 Joy St., Boston 8, Mass. Monthly.

EXPERIMENTS, DEMONSTRATION, AND CONSTRUCTION REFERENCES FOR TEACHERS AND CHILDREN

Arey, Charles K. *Science Experiences for Elementary School.* New York: Teachers College, Columbia University, 1942, 98 Pp.

Atkin, J. Myron and R. Will Burnett. Elementary School Science Activities Series. New York: Holt, Rinehart & Winston, Inc., 1960. Titles: *Air, Winds and Weather; Electricity and Magnetism; Working with Animals; Working with Plans.*

Baker, Tunis. *Baker Science Packet.* Educational Science Packet, 42 Carolin Rd., Upper Montclair, N.J., 1952.

Beeler, Nelson F. and Franklyn M. Bramley. Experiments in Chemistry. New York: Thomas Y. Crowell Company, 1952.

————. *Experiments with Airplane Instruments.* New York: Thomas Y. Crowell Company, 1953.

————. *More Experiments in Science.* New York: Thomas Y. Crowell Company, 1953.

Berger, Melvin and Frank Clark. Science and Music. New York: Whittlesey House, 1961.

Blough, Glenn O. and Marjorie H. Campbell. *Making and Using Classroom Science Materials in the Elementary School.* Dryden, 1954.

Branley, Franklyn M. *Experiments in the Principles of Space Travel.* New York: Thomas Y. Crowell Company, 1955 (also other titles).

Bruce, Guy V. *Experiments with Fuels and Fire.* National Science Teachers Association, 1201 16 St. N.W., Washington, D.C., 1961 (other titles: *Experiences With Heat; Experiences With Light and Color; Experiences With Magnetism and Electricity; Experiences With Sound; Experiments With Air;* and *Experiments With Water*).

Cooper, Elizabeth K. *Science on the Shores and Banks.* New York: Harcourt, Brace & World, Inc., 1960.

DeVries, L. *The Book of Experiments.* New York: The Macmillan Co., 1959.

Frank, Annette and Tillie S. Pine. *Science Experiences Related to the Social Studies.* New York: 69 Bank Street Publication, 1955.

Freeman, Mae and Ira M. *Fun With Chemistry.* New York: Random House, Inc., 1944.

————. Fun With Science. New York: Random House, Inc., 1956.

————. Fun With Scientific Experiments. New York: Random House, Inc., 1960.

Herbert, Don. *Mr. Wizard's Science Secrets.* Popular Mechanics, 1953.

————. *Mr. Wizard's Experiments for Young Scientists.* New York: Doubleday, 1959.

Hone, Elizabeth, et al. *Teaching Elementary Science: A Sourcebook for Elementary Science.* New York: Harcourt, Brace & World, Inc., 1962.

Leavitt, Jerome and John Juntsberger. *Fun-Time Terrariums and Aquariums.* Chicago: Children's Press, 1961.

Lemming, Joseph. *The Real Book of Science Experiments.* Garden City: Doubleday and Company, Inc., 1954.

Lewellyn, John. *Boy Scientist.* New York: Simon and Schuster, Inc., 1954.

Lynde, Carlton J. *Science Experiences With Home Equipment.* New York: D. Van Nostrand Co., Inc., 1955.

_____. *Science Experiences With Inexpensive Equipment.* New York: D. Van Nostrand Co., Inc., 1956.

_____. *Science Experiments With Ten-Cent Store Equipment.* New York: D. Van Nostrand Co., Inc., 1955.

Milgrom, Harry, ed. *Matter, Energy and Change.* Holt, Rinehart & Winston, Inc., 1961.

Nelson, Leslie W. and George C. Lorbeer. *Science Activities for Elementary School Children.* Dubuque Iowa: William C. Brown Company, Publishers, 1955.

Newbury, N. F. and H. A. Armstrong. *The Young Experimenter.* New York: Sterling Publishing Co., Inc., 1960.

Parker, Bertha. *Science Experiences Elementary School.* Evanston, Ill.: Harper & Row, Publishers, 1955.

Partridge, J. A. Natural Science Through the Season. New York: The Macmillan Company, 1955.

Podendorf, Illa. *The True Book of Science Experiments.* Chicago, Ill.: Chicago Press, 1954.

Schneider, Herman and Nina. *Let's Find Out.* New York: William R. Scott, Inc., 1946.

_____. *Let's Look Inside Your House.* New York: William R. Scott, Inc., 1948.

_____. *Science Fun With Milk Cartons.* New York: Whittlesey House, 1953.

Schwartz, Julius. *It's Fun to Know Why: Experiments with Things Around Us.* New York: Whittlesey House, 1952.

_____. *Now I Know.* New York: Whittlesey, 1955.

_____. *Through the Magnifying Glass: Little Things That Make a Big Difference.* New York: Whittlesey House, 1954.

Science II for Intermediate and Upper Grades. Darien, Conn.: Educational Publishing Co., 1958.

Selsam, Millicent E. *Underwater Zoos.* New York: William Morrow & Co., Inc., 1961.

Sheckes, Mary. *Building Children's Science Concepts.* New York: Teachers College, Columbia University, 1958.

Straight, G. M. *Company Science Experiments.* Hart Publishing Co., 1957.

Swezey, Kenneth M. *After Dinner Science.* New York: Whittlesey House, 1948.

Tannenbaum, Beulah and Myra Stillman. *Understanding Light.* New York: Whittlesey House, 1960.

UNESCO, *UNESCO Source Book for Science Teaching.* UNESCO Publications Center. 801 Third Ave., New York, N.Y., 1962.

Vessel, M. F. and H. Wong. *How to Stimulate Your Science Programs: A Guide to Simple Science Activities.* San Francisco: Fearon, 1957.

_____. *What is Space?* San Francisco: Fearon, 1958.

_____. *Journey into Space.* San Francisco: Fearon, 1958.

_____. *Water, A Resource.* San Francisco: Fearon, 1958.

_____. *A Trip to the Moon.* San Francisco: Fearon, 1959.

Wyler, Rose, *First Book of Science Experiments.* New York: Franklin Watts, Inc., 1952.

_____. *Experiment Book.* Eau Claire, Wisconsin: Hale and Co., 1953.

INDEX

INDEX